MANUAL FOR THE IDENTIFICATION OF MEDICAL BACTERIA

MANUAL
FOR THE IDENTIFICATION OF
MEDICAL BACTERIA

BY

S. T. COWAN

M.D., D.SC., F.C.PATH.

Administrative Director, Central Public Health Laboratory, Colindale
Deputy Director, Public Health Laboratory Service, England and Wales

AND THE LATE

K. J. STEEL

B.PHARM., PH.D., F.P.S.

Deputy Curator, National Collection of Type Cultures
Head, Media Department, Central Public Health Laboratory, Colindale

CAMBRIDGE
AT THE UNIVERSITY PRESS
1966

PUBLISHED BY

THE SYNDICS OF THE CAMBRIDGE UNIVERSITY PRESS

Bentley House, 200 Euston Road, London, N.W.1
American Branch: 32 East 57th Street, New York, N.Y. 10022

©

CAMBRIDGE UNIVERSITY PRESS
1965

First published 1965
Reprinted 1966

First printed in Great Britain by Adlard & Son Ltd., Bartholomew Press, Dorking, Surrey
Reprinted in Great Britain, by lithography, by Lowe & Brydone (Printers) Ltd, London

CONTENTS

PREFACE

Our 'Diagnostic Tables for the Common Medical Bacteria' were originally published in the *Journal of Hygiene*. The tables seemed to fill a need and the demand for reprints was so great that Cambridge University Press reprinted them in pamphlet form. Many inquired about the technical methods, and there were constant complaints that the methods were not described and that the text lacked details of the taxonomic problems. We resolved, therefore, to expand the original paper and to prepare a book which would give sufficient detail of media and methods to justify its description as a laboratory manual. Although designed for medical workers we hope that others will use it.

The value of a laboratory manual was impressed on one of us in 1935 at the British Postgraduate Medical School. Dr A. A. Miles had prepared a loose-leaf mimeographed manual to supplement (and improve on) a popular laboratory handbook. With this example in mind a manual suited to the special needs of the National Collection of Type Cultures was prepared, and contributions were made by other members of the Collection staff, particularly Mrs P. H. Clarke, Miss H. E. Ross, Miss C. Shaw, and Mr C. S. Brindle. The National Collection Manual in turn became the basis for the appendices to the present *Manual*.

In compiling the tables we sought information from various sources, including authoritative works such as the Reports of the Enterobacteriaceae Subcommittee of the International Committee on Bacteriological Nomenclature, and monographs such as Kauffmann's (1954) *Enterobacteriaceae*, Edwards & Ewing's *Identification of Enterobacteriaceae* (1962), and Smith, Gordon & Clark's (1952) *Aerobic Sporeforming Bacteria*. We found large gaps in published works, and in many instances our own data have been the only source of information. While we have taken great care in compiling and checking the tables, we are sure that the *Manual* is unlikely to be free from error. When such errors are detected we hope that the finders will let us know. We will also welcome data to fill up the few gaps in the tables.

It is with pleasure that we acknowledge our indebtedness to many friends and colleagues at home and abroad for facts and discussions that have helped to clarify our ideas. It is impossible to name them all but we could not have planned or written the *Manual* without the help of Dr R. E. Gordon, Dr P. R. Edwards, Dr W. H. Ewing, Dr T. Gibson, Dr Joan Taylor, Mrs P. H. Clarke, Miss C. Shaw, and Miss H. E. Ross. We also wish to thank Miss B. H. Whyte and Miss A. Bowman, the Colindale librarians, Miss M. I. Hammond who dealt skilfully with the manuscript, and Mr W. Clifford who made the figures.

LONDON, 1964   S.T.C.
                                                                                      K.J.S.

POSTSCRIPT

My colleague, Dr K. J. Steel, died suddenly on 25th September, 1964, between the completion of the manuscript and the proof stage of the book. His death at the age of 34 is a great loss for he seemed destined to reach the highest branches of bacteriology. In this *Manual* he was responsible for the whole of Appendices A to D and F and for much of Chapter 3; and he played a big part in revising and recasting the tables that form the heart of our work. I hope that the book will serve as a fitting memorial to a great collaborator and friend.

London, 1965   S.T.C.

INTRODUCTION

While all essential detail is given in the Appendices, it is assumed that the reader has some knowledge and experience of bacteriology and elementary chemistry and that the basic principles are understood. Thus we do not describe how to find the pH value of a medium, or how to make a normal solution; we do not give details of the use of anaerobic jars or the microscope. Serology is not discussed but we describe methods commonly used in the preparation of extracts for grouping streptococci, as the grouping finds a place in Table I*b*. We give details of sterilization temperatures and times as these so-called standard procedures vary from one laboratory to another.

This *Manual* is intended to help those who have isolated a bacterium and want to identify it. We do not describe the methods used by clinical bacteriologists to isolate the organism from the specimen sent to the laboratory; to do so would lead us into ever-changing fields where we do not now practise, and our recommendations might well be out of date, but *Clinical Bacteriology* by E. Joan Stokes (1960) will be found useful. We must stress, however, that before an identification is attempted the organism must be obtained in pure culture and we give some advice on how to recognize that a culture is impure and the steps to be taken to purify it.

Intelligent use of the tables demands technical skill and sensitive but specific methods for the individual tests. As in all determinative bacteriology, a true identification must be based on careful work, and our diagnostic tables will not help the man who is in too much of a hurry to carry out all the tests needed. Because the tables were constructed from many sources we do not stipulate particular methods, but those given in Appendices D and E will be found satisfactory. Three points need to be emphasized about the tables: (i) they cannot be considered in isolation; they must be taken in conjunction with other evidence, such as colony form, that cannot be included in them. (ii) The tables do not characterize an organism; all they do is to focus attention on the tests most valuable for differentiation. (iii) The tables do not form part of any classification but they may draw attention to similarities and relations that are not otherwise apparent; these are discussed briefly in Chapter 9.

In general the tables make possible the identification of species which can often be broken down into serotypes or phage types. However users of this *Manual* will seldom have the facilities to work out the antigenic structure of the species they isolate; this is a task for a reference laboratory. Those who aspire to do this work themselves should consult the excellent practical manual by Edwards & Ewing (1962), which spotlights the problems and, for the Enterobacteriaceae, gives all essential details.

In Chapters 6 and 7 we give brief definitions (minidefinitions) of the groups (or genera) that appear in the tables. For the sake of brevity we have used phrases which we hope will be understood but which may cause a little difficulty to readers whose native language is not English. Thus we write 'Facultatively anaerobic' for 'Aerobic, facultatively anaerobic', and ask our readers to assume that all bacteria are aerobic unless we state that they are anaerobic. We also use the word 'sugars' for the longer but more correct 'carbohydrates'.

In plan the *Manual* falls into two parts: the first, divided into chapters, is discursive; the second, made up of appendices, is instructive.

The heart of the *Manual* is contained in Chapters 6 and 7, which are made up of the main diagnostic tables, numbered in roman, and with subsidiary tables bearing letters in italic which correspond to the columns of the Table-figs. I and II. The use of the diagnostic tables, and the significance of the signs used in them are described in Chapter 5. In other parts of the book the tables have arabic numerals and are numbered sequentially in both chapters and appendices. The appendices are written tersely; there is free use of abbreviations (which conform to British Standard 1991 : Part I : 1954), chemical formulae, and prescription-like recipes for media.

1

CLASSIFICATION AND NOMENCLATURE

Taxonomy can be likened to a cocktail; it is a mixture of three components skilfully blended so that the outsider relishes the whole and cannot discern the individual ingredients. In taxonomy the ingredients are: (i) *classification*, or the orderly arrangements of units, (ii) *nomenclature*, the naming or labelling of units, (iii) *identification* of the unknown with a unit defined and named by (i) and (ii). The subdivisions should be taken in the order indicated, for without adequate classification it is impossible to name rationally, and without a system of labelled units it is impossible to identify others with them and communicate the result to a third person.

Before discussing identification, the subject of this *Manual*, we must first deal briefly with the principles of classification and nomenclature; but since this book is essentially a practical manual, theoretical considerations of the validity of bacterial species (Lwoff, 1958; Cowan, 1962) have no place here. For a book of this kind we must accept the bacterial species as a convenient unit, but as it so obviously has different values in different groups of bacteria we do not attempt to define it. We recognize subdivisions of species either as varieties (biotypes) or as serotypes, but we cannot accept Kauffmann's (1959*a*, *b*; 1963*b*) contention that the serotypes or the phage types of the various members of the Enterobacteriaceae should be equated with species. The collection of similar species into larger groups (genera), and similar (we do not say related) genera into families, are convenient groupings and have found common usage. However, we do not believe that these are phylogenetic groupings and we are not willing to combine families into even larger groups (orders) which we regard as artificial and highly speculative. The different kinds of bacteria are not separated by sharp divisions but by slight and subtle differences in characters so that they seem to blend into each other and resemble a spectrum (Figs. 1*a* and *b*). The spectrum-like intergrading of different kinds of bacteria is confirmed by a newer method of grouping, namely on the base composition of the deoxyribonucleic acid (DNA) of the bacterial cell (Vendrely, 1958). The DNA of a bacterial group is homogeneous (Rolfe & Meselson, 1959), and different groups have different DNA compositions. Marmur, Falkow & Mandel (1963) collect the results of numerous workers and summarize in a table the DNA-base composition of many bacteria. These techniques are not applicable to day-to-day diagnostic work but the results are of fundamental importance to the taxonomist.

A theoretical classificatory scheme divides the higher ranks into two or more kinds of a lower rank, for example, *Bergey's Manual* (1923–57) divides the kingdom Bacteria into orders and continues the breakdown through families, tribes, genera, and species.

We suggest that a pragmatic classification should be built up from the basal unit (species); basal units which share a number of characters are combined to form the next higher unit (genus), and the common characters become those which are important in the definition or characterization of the genus. The stressing of certain characters (which we say are important characters because they are significant in identification), differs from the Adansonian concept (that it is proper to apply to orthodox theoretical classification (Sneath, 1957*a*)), in which each character has equal merit in the eyes of the taxonomist.

What we call 'important characters' may be of three kinds: (i) *specific*, as the ability to produce coagulase by *Staphylococcus aureus*; (ii) *distinguishing* characters which, while not specific, are useful in separating organisms that are otherwise very similar. An example is indole production by *Proteus vulgaris*, which distinguishes it from *P. mirabilis*; (iii) characters *shared* by all members of a group; thus, acid-fastness is an important character of mycobacteria (since all members are acid-fast) but not of the nocardias (only some of which are acid-fast).

Needless to say, there are degrees of importance and it would be feasible to continue the list; but we think that we have said enough to illustrate the point that characters can have an importance in a pragmatic scheme that they are denied in an Adansonian classification.

Until recently taxonomists paid little attention to the type of carbohydrate breakdown; this is characteristic of an organism and of great informative value to the diagnostician. In this connexion we follow Hugh & Leifson (1953) and use the terms 'oxidative' and 'fermentative' though it is not at all certain that these words describe accurately what is happening in the test, which we shall refer to as the Oxidation–Fermentation (O–F) test.

We think that a practical classification should be based on characters that are easily determined; consequently we cannot use features that demand difficult techniques or special apparatus. Thus, cytological details of the bacterium such as cell walls, septa, nuclei, and fimbriae do not find a place in our scheme although we are well aware of their importance and know that to add them would increase the weight of our arguments and support our general conclusions. Again, because it is difficult, even with an electron microscope, to obtain an accurate picture of the arrangement of flagella on bacteria, we have placed little weight on this character which, in all except the most rigidly Adansonian taxonomy, is given a very important place.

The classification we use is built on a wide range of characters; the identification of each unit is based on the same characters and it is not necessary to make the hypothetical (and sometimes absurd) assumptions of classical taxonomy. By omitting the type of flagellation we do not need to postulate that *Shigella* species, if they had any, would have peritrichous flagella.

The Gram-positive and Gram-negative bacteria can each be considered as a continuous series (Fig. 1*a* and *b*). Some of the genera shown in these figures (e.g. *Leuconostoc* in Fig. 1*a* and *Flavobacterium* in Fig. 1*b*) are dealt with only summarily in this *Manual*, but are mentioned because they may be met in medical bacteriology either as contamin-

Fig. 1 *a* Gram-positive genera dealt with in the *Manual*; *b* Gram-negative genera dealt with in the *Manual*.

ants or as suspected pathogens. We cannot discuss all the ways in which our scheme differs from those found elsewhere, but we think that some explanation may be helpful.

We use the generic name *Sarcina* in a narrower sense than most authors, and confine the genus to the anaerobic packet-forming Gram-positive cocci. *Gaffkya* does not find a place in our scheme, and tetrad-forming cocci are included in *Micrococcus*. In distinguishing between *Staphylococcus* and *Micrococcus* we are following the present trend of basing the distinction on the method of carbohydrate breakdown.

The three species *Bordetella pertussis*, *B. parapertussis* and *B. bronchiseptica* each produce a similar endotoxin-like substance but otherwise have little in common. The growth requirements of *B. pertussis* are complex and distinctive, and justify its segregation in a separate genus (*Bordetella*). In the past *B. bronchiseptica* has been placed in many different genera including *Brucella*, *Haemophilus*, and *Alcaligenes*; as it is motile we do not think that it fits well in *Brucella*; it is not haemophilic, does not need either *X* or *V* factors and, as it has many features of the type, *Alcaligenes faecalis*, we place it in the genus *Alcaligenes*. *B. parapertussis* is not nutritionaliy exacting and we place it in *Acinetobacter*, a genus created by Brisou & Prévot (1954) for non-motile organisms previously grouped in *Achromobacter*. The glanders bacillus and *Moraxella lwoffii* are also included in *Acinetobacter* (Steel & Cowan, 1964). *Bacterium anitratum* presents problems of classification (Lautrop, 1961) and we have followed Brisou & Prévot (1954) and placed it in *Acinetobacter*.

In some groups (for example, *Klebsiella*) our own work has made us unwilling to accept classifications based mainly on serology and, being prejudiced in favour of our own schemes, we give them here. The organisms of haemorrhagic septicaemia form the original *Pasteurella* group, and we retain this generic name coupling it with the specific epithet *multocida*.

We had to make up our minds about the worth of the genera *Mima*, *Herellea*, and *Colloides*, and to decide whether they should be included in the tables. Our experience of cultures bearing these names is that they can be identified as species of well-established genera, and we agree with Henriksen (1963) that they are unnecessary taxonomic encumbrances. Our judgement is fallible and we do not expect all readers to agree with us.

We have left out of our scheme such organisms as *Mycoplasma* (PPLO group), *Leptospira* and other spirochaetes which are diagnosed on morphological and serological grounds and on their pathogenicity for various animals. For details concerning the identification of these organisms see Madoff (1959) and Babudieri (1961).

NOMENCLATURE

We do not propose to discuss the problems and principles of nomenclature, but we must point out that as nomenclature is secondary to classification there may be more than one correct name for a bacterium. Nomenclature is subject to the Rules and Recommendations of the Bacteriological Code. There are not, and can never be, any rules for classification. Classification is subjective and a matter of opinion, and it is within the rights (if not the competence) of each worker to classify bacteria as he will. The classification adopted determines the names to be appended to the organisms, and the rules of nomenclature will guide us to choose the correct names. If a worker believes that all rod-shaped organisms should be grouped together into one genus, he is entitled to name the diphtheria organism *Bacillus diphtheriae*, but if he thinks that rod-shaped bacteria can be split up into different groups he can use a name such as *Corynebacterium diphtheriae*; each name is correct within its own taxonomic scheme or classification, and would be wrong in the other scheme.

To help our readers to find a particular bacterium, we have included in the Index not only the specific epithets we use in this *Manual*, but also many (though obviously not all) of the synonyms with which they may be familiar. We have tried to include the names used in the current editions of *Bergey's Manual* (1957) and *Topley & Wilson's Principles* (1964).

One of the aims of the Bacteriological Code is to stabilize nomenclature; this is an impossibility for nomenclature is itself dependant on everchanging ideas on classification. The rediscovery and application of an old or the development of a new technique may act on taxonomists as a blood transfusion.

Sometimes, an organism remains unclassified for decades after its discovery and characterization. Morgan's No. 1 bacillus (Morgan, 1906) needed the insight of Rauss (1936) and the discovery that under the right conditions it could be made to swarm, to recognize it as a species of *Proteus*. It was the rediscovery and application of the phenylalanine test that made Singer & Bar-Chey (1954) see that Stuart's 29911 (Stuart, Wheeler & McGann, 1946) or Providence group was a *Proteus* species.

It is often easier to create a new genus or species than to do the comparative work necessary to put an organism into its rightful place in an existing genus or species. The temptation to designate a new genus or species should be resisted; it would be if people realized that the ability of a taxonomist is judged as inversely proportional to the number of new taxa he has created.

Many workers use common names (in the vernacular of the country) in preference to scientific names that are subject to change. Since English is now the language of science, common English names are widely understood, but French or German equivalents may present difficulty to English-speaking people (e.g. Bacteridie de charbon = der Milzbrandbazillus = the anthrax bacillus = *Bacillus anthracis*). The great advantage of the latinized binomial is that it is accepted throughout the world and the same word should have the same meaning everywhere.

Nomenclature often presents difficulties because a change in name may be necessary when an organism is moved from one group to another. Sometimes the nomenclatural difficulties arise because the Rules, first published in 1948 (Buchanan, St John-Brooks & Breed, 1948), revised and annotated in 1958 (Buchanan *et al.* 1958), were made retroactive. This means that we should apply them to names first used in the last century, long before a Bacteriological Code was thought of, and in some instances, before the organism named had been isolated and characterized.

5

Another source of confusion is due to the well-intentioned efforts of workers to give a meaning to the specific epithet, and to make the epithet appropriate. More than 20 years ago one of us was concerned with an ill-conceived attempt to apply an appropriate epithet 'pyogenes' to the generic name *Staphylococcus* because the legitimate epithet 'aureus' was inappropriate when applied to strains that produced white colonies. In more recent times Foster & Bragg (1962) suggested that various specific epithets for *Klebsiella*, correctly proposed (by the Rules), should be transposed (which would greatly add to confusion) because, as originally proposed, they seemed to them to be inappropriate.

Another source of confusion is the re-use of a discarded name for a newly described genus or species. An example is the use of *Aerobacter* (a later synonym of *Klebsiella*) for a group of motile organisms which share several characters with non-motile organisms formerly named *Aerobacter aerogenes*. This confusion was remedied by its authors (Hormaeche & Edwards, 1960) who withdrew their proposal and substituted the new generic name *Enterobacter*. Unfortunately some authors continue to use the name *Aerobacter* for both motile and non-motile organisms.

2

IMPORTANCE OF PURE CULTURES

Many difficulties in identification are due to the use of an impure culture as starting material. Before an organism can be identified it must be obtained in what we glibly describe as a 'pure culture'. By this we mean the descendants of a single colony obtained after plating the material in such a way that much of the growth consists of well-isolated colonies; it is only an assumption that these have developed from a single organism or a single clump of similar organisms. In routine diagnostic bacteriology a single plating may have to suffice but a replating can always be made with advantage, and, as will be explained below, is essential when highly selective and inhibitory media are used for the primary plating.

Our 'pure culture' is one that generally breeds true, that is, when replated the majority of the daughter colonies will be like the parent, but we know that occasionally (perhaps once in several million times) a bacterial cell will mutate and the colony developing from it will consist of organisms that have changed a character. Our 'pure culture' retains its original characters because the chances are, on an ordinary nutrient medium, millions to one against picking the mutant, and also because once satisfied that our culture is pure we stop picking isolated colonies (lest, perchance, the mutant is picked) and we subculture from a sweep (or pool) of several colonies.

When two organisms are grown together as in an impure culture, one of four things may happen: (i) each organism may grow independently; (ii) one may produce a substance that will enable the other to grow (symbiosis) or grow better in the particular medium; (iii) one may produce a substance that inhibits the growth of the other; (iv) one may grow faster than the other and deprive the second of some essential part of its food supply. In (i) and (ii) a characterization of the impure culture will probably yield a summation of characters unless one organism produces say, acid and the other an equivalent amount of alkali to neutralize it. In (iii) and (iv) the characterization will be that of the organism which grows at the expense of the other. In (i) and (ii) an organism A (characterized as $x+$, $y-$, $z-$) growing with B ($x-$, $y+$, $z-$) in mixed culture $(A+B)$, might be characterized as $x+$, $y+$, $z-$, which might be characteristic of a third organism C, and the mixture would inevitably be misidentified.

Often the bacteriologist is looking for a particular organism, e.g. a shigella in faeces or *Corynebacterium diphtheriae* in a throat swab, and many isolations are made on selective or differential media which contain substances that inhibit the growth of some (unwanted) organisms. The inhibitory substance(s) does not kill the unwanted organism but merely suppresses or retards its growth on that medium; when an inhibited organism forms part of a colony made up mainly of the suspected pathogen, subculture to another medium will result either in further suppression of growth of the unwanted, or, in the absence of its inhibitor, a resumption of growth in competition with the strain it is desired to isolate. From an inoculum of faeces on deoxycholate citrate medium a colourless colony (indicating a non-lactose fermenter) is likely to be made up of non-lactose fermenters and a few suppressed lactose fermenters. Subculture to lactose peptone water will allow the lactose fermenters to grow and produce acid from the lactose and, unless the colony is replated on a non-inhibitory medium, the presence of the non-lactose fermenters may be overlooked. A routine should be so developed that, before a culture is assumed to be pure, colonies picked from a selective medium are replated on a non-inhibitory and preferably an indicating medium. For, until a culture is known to be pure, it is a waste of time to attempt any characterization tests.

The reader may think that we have laboured the presence of mixed colonies, but experience has shown that many of the cultures that are difficult to identify are, in fact, mixed and came from colonies on inhibitory media, and we cannot stress too much the importance of obtaining a pure culture before attempting to identify it. While inhibitory media are the main source of impure cultures, other causes are sufficiently common to warrant mention here. The presence of a 'spreader' on a plate may be difficult to detect; this spreading growth will also cover any discrete colonies on the plate. The most troublesome spreading organisms are members of two genera, *Proteus* and *Clostridium*, and different methods must be used to purify cultures contaminated by them.

Proteus species grow readily on most media but swarming can be inhibited by bile salts and by substances in some of the selective and inhibitory media on which *Proteus* organisms will produce discrete colonies. Thus, a culture contaminated by a *Proteus* species can be plated on MacConkey agar; if however, the wanted organism will not grow on this medium the contaminated culture should be spread on plates of a richer nutrient medium in which the agar concentration has been increased to 7 % (Hayward & Miles, 1943).

It is much more difficult to purify a culture contaminated by a *Clostridium* species. This difficulty of freeing a culture from a clostridial contaminant applies also to separating one *Clostridium* species from another and explains why it takes so long to identify most cultures of this genus. Since more than one species of this genus may be found in the same material, it is not surprising that the original descriptions of many so-called species of *Clostridium* were based on mixtures of two or more species.

The separation of *Clostridium* species may entail a long series of platings and selection of colonies unless one of the mixture happens to be a pathogen with invasive properties.

Such an organism might be isolated from a remote site (say the surface of the liver) when an animal dies after subcutaneous or intramuscular inoculation of the mixed culture in a hind limb. Separation may be achieved when the spores of the strains making up the mixture differ in their resistance to heat or when one of the strains is motile and the other non-motile. The separation of two pathogens may depend on the ability of the bacteriologist to recognize which species (or even toxin types) are present. Much information can be obtained from *in vitro* tests, such as lecithinase production on egg-yolk medium, before going on to *in vivo* tests in animals.

The contamination of bacterial cultures by the pleuro-pneumonia-like organisms (or PPLO) is not believed to be a serious hazard, but our knowledge of these organisms is much less than that of ordinary bacteria, and their presence may escape detection. The PPLO grow slowly and generally only on media enriched with blood or serum, and if they are initially present as contaminants they are likely to be outgrown by the more hardy and less fastidious bacteria. However, they should be borne in mind and their presence suspected when bacterial cultures show inconsistencies on repeated testing. Bacterial cultures that have been isolated on media containing antibiotic or from patients treated with antibiotics, may show g, L or other aberrant forms, which may be confused with PPLO because they grow slowly and produce very small colonies.

3

MEDIA: CONSTITUENTS AND STERILIZATION

Media preparation seldom receives the attention it deserves; moreover, the media room is often overcrowded and understaffed, and the conditions in which media-makers work are usually the worst in the laboratory. Complaints about media, both commercial and home prepared, are so common that some laboratories have opened a control department adequately staffed to be able to watch media making in all its stages and to test the final products. In this chapter we shall discuss the general aspects of media making; formulae for the different media will be found in Appendix A, beginning on p. 98.

The majority of the commonly used culture media are now commercially available as dehydrated products which are reconstituted by the addition of distilled water and then sterilized in the conventional manner. The manufacturer's directions for reconstitution should be followed for best results. The advantages of dehydrated media include ease of preparation without the necessity of pH adjustment or phosphate removal, batch to batch uniformity which is often greater than with laboratory prepared media, convenience for the preparation of small quantities, ease of storage, and economy especially in saving time and labour. Against these must be set certain disadvantages, primarily, the absence of control by the user. Most of the dehydrated products are hygroscopic but this can be overcome by the use of plastic or foil sachets containing sufficient for one batch of medium. Dehydration is not suitable for media containing blood, other thermolabile components, or egg. An important consideration where dehydrated media are widely used, is that technical staff are not adequately trained in media preparation.

MEDIA CONSTITUENTS

For a fuller account of peptone, meat extract, yeast extract, gelatin, agar, and bile salts reference may be made to the Special Report of the Society for General Microbiology on constituents of bacteriological culture media (Report, 1956a).

Agar can be obtained as shreds, flakes, granules or powder and is made from certain types of sea-weed; it has unusual gelling properties which make it useful in bacteriology. When mixed with cold water agar does not go into solution; as a consequence it can be washed to free it from soluble saline impurities. The concentration to be used depends on the geographic source or species of the sea-weed from which the agar is made, and on the purpose for which the medium is intended (Table 8, p. 98). In the formulae for media described in this *Manual* the concentration of agar relates to the product from

Japanese sea-weed. In addition to the agar concentration other factors will affect gel strength; for example, repeated melting of the medium or sterilization at a low pH value will decrease it.

Peptone is a product of varying composition made by acid or enzymic hydrolysis of animal or vegetable protein, such as muscle, liver, blood, milk, casein, lactalbumin, gelatin, and soya bean. The exact composition will depend on the raw material and the method of manufacture. No two batches of peptone are exactly alike but commercial firms now try to produce peptones in which the measurable constituents are present within certain defined limits. For many kinds of media the make or type of peptone is immaterial but for certain tests a particular type may be specified (e.g. Eupeptone no. 1 for British Standard 541 : 1934). This does not mean that all other types are unsuitable, more often than not it means that other peptones have not been tried. Certain batches of peptone, however, may be quite unsuitable for a particular purpose, and before being taken into use a peptone should be tested. In Appendix B on Media Control we discuss this problem in more detail and give examples of fallacious results due to the use of unsuitable peptones. Our own experience of post-war peptones is limited to English products such as Evans, Oxoid and Benger's, and American such as Difco and BBL, but we are assured that other peptones (e.g. the Danish Orthana) are equally suitable.

Meat. Beef heart, muscle, and liver are commonly used but calf brain, veal, spleen, and placenta also have a place in media preparation. The quality of meat and other tissues varies with the age and health of the animal and with the conditions under which it was slaughtered. As far as we know the effect on media of using meat 'tenderized' by papain has not been investigated. To minimize variations the preparation of meat media requires extensive quality control, and this may be impracticable for small laboratories. In these circumstances, commercial meat extracts or dehydrated meat media are often more convenient. When meat media are to be used as the basis for fermentation studies, they should be tested for the absence of fermentable carbohydrate.

Meat extract. Commercial meat extracts contain soluble organic bases, protein degradation products, vitamins, and minerals. As these extracts are readily available and easy to use they have largely superseded fresh meat infusions which are both time-consuming to prepare and variable in quality.

Yeast extract is made from bakers' or brewers' yeast and is a rich source of amino acids and vitamins of the B-complex. In culture media it is used to supplement or replace meat extracts. In our laboratory we have replaced beef extract (1 %) by yeast extract (0·3 %) in nutrient broth without significant change in the growth-promoting capacity.

Blood. The choice of blood is often a matter of convenience and depends on the animals kept by a laboratory. When bought from a commercial source we commonly use horse blood, but the blood of other species (man, goat, rabbit, sheep) may be used for special purposes. Sheep blood agar can be used for detecting the different haemolysins of staphylococci (Elek & Levy, 1954); sheep and goat blood are said to be lysed by el-Tor vibrios, but human blood may also be used. Sodium citrate is said to be inhibitory to staphylococci (Rammell, 1962). Our preference is for defibrinated horse blood; it should be relatively fresh and should not be used when haemolysis is obvious. Blood must be stored in a refrigerator but should not be allowed to freeze; all blood products must be tested for sterility.

Plasma is used for demonstrating coagulase activity. In medical bacteriology human plasma is preferred but rabbit plasma may be used. As some bacteria utilize citrate, oxalated plasma is better but citrated plasma may be used when heparin is added (Harper & Conway, 1948). Plasma may be obtained by removing the supernatant of blood + anticoagulant in which the red cells have settled. Blood samples obtained for biochemical examination and containing sodium fluoride or ethylenediaminetetra-acetic acid ('sequestric acid') are to be avoided. Liquid plasma is an unstable product liable to coagulate or to form particles which cause a turbidity or deposit. It should not be filtered. Plasma should be stored in a refrigerator but should not be frozen. Dehydrated plasma is available commercially.

Serum is prepared from blood, collected without addition of an anticoagulant, by removal of the liquid which separates when the clot contracts. Alternately it may be citrated plasma clotted by calcium. Serum should be sterilized by filtration. Horse serum may contain a maltase and an amylase and it is essential that these be inactivated by heat before addition to maltose- or starch-containing media (Goldsworthy, Still & Dumaresq, 1938). Hendry (1938) reported that the maltase was inactivated at 75° C for 30 minutes but not at 55° C for 4 hours; Goldsworthy *et al.* (1938) recommended heating serum at 65° C for 1 hour. Horse serum kept at 0–4° C for a month or longer may show a deposit, believed to contain calcium, lipids and protein (Roche & Marquet, 1935) and this deposit may be mistaken for bacterial contamination.

Ascitic and **hydrocele** fluids are preferred to serum by some workers in hospitals. Most laboratories do not use them because they are not generally available.

Bile contains several bile acids as compounds conjugated with amino acids; bile acids can also form addition compounds with higher fatty acids and other substances. Bile also contains the pigments bilirubin and biliverdin. Fresh ox bile (ox gall) has been superseded either by bile extract, dehydrated bile or bile salts. Bile extract, a dark yellowish green plastic material, is prepared by concentration of fresh bile, extraction with 90 % ethanol, and evaporation of the ethanolic extract. A 10 % solution of the dehydrated product is equivalent to fresh bile.

Bile salts. Commercial bile salts are prepared by extracting dried ox or pig bile with ethanol, decolorizing the extract with charcoal, and precipitating the bile salts with ether to form a water-soluble yellowish-brown hygroscopic powder. When prepared from ox bile the salts consist mainly of sodium taurocholate and sodium glycocholate with smaller amounts of the sodium salts of taurodeoxycholic and glycodeoxycholic acids. The bile acid conjugates may be hydrolyzed by alkali, and it is possible to prepare sodium cholate or deoxycholate but these substances are not chemically pure. Several workers (Mair, 1917; Downie, Stent & White, 1931) showed that in bacteriology deoxycholic acid is the most active component of bile and its effects were studied by Leifson (1935).

Gelatin is the protein obtained by extraction of collagenous material, and is available as sheets, shreds, granules or powder. A gelatin of pharmaceutical or edible grade should be used for culture media. When immersed in water below 20° C, gelatin does not dissolve but swells and imbibes 5–10 times its weight of water. Solution is effected by heating and the solution gels on cooling to about 25–35° C. Gelatin has little nutritive value but is used in culture media as a substrate for detecting gelatinase activity. As with agar gels, excessive heating is detrimental and destroys the setting properties.

Carbohydrates. The bacteriologist uses carbohydrates (collectively called 'sugars') to enrich media for growth, pigmentation, and to determine whether the organism can produce acid or acid and gas from them. The carbohydrates generally used are listed in Table 5 (p. 94), which also includes glycosides and polyhydric alcohols, with concentrations of aqueous solutions suitable for addition to media. The concentration of carbohydrate used in oxidation and fermentation studies is 0·5–1 %; we prefer 1 % carbohydrate as reversion of the reaction is then less likely. Some carbohydrate solutions may be sterilized by autoclaving whereas with others decomposition may occur. Durham (1898) recommended steaming for 'sugars' but Mudge (1917) found that maltose and lactose suffered greater hydrolysis when steamed on three days than when autoclaved at 121° C for 15 minutes. Smith (1932) showed the adverse effect of heat and the accelerated decomposition of glucose and maltose in the presence of phosphate. Solutions are often sterilized by momentary autoclaving or by steaming but it is better to sterilize them by filtration.

We have deliberately omitted dextrin from the list of carbohydrates. White dextrin is generally prepared by heating starch, which has been moistened with a small volume of dilute nitric acid and dried, at 100–120° C; it contains up to 15 % of starch, the remainder consists of erythrodextrin. Inferior grades are prepared by roasting starch without acid at 150–250° C, and have a yellow colour; they are hydrolyzed to a greater extent than white dextrin and may contain appreciable quantities of maltose. Because of its variable composition, we do not recommend the use of dextrin. Soluble starch is prepared by treating potato starch with dilute hydrochloric acid until, after washing, it forms a limpid, almost clear solution in hot water; it is insoluble in cold.

13

INDICATORS

pH indicators are incorporated in some culture media and give visual evidence of pH changes occurring during the growth of bacteria. Indicators for this purpose must be non-toxic in the concentrations used; some samples of neutral red may inhibit growth of *E. coli* in MacConkey broth (Childs & Allen, 1953). With some bacteria (e.g. *Actinomyces israelii*) we have observed better growth in media containing ethanolic than in media with aqueous indicator, showing that the solvent was being used as a readily available carbon source. Where the indicator is prepared as its sodium salt it is preferable to use water as the solvent. Table 4 (p. 93) lists the pH indicators commonly used; the concentrations recommended are for the purpose of adding concentrated indicator solutions to culture media and are not necessarily suitable for the colorimetric determination of pH values. Many new indicators and mixtures now used in chemistry have not yet been applied to bacteriology.

Indicators of oxidation-reduction potential (redox indicators) have limited use in culture media. Examples are methylene blue or resazurin in thioglycollate media and methylene blue in milk (Ulrich, 1944).

The use of tetrazolium compounds (e.g. 2:3:5-triphenyltetrazolium chloride) as indicators of bacterial growth has been advocated, for example in motility media (Kelly & Fulton, 1953) and in KCN broth (Gershman, 1961). As bacterial growth occurs the colourless reagent is reduced to an insoluble red formazan.

STERILIZATION OF MEDIA

(a) HEAT

Sterilization may be a misnomer when it is applied to the processes to which media or media constituents are subjected. In some cases, for example, Tyndallization, the heat applied is sufficient only to kill vegetative bacteria. Again, media that appear to be sterile may contain viable spores of thermophils that are incapable of growing at the temperatures at which sterility tests are normally carried out (37° C). Labile media constituents that are normally kept at about 4° C may contain organisms that grow at room temperature (in England about 15° C) but not at 37° C; such material will pass the usual sterility tests. However, we do not think that we should attempt to qualify the words sterility or sterilization, for to write of partial sterility is a contradiction in terms.

The lethal action of heat depends both on the temperature and the time for which it is applied; the higher the temperature the shorter the time needed to destroy micro-organisms. Sporing bacteria are more resistant to heat than vegetative bacteria, but all sporing forms are not equally resistant. Some, such as *Bacillus subtilis* spores, are killed by a short exposure to 100° C; others, such as those of *B. licheniformis* and *B. stearo-thermophilus*, may resist boiling for hours or survive autoclaving at low pressures for short times.

Autoclaving. An autoclave is a pressure vessel and must be regarded as potentially dangerous. When air has been expelled and the vessel is filled with saturated steam there is a relation between temperature and pressure (Table 1); if air is present, the temperature will be lower than that corresponding to the steam pressure.

Overheating is detrimental to most media, but autoclaving is the most satisfactory method of sterilizing material or media that will withstand temperatures over 100° C, the routine temperature-time combination being 115° C (10 lb) for 20 minutes. The rate of heat penetration into large containers is slow, especially when they contain agar.

Table 1. *Relation between steam pressure and temperature*

Atmospheres	Pressure (*lb/in²*)		Temperature ° C
	Absolute	Above normal	
1	15	0	100
	20	5	108·5
	25	10	115·5
2	30	15	121
	35	20	126

When the volume of medium exceeds 1 litre the time, but not the temperature, should be increased to ensure that the whole contents are maintained at the required temperature for the correct time. The temperature inside the autoclave should be allowed to fall to 90° C or below before opening it to remove the contents.

Containers such as test tubes, flasks and bottles should be of a capacity sufficient to allow a generous head space; an exception is the container of Stuart's (1959) transport medium, which is completely filled.

'Momentary autoclaving' (Davis & Rogers, 1939). Heat or steam is turned off as soon as the autoclave reaches the required temperature (e.g. 121° C), the valve opened when the temperature falls to 100° C, and the medium is taken out between 80–90° C.

Steaming is the process of exposing the medium to the vapour of boiling water but the medium itself seldom reaches 100° C. It is carried out in a non-pressurized vessel, a steamer. Sterilization by steaming may be carried out once only, or on three successive days when it is a high temperature form of fractional sterilization. Sterilization by boiling or steaming is clearly a misnomer, as these processes cannot be relied upon to ensure sterility. They may be necessary when media cannot be autoclaved without detriment to their constituents, for example those containing selenite or tetrathionate. Many of the media which cannot be sterilized by autoclaving are enrichment or selective media for isolating particular organisms from a mixed flora, and in these sterility is not essential.

Tyndallization (or fractional sterilization) has limited use in the media department and is only suitable for nutrient media in which spores can germinate. It is used for litmus milk which is heated at 80° C for one hour on three successive days but our experience shows that this time-consuming process is unnecessary and that autoclaving at 115° C for 10 minutes does not damage the milk.

Inspissation is fractional sterilization carried out at a temperature sufficiently high to coagulate serum or other heat labile constituents (e.g. egg white) and consists in heating at 75–80° C for one hour on three successive days. An alternative method of inspissation using the autoclave will be described in Appendix A (p. 102). Other methods were described by Levin (1943), Foster & Cohn (1945), Spray & Johnson (1946), and Brown (1959).

(b) FILTRATION

Sterilization by filtration has the advantage that it is a process suitable for solutions of thermolabile materials; its disadvantages include the possibility of hidden defects in the filtration apparatus, the need for pre-sterilization of the apparatus, the possibility of adsorption from dilute solutions and of pH changes, and difficulty in cleaning filters after use. Filtration is not only a mechanical sieve action depending on porosity and thickness of the filter but is also a complex physico-chemical procedure involving the charge on the filter and the pH of the solution.

Bacterial filters may be made of porous porcelain, kieselguhr (diatomite), asbestos, sintered glass, or cellulose esters. Doulton and Pasteur-Chamberland candles or cylinders are made of porous porcelain and are available in varying porosities not all of which are suitable for bacterial filtration. Berkefeld and Mandler filters are made from kieselguhr.

Asbestos pads have the advantage that the pad is used once only and then discarded, but their many disadvantages should make us consider whether their continued use is justifiable. Asbestos pads often impart an alkaline reaction to the filtrate and this cannot always be prevented by washing the pad before use; however this alkalinity is not significant with well-buffered media. Release of calcium and magnesium ions from the pad may produce incompatibilities and induce the clotting of plasma. Adsorption phenomena are not uncommon and some pads tend to shed fibres into the filtrate. Asbestos, kieselguhr, and porcelain filters carry a negative charge.

Sintered or fritted glass filters are available in varying porosities, No. 5 being suitable for bacterial filtration; it is usually available as a 5/3 filter consisting of a No. 5 supported on a No. 3 for mechanical strength. Sintered metal filters are not widely used in bacteriology as they are not completely inert to the action of materials likely to be found in culture media.

Collodion filters have largely been replaced by the more convenient membrane filters composed of cellulose esters which are stored in the dry state, and although somewhat brittle they have good wet strength and may be sterilized by autoclaving.

4

CHARACTERIZATION

The difference between characterization for classification and for identification lies not so much in the tests as in the emphasis placed on the results of the tests. Although it is not universally accepted, most taxonomists now support the Adansonian concept that, in classification, equal weight should be given to each character or feature. The relations between strains can be calculated and expressed either as similarity of positive characters (Sneath, 1957*b*) or by taking into account both positive and negative features (Hill *et al.* 1961; Floodgate, 1962; Lockhart & Hartman, 1963); the results of such comparisons can be analyzed laboriously by making a large number of calculations, or more easily by letting a computer do the hard work (Sneath & Cowan, 1958).

Although we accept the Adansonian concept for classification, for identification we attach much weight to some characters, regarding them as having great differential value, less weight to others, and finally, no weight at all to some features. Excessive weighting is given to coagulase production by the staphylococci; heavy weighting is placed on the urease and phenylalanine deaminase systems in identifying *Proteus* species, and on urease in distinguishing between *Alcaligenes faecalis* and *A. bronchisepticus*. Little emphasis is placed on gelatin hydrolysis or liquefaction by staphylococci or micrococci but more weight is given to the same test among the enteric bacteria or the pseudomonads. The variable weighting attached to these characters is largely based on experience but it is likely that the assimilation of data from a wide range of bacteria and subsequent analysis by the computer will, in the future, enable us to express the value of a feature in a quantitative manner.

If we had ready access to a computer we should be able to use an almost unlimited number of characters or features, but with tables we are restricted by our memory or limited by our ability to recognize similarities and differences when making multiple comparisons simultaneously. These limitations led us to develop the mechanical aid we named the Determinator (Cowan & Steel, 1960, 1961) and to construct tables suitable for it. In the original Determinator we were restricted by its size to about 25 features, but in the simplified form this limitation was removed and, in theory at least, we could use 50 or more features in the tables. However, by judicious selection (and weighting) we kept down the number of features used in the individual tables and made the identification in stages. At one time we intended to make tables with the smallest number of

17

tests essential for identification. In the event we included in each second-stage table sufficient detail to provide an adequate, but not exhaustive, characterization.

CHOICE OF CHARACTERS

In choosing characters for the tables we leaned towards those that seem to be most constant and to tests that give most reproducible results. Unfortunately, nearly all tests are influenced by factors that are difficult to control, and we are not yet in a position to specify any standard methods. All we can do is to recommend that the materials used (media and reagents) should be controlled as far as it is possible to control them (see Appendix B), and that environmental factors such as temperature, and the time at which a test is done should be standardized. We would emphasize the desirability of keeping to the same method of doing a test so that its idiosyncrasies and difficulties become known, and, within the one laboratory, the results become reasonably comparable. We have made innumerable comparative tests but seldom could we say unequivocally that one method was better than all the others. To keep our results reasonably comparable we chose certain methods and these became our laboratory standards. Often the choice of method was a compromise between two, sometimes conflicting demands: firstly to know the truth, and secondly, to be able to distinguish between two otherwise similar organisms. It is essentially a compromise to express qualitatively (as positive or negative) what is really a quantitative reaction. An example is the production of hydrogen sulphide; when an organism is grown in a medium with an adequate sulphydryl content, and a sensitive indicator (lead acetate paper) is used, the ability to produce even small amounts of H_2S can be detected. However, with a medium deficient in $-SH$ compounds and a poor indicator (ferrous chloride), only an organism with great ability to produce H_2S is positive in the test.

Sometimes a test is carried out by different methods when dealing with different groups of organism. Again taking H_2S production as the example; in the genus *Brucella* the organism is grown on a medium rich in $-SH$ compounds and lead acetate papers are changed each day so that the result of the test can be expressed as 'H_2S produced on the first two days' or 'from the 1st to the 5th day'. We do not know of any other group of organisms in which this technique is used, and its application to other groups might give us information of value. On occasion we shall find it necessary to indicate the method to be used to obtain the results given in a table.

CHARACTERS NOT USED IN THE TABLES

Certain features are not used in our diagnostic tables because they are subjective, for example, the smell of staphylococci growing on agar is unmistakable but also indescribable. The recognition of the finer shades of pigments is a subjective observation;

we try to keep to the primary colours and eschew such indefinite subdivisions as baby-wool pink, coral red, and sky blue used by the female members of our staff.

Normally we do not describe colony morphology as this will vary with the medium on which the organism is grown and, except in bacteria such as *Corynebacterium diphtheriae* var. *gravis*, is seldom sufficiently characteristic to have diagnostic value. We do not consider that the descriptions of stroke cultures on agar slopes are worth the paper they are written on, and we rarely pay any attention to the type of growth in broth except to note the presence or absence of a pellicle. In a few cases (e.g. *Clostridium tetani* and *Bacillus anthracis*) the type of growth in gelatin stab cultures is characteristic but the fir-tree and inverted fir-tree growths can only be seen when the gelatin columns are deep and the cultures are incubated at about 22° C. On the whole we pay little attention to the type of liquefaction of gelatin and are content to record the test as 'gelatin liquefied' or 'not liquefied'.

Thus the reader will not find in this *Manual* diagrams of the different shapes, edges, surfaces, and elevations of colonies, and of the shapes of liquefaction seen in gelatin stab cultures; the elimination of these relics of nineteenth-century bacteriology makes unnecessary a glossary of descriptive terms that now have but limited use. However, lest we should be accused of too biochemical an approach to classification and identification, we must state our belief that cell morphology has an important place in characterization and we deprecate the tendency to abandon the microscope for the spectro-photometer and other instrumental aids.

We do not describe any serological techniques since serology plays its part in classification and identification only in the finer subdivisions made for epidemiological purposes. For those who wish to pursue serological analysis we recommend the monographs by Kauffmann (1954) and by Edwards & Ewing (1962); the latter is essentially a practical treatise and contains such relevant and important details as the identity of the best strains to use for immunization and absorption. However, one of the primary subdivisions of the streptococci is by the method of grouping introduced by Lancefield (1933) and this finds an important place in Table I*b*. The method of preparing extracts of streptococci is described in Appendix D.

It is possible to say in general terms that certain organisms are sensitive or resistant to a particular antibiotic but because so many strains come from patients who have been treated with antibiotics it is likely that strains isolated during treatment represent the antibiotic-resistant survivors. Sensitivity to antibiotics, therefore, is not a character that has much diagnostic value among the medical bacteria. Among strains made resistant *in vivo* the other characters do not change (Brown & Evans, 1963). In other fields Shewan, Hobbs & Hodgkiss (1960) found that the sensitivity to anti-biotics and bacteriostatic agents was of help in identifying various pseudomonads and vibrios.

TESTS USED IN THE TABLES

When we prepared our tables we started with the Gram reaction and for the next sub-divisions used cytology and fundamental reactions such as ability to grow in air, catalase, oxidase production, and the method of carbohydrate breakdown. One of the advantages of a table is that several characters of different groups can be seen simultaneously and compared, a feat that is impossible with the genealogical type of chart. We were surprised to find that on the results of a limited number of selected tests we could place most bacteria into a genus or a small group of genera.

PRIMARY TESTS

Gram reaction. Gram did not describe a stain but a method in which he used stains and solutions devised by others; to this day we do not fully understand its mechanism, but we do know that the reaction to Gram's method is a stable characteristic of a bacterium. Gram-positivity (the ability to resist decolorization with ethanol or acetone) is a feature of relatively young bacterial cells of some species; as they age, the cells lose this characteristic and apparently become Gram-negative. It is important, therefore, to examine young cultures, preferably before the end of the logarithmic growth phase. Genuinely Gram-negative bacteria do not retain the first stain which is easily removed by the decolorizing agent. Thus, as in many other tests, a positive finding (in this case retention of the purple stain) has much more significance than a negative which may, in fact, be false due to (i) the age of the culture, or (ii) excessive decolorization with powerful solvents such as acetone. There are many variations of Gram's method (and each works well in the hands of those who practise it); the one we use under the name of Lillie's modification is simple and students obtain good results with it but, as acetone is used, the decolorization can be overdone. A recent modification by Preston & Morrell (1962) is claimed to be foolproof.

Morphology may be affected by the medium on which the organism is grown and the temperature of incubation.

Acid-fastness is shown when an organism resists decolorization with strong acids or mixtures of ethanol and mineral acid; this is a characteristic shown by few bacteria and when positive it is diagnostic of mycobacteria, though one species, *M. rhodochrous*, is only feebly acid-fast. Nocardias are sometimes acid-fast but seldom resist the vigorous decolorization which mycobacteria successfully endure. Ziehl-Neelsen's method is used to demonstrate acid-fastness but methods using a cold stain have also been described.

Spores are stained by a modification of Moeller's method (itself a modified Ziehl-Neelsen method) in which decolorization is effected by ethanol. The staining method is simple and seldom causes difficulty but the young spore does not resist decolorization and it may or may not take up the counterstain. In older cultures some bacilli may shed their spores so that in the rod-shaped bacterium an unstained area is seen, and stained spores may lie free of the cells from which they developed. An indirect method of showing the presence of spores is to show that a culture can survive heating at 80° C for 10 minutes.

A problem that faces the diagnostician is the tendency for sporing organisms to lose the ability to produce spores. The asporogenous state may be permanent, or it may be a temporary reaction to an environment, when a change of medium or temperature of incubation may suffice to restore the strain's ability (or need) to form spores. Sub-culture to a starch-containing medium such as potato agar, is often successful in restoring the ability of an aerobe to form spores; in other instances a deficiency of manganese in the medium is the cause of the asporogenous state and the remedy is the addition of a 'trace elements' supplement. Often the cause is unknown and the best general advice we can give, based on the restoration of many asporogenous strains of *Bacillus* in the National Collection of Type Cultures to the sporing state, is to grow the cultures on a medium containing soil extract (p. 123).

In connexion with the acid-fast and spore-forming characters of organisms, certain other problems need to be discussed. Should we stain every culture by Ziehl-Neelsen's and Moeller's methods or apply heat-resistance tests, or do we restrict these tests to Gram-positive organisms or to those cultures which, by morphology, colony form, rate of growth, and other characters, we suspect may be acid-fast or able to produce spores? We do not know of any Gram-negative bacteria that are genuinely acid-fast and we think that it is reasonable to omit the Ziehl-Neelsen staining of Gram-negative organisms. Should we stain all cultures for spores and, failing to find them, try again after growing the cultures on soil extract agar or other spore-encouraging medium? We know that these tests are not done as a routine and, as the majority of cultures will show negative results we cannot advise that the search for sporing forms be made in all cases. All we would stress is that when spores are not looked for a mental note should be made that they have not been excluded, and their possible presence borne in mind.

Motility may be studied in a hanging-drop or other wet preparation. Some strains are only sluggishly motile when first isolated; motility may be speeded by using Craigie's technique (Craigie, 1931; Tulloch, 1939) in which the inoculation is made into a central tube of sloppy agar and, after incubation, a subculture is made from those organisms that, by their motility, have migrated outside the central tube. Motility may be inferred by observing the spreading growth in a semisolid agar (Tittsler & Sandholzer, 1936) which may be seen better when a tetrazolium dye is incorporated in the medium; as the organisms grow the dye is reduced, and the medium changes colour (Kelly & Fulton, 1953). The temperature of incubation is important: most motile organisms are motile at lower temperatures (e.g. 15–25° C) and may not be motile at their optimal temperature (e.g. 37° C) for growth.

The problem pertaining to motility is: do we test all strains or only rods? If we only examine the rods we shall overlook the motility of many strains of *Streptococcus faecalis*, of *Micrococcus agilis*, and other cocci. When these tests become part of the daily routine they do not take up much extra time; they are only time consuming and upsetting of routine when they are 'special tests'. Our remarks refer to the motility shown by aerobic organisms; anaerobes present special problems in that motility will be inhibited by the air in hanging-drop preparations. Capillary tube preparations, sealed at each end, from cooked meat cultures, are more likely to show motility in clostridia.

Some bacteria (cytophaga) are motile by a gliding movement and to observe this special media and techniques are necessary. This type of movement is not only affected by the concentration of agar in the medium, but also by the concentration of peptone. Such organisms are not likely to be found in pathological specimens because the methods used by medical bacteriologists are not suitable for showing this gliding motility. Lautrop (1961), Halvorsen (1963) and Piéchaud (1963) found it in *Bacterium anitratum* (*Acinetobacter anitratus*) and *Moraxella lwoffi* (*A. lwoffii*).

The **catalase** test is simple and seldom causes difficulty; a few strains (e.g. *Aerococcus viridans*) produce a weakly positive reaction which may easily be missed by those looking only for strong reactions. Gagnon, Hunting & Esselen (1959) devised a method that might be applied to bacteriology; the material under test was spread on disks of filter paper which were dropped in 3 % H_2O_2; when catalase was present the evolution of oxygen quickly brought the disks to the surface. Thomas (1963) suggests a slide method which she claims to be sensitive and easy to read. Dacre & Sharpe (1956) recommend a medium of low glucose content to detect catalase production by certain atypical lactobacilli.

The **oxidase** test has been used to pick out colonies of *Neisseria* species in mixed cultures (Gordon & McLeod, 1928; McLeod *et al.* 1934; McLeod, 1947), but its wider use originated with the test devised by Kovacs (1956) to distinguish pseudomonads from the enteric bacteria. When due precautions are taken to avoid oxidation of the reagent, the test is sensitive and useful in classification and identification (Steel, 1961). Leclerc & Beerens (1962) use a similar technique to Kovacs' but substitute the more stable dimethyl for the tetramethyl compound. Brisou *et al.* (1962) suggested a modification of Kovacs' method that is said to make the result of the test more clear-cut and easier to read. In the U.S.A. the term cytochrome oxidase is used for the reaction, and the methods used are those of Gaby & Hadley (1957) and Ewing & Johnson (1960).

Carbohydrate breakdown. The so-called 'fermentation tests' were used by the early bacteriologists to distinguish one organism from another and elaborate diagnostic tables were based on them (see for example Castellani & Chalmers, 1919). The introduction of the simple gas tube (Durham, 1898) and indicators enabled the production of gas and acid to be detected by inspection.

The failure to standardize methods has led to discrepant results in the hands of different workers, and it is only within the last decade that taxonomists have given adequate thought to the significance of acid production by a bacterium growing in a medium containing a carbohydrate. In such a medium we provide peptones which, during growth of the organism, are broken down to substances which are alkaline in reaction; if, in the medium, there is a carbohydrate, alcohol, or other substance commonly called a 'sugar' that can be broken down by the bacteria either by oxidation or by fermentation, acid will be produced, but it will be detected by an indicator in the medium only when the acid produced from sugar exceeds the alkali from peptone. The visibility of the reaction is also influenced by (i) the buffering properties of the medium, and (ii) the indicator used, e.g. bromthymol blue shows acid production when the pH value falls to 6·0 or less, whereas bromcresol purple does not change colour until the pH has fallen to about 5. Peptone water sugars, which are commonly used in this country and continental Europe, have less buffering power and yield less alkali than the broth-based sugars used extensively in the U.S.A. and elsewhere. With peptone water sugars we normally use Andrade's indicator (which becomes pink at about pH 5·5) or bromcresol purple (yellow at about pH 5), and it is fortunate that with the Enterobacteriaceae these give approximately the same results as broth based sugars with bromthymol blue (yellow at about pH 6·0).

Some bacteria will not grow on simple media and need an enriched sugar medium. Streptococci and corynebacteria are grown in media containing serum; neisseria in media enriched by serum or ascitic fluid; haemophilic bacteria in sugar media to which X and V factors have been added. Organisms which oxidize sugars do not always show much acid production when they are grown in tubes of liquid media, and more reliable results are obtained by growing them on the surface of solid media, which exposes the organism to an adequate supply of air. Some oxidizers (such as *Pseudomonas* species) do not give reliable 'sugar reactions' on peptone-containing media, and these should be grown on media with an ammonium salt as the main nitrogen source.

The O–F test. To find out whether the attack on sugar is by oxidation or fermentation, the O–F test is made by growing the bacterium in two tubes of Hugh & Leifson's (1953) medium; the medium in one tube is covered with a layer of soft paraffin (petrolatum). Oxidizers show acid production in the open tube only, fermenters show acid in the paraffin-covered tube, and usually in the open tube. The usual sugar included in the Hugh & Leifson medium is glucose but, because of the occurrence of organisms which do not attack glucose but break down other sugars (Hugh & Ryschenkow, 1961; Koontz & Faber, 1963) the need for a test using the basal medium + maltose or pentoses

3

23

should be considered. Various modifications to the medium have been suggested, and to avoid confusion we do not use the term 'Hugh & Leifson test', but prefer the more descriptive term Oxidation–Fermentation (O–F) test.

In connexion with the O–F test two points deserve mention: (i) the organism may not be able to grow in the Hugh & Leifson type medium, in which case the test must be repeated using a basal medium enriched with 2 % serum or 0·1 % yeast extract; (ii) the organism may grow but not produce acid in either tube. This result should be confirmed by inoculation of media with other kinds of base + glucose. Leifson (1963) found that bromthymol blue was toxic to some bacteria, and modified the O–F medium for marine organisms.

The O–F test is one of the most important tests carried out in the early stages in the identification of aerobic bacteria. Most genera are composed of bacteria that either oxidize or ferment glucose; when a genus contains some species that attack glucose by oxidation and other species by fermentation, there would seem to be reason to reconsider the taxonomy of the genus and the desirability of dividing it (see Chapter 9).

Some organisms do not appear to be able to attack a sugar readily, and often show acid production only after several days of incubation. Lederberg (1950) found that this delay was due to failure of the sugar to reach the inside of the bacterial cell, and a test (the ONPG, q.v. p. 34) was devised to reveal quickly the potential fermentative power of the 'late lactose fermenters'.

The **ability to grow in air** is a character shared by all bacteria except the strict anaerobes; it is a feature needed in Table I for the identification of certain anaerobes (especially *Clostridium welchii*) in which spore formation may be difficult to show, and which, without this line, would appear to be placed among the lactobacilli, corynebacteria, or other Gram-positive rods.

SECONDARY TESTS

Aesculin hydrolysis is a test of value for streptococci and some other groups, and may be demonstrated in one of two ways. The usual method is to incorporate the glycoside in a nutrient base together with a ferric salt; hydrolysis is indicated by a brown coloration due to reaction of the aglycone (6:7-dihydroxycoumarin) with the iron. Alternatively, the use of the glucose portion of the molecule can be detected by acid or acid and gas production.

Bile solubility is used to distinguish pneumococci from the viridans types of streptococci; however, the test is not specific for *Streptococcus pneumoniae*. The pneumococcus differs from other streptococci in having an autolytic enzyme which can be demonstrated by allowing a digest broth culture to age in the incubator; at 24 hours the broth is turbid; after a few days the medium will become clear. Bile and bile salts activate the autolytic enzyme, and so will not produce clearing of a heat-killed culture or one that is too acid; the suspension to be tested should be about pH 7·2. At one time crude bile was used for the test but the isolation of various bile salts in a pure state showed that certain of them were more active than others (Downie *et al.* 1931). Sodium deoxycholate is used as it can be obtained in a reasonable state of purity.

Citrate utilization is tested in Koser's (1923) citrate medium or in a similar medium solidified by agar (Simmons, 1926); Vaughn *et al.* (1950) believe that the addition of agar invalidates the test. The medium must be in chemically clean tubes. In tests of this kind the inoculum should be small and free from medium on which the organism has grown. To avoid carry-over, use a straight wire instead of a loop, and inoculate from a light suspension in water, saline or buffer. All positives should be confirmed by sub-culture (again using a wire) to another tube of the same medium.

Other citrate media, such as Christensen's, contain additional nutrients and do not test the ability of the organism to use the citrate radical as a sole carbon source. An organism growing in Koser's or Simmons' medium will grow on Christensen's medium, but one growing on Christensen's medium may not grow on the other two media (but see Piéchaud & Szturm-Rubinsten, 1963).

The **coagulase** test was developed from observations that certain staphylococci clotted plasma from the goose (Loeb, 1903), man, horse, and sheep (Much, 1908), and Gratia (1920) introduced the name staphylocoagulase for the active agent. At least two sub-stances go to make up staphylocoagulase, bound and free coagulases, but the tube methods of carrying out the coagulase test do not distinguish between them; the slide test (Cadness-Graves *et al.* 1943) detects bound coagulase.

The type of plasma used in the test may affect the result; the anticoagulant should not be citrate alone for this will be removed by citrate-using bacteria such as *Klebsiella aerogenes* (Harper & Conway, 1948) or certain streptococci (Evans, Buettner & Niven, 1952), with the result that a clot will form after prolonged incubation and give the (false) appearance of a delayed positive coagulase test. Harper & Conway recommend that heparin be added to citrated plasma to prevent clotting of fibrin when the citrate is withdrawn. A filterable coagulase-like factor produced by some streptococci will not clot heparinized plasma (Wood, 1959). The species of animal from which the plasma is derived is important; for staphylococci of human origin plasma from man or rabbit should be used, sheep or bovine plasma gives fewer positives and guinea-pig plasma gives even fewer. When strains from animals other than man are under test, it is advisable to run the test with plasmas of several animal species, including the one from which the strains were isolated.

The coagulase test is simple, so simple that there are almost as many ways of doing it as there are bacteriologists. Williams & Harper (1946) compared many of the methods, and those given in Appendix D are based on their recommendations and our own experience and preference. We draw attention to points that we regard as important. Occasionally a strain will be isolated that produces so much fibrinolysin early in its growth that a clot from coagulase action never becomes visible. Sometimes a small clot forms early but lyses quickly; for this reason a reading should be made an hour after the test has been put up. Some strains produce only small amounts of coagulase and the clot may only be seen after overnight incubation. Each batch of plasma should be tested to show that it is suitable for the coagulase test; filtered plasma is generally unsuitable. Positive and negative controls should be included in the tests put up each day. The use of fibrinogen was investigated by Cadness-Graves et al. (1943) and was found to be a suitable substitute for plasma. Dried plasma can also be used (Colbeck & Proom, 1944).

Decarboxylases for amino acids are characteristic for different bacteria within the Enterobacteriaceae (Møller, 1954 a, c). Initially the determination of the decarboxylases was a research problem but Møller (1955) developed simpler technical methods so that the decarboxylase pattern became a useful taxonomic tool at a higher level than antigenic structure. Glutamic acid decarboxylase, which is characteristic of *Escherichia*, *Shigella*, and *Proteus* (including Providence), cannot yet be determined simply, but arginine dihydrolase, and lysine and ornithine decarboxylases can now be detected simply by observing the colour change of an indicator. Falkow (1958) introduced even simpler tests but we found that they were not satisfactory with klebsiellas; they cannot, therefore, be used with organisms of unknown identity. Arginine is hydrolyzed by some but not all streptococci and corynebacteria (Niven, Smiley & Sherman, 1942); methods of detecting arginine hydrolysis by pseudomonads are described by Sherris et al. (1959) and Thornley (1960). Steel & Midgley (1962) surveyed many different genera and found the decarboxylase pattern informative.

Digestion of meat, inspissated serum, Dorset egg or casein is used as an indicator of proteolytic activity. At one time gelatin liquefaction was used to detect proteolysis, but gelatinase is not a true proteolytic enzyme.

Ethylhydrocuprein or **optochin inhibition** of the pneumococcus was described by Moore in 1915, but as a diagnostic test it has had a chequered career. Soon after its introduction it fell into disrepute and, as a means of distinguishing pneumococci from viridans streptococci, it was superseded by the bile solubility test, especially when the more highly purified bile salts became available (Downie et al. 1931). Recently the optochin test has come into its own again; ethylhydrocuprein is applied to localized areas of a plate by impregnated paper disks (Bowers & Jeffries, 1955; Bowen et al. 1957). In the concentration recommended by Bowers & Jeffries a small zone (1–2 mm beyond the disk) of inhibition may occur with a few viridans streptococci but pneumococci are inhibited more obviously and the zone extends 5 mm or more. The advantage of the optochin test over bile solubility is that the disk can be applied to any plate culture of the organism under test, whereas for bile solubility the suspension or broth culture must be of about neutral pH value. When small zones of inhibition are ignored and 5 mm is the minimum to be recorded as positive, the specificity of the optochin test for the pneumococcus is claimed to be high. Bowers & Jeffries (1955) found that only one of 243 pneumococci failed to be inhibited; the exception was found to be avirulent for mice and was thought to be in the R form (however, the R pneumococci are bile soluble).

Gelatin hydrolysis or **liquefaction** is shown by a test in which the organism grows in a nutrient medium solidified by gelatin; the disadvantages of the liquefaction test are (i) different samples of gelatin vary in gelling power; (ii) the cultures are incubated at a temperature (22° C) below the melting point of the medium (about 25° C) and mesophilic organisms may grow very slowly or not at all; (iii) some bacteria will not grow in the medium. To overcome the second of these difficulties the cultures may be incubated at the optimal temperature for growth and later refrigerated to see whether the gelatin has retained its gelling property; a suitable control is uninoculated medium exposed for the same length of time to the same temperature.

Gelatin stab cultures may need weeks of incubation before showing liquefaction. Hucker (1924a), working with micrococci, found a curious relation between length of incubation and the first appearance of liquefaction; when the number of liquefying strains was plotted against duration of incubation there were two peaks, one after about 1–2 weeks, the second after about 3 months incubation. The significance of tests of such long duration is doubtful (the gelatin may be denatured) and they are quite useless in identification work. However, the gelatin stab test should not be discarded; some species will liquefy it overnight, others will take longer, and these differences may be helpful in distinguishing between species (e.g. *Enterobacter cloacae*, which takes a week or more, and *Serratia marcescens*, which liquefies gelatin in 1–2 days). For identification work the duration of incubation must be limited to a reasonable period, and we suggest that one of the rapid methods should be run in parallel. Frazier's (1926) test has the advantage that the gelatin is in agar and the medium does not melt at 37° C. After growth of the organism, the plate is flooded with an acid mercuric chloride solution which reacts with the gelatin in the medium to produce an opacity; where gelatin has been hydrolyzed the medium remains clear.

A rapid method devised by Kohn (1953) uses gelatin-charcoal disks hardened by formaldehyde; these do not melt at 37° C and can be added to peptone water cultures which are then returned to the incubator; preformed or induced enzyme will hydrolyze the gelatin and liberate the charcoal particles. Our experience with these disks is limited but there seem to be uncontrolled factors that produce considerable variations between different batches of disks. However, Lautrop (1956a), using Difco gelatin, reported favourably on the method. Green & Larks (1955) devised an even quicker micromethod in which Kohn's disks were used (see Appendix E). Thirst (1957b) and Hoyt & Pickett (1957) developed microscope-slide techniques which were similar to one described by Pickford & Dorris (1934), who found that the gelatin of photographic plates and film could be removed by proteolytic enzymes and bacteria. LeMinor & Piéchaud (1963) describe a method in which the silver sulphide of exposed and developed film can be seen to be released when the gelatin is liquefied.

Gluconate is converted by some bacteria to 2-ketogluconate which can be detected by the appearance of a reducing substance in the medium. Haynes (1951) found this test helpful in identifying *Pseudomonas aeruginosa*. Shaw & Clarke (1955) simplified the test and reported that it was useful for klebsiellas. When *Klebsiella* species were compared with *Enterobacter*, Cowan et al. (1960) found that klebsiellas with IMViC reactions $- - + +$ and *Enterobacter* species were gluconate-positive, but the klebsiellas with other IMViC reactions were often gluconate-negative.

Growth or failure to grow on specified media can, depending on the media themselves, indicate (i) nutritional needs; (ii) sensitivity or insensitivity to substance(s) in the medium; (iii) ability to use a specified compound as source of particular elements. Examples of the characters revealed are: (i) growth on blood agar but not on the basal medium indicates a need for enrichment with blood; (ii) (a) failure to grow on MacConkey accompanied by growth on nutrient agar, shows sensitivity to bile salt; (b) growth on media containing 6·5 % NaCl shows an unusual degree of salt tolerance; (iii) failure to grow on Koser's citrate medium shows that the organism cannot use citrate as carbon source under the conditions tested. These utilization tests must be adequately controlled to prevent carry-over from the medium on which the inoculum was grown (see citrate utilization, p. 25).

Haemolysin production and **haemolysis** are not always cause and effect, and the ability to produce a soluble haemolysin is not necessarily associated with zones of haemolysis on blood agar plates (Elek & Levy, 1954). Streptococci produce haemolytic zones on the surface of blood agar made from the blood of most animal species and these organisms are rightly named haemolytic streptococci. The haemolysins produced by streptococci may be oxygen-labile (streptolysin O) or oxygen-stable (streptolysin S) and they need different conditions for their production; on blood agar plates, however, similar zones of haemolysis are produced. Brown (1919) studied the haemolytic zones around streptococcus colonies in poured plates and labelled the types of haemolysis α (green zone, cell envelopes intact), β (clear, colourless zone, cell envelopes dissolved) and γ (no action on red cells). The term γ-haemolysis is an anachronism and describes a negative result.

28

The application of the first two terms, α and β, has been extended to the haemolytic zones seen around colonies on the surface of blood agar, and although this is not in accordance with Brown's usage, it is a convention that is well understood.

Streptococci that produce α-haemolysis or green zones on blood agar are often described as the 'greening streptococci'. The species name *Streptococcus viridans* has been attached to several different kinds of greening streptococci, but as the species has never been adequately characterized, the name is now seldom used.

Staphylococci behave differently on plates made with the blood of different species and it is misleading to speak of haemolytic staphylococci because the haemolysis may be due to a haemolysin or to a lipolytic enzyme (Orcutt & Howe, 1922). The soluble haemolysins can be used to detect the toxins produced by some strains of staphylococci; thus rabbit cell haemolysin is one manifestation of α-toxin, and sheep cell 'hot-cold' lysin is a characteristic of β-toxin. These toxins are not used in characterizing different species of *Staphylococcus* and so do not appear in our diagnostic tables.

Among strains of *Clostridium*, however, the different kinds of toxin produced may determine the species, and as some of the toxins are haemolytic, these could appear in tables showing the finer subdivision of the genus. The haemolytic activity of certain vibrios is said to have distinguishing value; with these organisms not only is the species of red cell attacked important, but also we should know whether calcium is needed for or inhibits haemolysis (De *et al.* 1954).

Hippurate may be hydrolyzed to benzoate by bacterial action, and the ability to do this is limited to certain bacteria, of which it is an important characteristic. The end-product is tested for by the addition of ferric chloride which precipitates both hippurate and benzoate but the hippurate is more readily soluble in excess. The final concentration of iron is critical and to find the optimal amount of $FeCl_3$ to add, uninoculated tubes of medium, on which a titration can be made, are incubated with the test cultures.

The methods of Ayers & Rupp (1922) and Hare & Colebrook (1934) for streptococci use a relatively rich basal medium in which the organism will grow without hippurate. The Hajna & Damon (1934) method for coliforms uses Koser's medium (without citrate) as a base and the test becomes a test of the organism's ability to use hippurate as a source of carbon as well as its ability to hydrolyze it. Thirst (1957a) added an indicator so that the growth may be seen more readily.

Hydrogen sulphide production by bacteria is such a common feature that, of itself, it has little differential value. The H_2S test is one that can be made as sensitive as a worker wishes (for a review see Clarke, 1953a); with an adequate sulphur source (cysteine) and a delicate indicator (lead acetate papers) almost all the enteric bacteria can be shown to have the ability to produce H_2S. Tested in this way we obtain an accurate estimate of an organism's katabolic power in relation to sulphur compounds but we can not distinguish readily between those organisms that have much and those that have little ability to produce H_2S. With a poor medium or a less sensitive indicator (ferrous chloride or lead acetate in the medium) we detect only the strong H_2S-producers. This is the kind of test used by the enterobacteriologists who have developed tests of low sensitivity that make possible clear distinctions between *Escherichia* and *Salmonella* and even between different salmonellas. Two media yield results of this kind, ferrous chloride gelatin and triple sugar-iron agar (TSI); both are recommended by the international Enterobacteriaceae Subcommittee (Report, 1958), and their formulae are given in Appendix A. Lead acetate papers are not only ten times more sensitive than lead acetate in the medium, but they eliminate the toxicity of lead for the growing bacteria (ZoBell & Feltham, 1934). In the Brucella group the time of H_2S production may be significant; this is found by changing the lead acetate papers each day.

Indole is volatile and can be detected either by testing the medium with *p*-dimethylamino-benzaldehyde or by a paper strip impregnated with oxalic acid held near the mouth of the test tube by the cotton plug. Both methods are sensitive and usually give the same result; occasionally all the indole volatilizes and only the paper strip is positive. Extraction of the indole from the liquid culture increases the sensitivity of the test; ether, xylol and petroleum have been used, but all are potentially dangerous if, following the usual bacteriological techniques, the mouth of the tube is flamed. Kovács' (1928) reagent has the advantage that the solvent (amyl alcohol) is present in the test solution. Oxalic acid papers (Gnezda, 1899; Holman & Gonzales, 1923) and papers soaked in *p*-dimethylaminobenzaldehyde (Gillies, 1956) are sensitive indicators of indole.

Temperature of incubation may affect the result; Taylor (1945–6) found three strains of *Escherichia coli* that were indole-negative at 37° C but positive at 30° C. Some organisms (e.g. *Clostridium* spp.) may break down indole; Reed (1942) found that with some species this happened so slowly that indole could always be detected in cultures 1–10 days old, but *C. sporogenes* used it so quickly that they gave negative results when cultures were grown for only one day in a medium containing 1 mg indole/100 ml broth.

The **KCN** test distinguishes those bacteria that can grow in the presence of cyanide and those that cannot grow in the stated concentration. When we report a strain as KCN-positive we mean that it is resistant and that it grows in Møller's (1954*b*) KCN-medium. KCN-negative strains, i.e. those that do not grow, should be subcultured to the basal medium without KCN; if they cannot grow in the basal medium the test is without significance. Møller (1954*b*) used waxed corks to prevent loss of cyanide from the tubes; these are unpleasant to handle and we prefer to use small screw-capped bottles (Rogers & Taylor, 1961).

Those who use the test assume certain responsibilities; KCN and HCN are extremely toxic and the KCN solution should be kept in a locked cupboard. After use the cyanide in the medium should be destroyed by adding ferrous sulphate and alkali before the tubes or bottles are put in the autoclave.

Lecithovitellin (LV) is the lipoprotein component of egg-yolk and can be obtained as a clear yellow liquid by mixing egg-yolk with saline. This liquid becomes opalescent when mixed with certain bacterial toxins or lecithinases; flocculation and separation of a thick curd of fat may follow. When lecithinase-forming organisms are grown on a solid medium containing LV, the lecithinase diffuses into the agar and produces zones of opalescence around individual colonies. This reaction can be inhibited by adding certain antitoxic or antilecithinase sera to the surface of the medium before inoculation. Lipolytic organisms also produce an opalescence on LV agar and it is often accompanied by a distinctive 'pearly layer' or iridescent film; the presence of free fatty acid can be demonstrated by treating the medium, after incubation, with copper sulphate solution (Willis, 1960b). The ability to produce an opacity on LV agar is useful in the division of the genera *Bacillus* and *Clostridium*, but other organisms, such as *Pseudomonas aeruginosa* and *Staphylococcus aureus*, may give positive reactions.

The LV reaction is not due solely to a lecithinase, and Willis & Gowland (1962) consider that separation of insoluble protein, splitting of fats from lipoprotein complexes, and coalescence of particles of free fat are all involved. In many laboratories medium containing human serum (Nagler, 1939) has been replaced by egg-yolk medium.

The **malonate** test was introduced by Leifson (1933) to help distinguish *Escherichia coli* from *Klebsiella aerogenes*, and with these organisms he found a perfect correlation with the V–P test. Shaw (1956) showed that most strains of the Arizona group were malonate-positive and most other kinds of salmonella were malonate-negative. Both these groups are V–P negative and there is clearly no correlation between the malonate and V–P tests. The test was described as a fermentation by Leifson and as a utilization by Shaw in spite of the fact that she added yeast extract to stimulate growth.

Milk (usually as litmus milk or bromcresol purple milk) is a good nutrient medium in which most organisms will grow and it has a fairly constant composition since man only interferes by removing the cream and adding an indicator. Although highly esteemed elsewhere, in the medical laboratory litmus (or bromcresol purple) milk occupies a secondary position and most bacteriologists believe that the information it gives can be obtained more certainly in other media. An objection to milk is that unless a change takes place in the appearance of the medium (e.g. acid or clot formation) one cannot be sure that growth has occurred.

Milk contains lactose, galactose, a trace of glucose, casein, and mineral salts. Acid production from the fermentation of lactose is shown by a change in colour of the indicator, and, when much acid is produced, by the formation of a clot. But another form of clot may be produced by rennet; in this case the clot forms and later, like the fibrin clot in blood, contracts and expresses a clear whey. By contrast the acid clot does not contract. When the bacterium also produces proteolytic enzymes the clot may be peptonized. Apart from the rennet clot (for which milk is a unique medium) all the other reactions can be detected more easily by using media appropriate for each reaction.

The **MR (methyl red)** test and **V–P (Voges–Proskauer)** test for acetylmethylcarbinol or acetoin may be carried out on the same tube of culture and are discussed together. The tests are mainly used to distinguish various coliform organisms from each other; all these ferment glucose vigorously and the pH value of the glucose medium falls quickly. When methyl red is added after overnight incubation the cultures of all these organisms will be found to be acid to the dye, i.e. MR-positive. After further incubation *Escherichia coli* cultures produce even more acid and in spite of phosphate buffer in the medium may be self-sterilizing; the MR test remains positive. *Klebsiella aerogenes* cultures, on the other hand, decarboxylate and condense the pyruvic acid to form acetylmethyl-carbinol, the pH value rises and, when methyl red is added, the colour is yellow, i.e. MR-negative. Nowadays there is a tendency to do biochemical tests earlier but the temptation to speed up the MR test must be resisted; the MR should never be read until the cultures have been incubated for at least 2 days at 37° C or 3 days at 30° C. The reaction cannot be accelerated by increasing the glucose content of the medium; Clark & Lubs (1915) found that, in media with much above 1 % glucose, cultures of *K. aerogenes* did not revert to become MR-negative.

The V–P test can be carried out in many ways and almost any desired degree of sensi-tivity can be obtained. It is now generally thought that the older methods (Harden & Norris, 1912) are too slow and insensitive, but there is less agreement about the method to be recommended or the sensitivity that gives the best differentiation between taxa. Although Clark & Lubs (1915) specified 30° C for the test, the MR and V–P tests were often carried out on cultures that had been incubated at 37° C. For many years water bacteriologists have recommended 30° C (Report, 1956b) and we now know that some enteric bacteria such as the Hafnia group are often V–P negative at 37° C but positive at 30° C or lower. In a comparative trial we found that incubation for 5 days (at 30° C) was the minimum time needed to detect by Barritt's method (1936) all the positives among the enteric bacteria; for other organisms (e.g. staphylococci) longer incubation up to 10 days gave more positive results. Others have reported that acetylmethyl-carbinol may be broken down and used as a carbon source by various coliforms (Linton, 1925; Paine, 1927; Ruchhoft *et al.* 1931; Tittsler, 1938), *Bacillus* species (Williams & Morrow, 1928) and staphylococci (Segal, 1940). Taylor (1951) found that O'Meara's (1931) fumarate medium prevented the breakdown of acetylmethylcarbinol by soft-rot bacteria and allowed it to accumulate.

32

Outside the field of enteric bacteria it has been found that phosphate may interfere with the production of acetoin; Smith, Gordon & Clark (1946) recommend a medium in which the phosphate is replaced by NaCl, and Abd-el-Malek & Gibson (1948b) use a simple glucose peptone broth without salt or phosphate. For several years we compared glucose phosphate broth with the media recommended by Smith et al. and by Abd-el-Malek & Gibson, and we came to the conclusion that glucose peptone was the most suitable for *Bacillus* and *Staphylococcus* and glucose phosphate broth was best for the enteric bacteria and most other organisms.

After comparing methods for the V–P test over several years we chose Barritt's (1936) method as our standard; the sensitivity was found to be midway between O'Meara's (1931) and Batty-Smith's (1941) methods. For a useful review of the V–P test see Eddy (1961).

Niacin (nicotinic acid) production is a characteristic feature of human tubercle bacilli and distinguishes them from bovine tubercle bacilli and other mycobacteria (Pope & Smith, 1946). Several modifications of the test method have been devised; all are based on the extraction of niacin from the bacterial growth and subsequent detection by a colorimetric reaction. Users of the test must exercise caution as one of the reagents (cyanogen bromide) is lachrymatory and toxic.

Nitrate reduction may be shown either by detecting the presence of one of the breakdown products, or by showing the disappearance of nitrate from the medium. The products of reduction may include nitrite, hyponitrite, hydroxylamine, ammonia, nitrous oxide, or gaseous nitrogen. The first test to be applied aims at showing the presence of nitrite. When this test is negative (i.e. nitrite is not detected) we test the medium to see whether there is residual nitrate; if this test also is negative we know that the first stage of the breakdown has been completed and the nitrite further broken down.

Test	Result	Interpretation
(i) For nitrite	colour not changed (negative)	nitrite not present (see (iii) below)
(ii) For nitrite	red colour (positive)	nitrate reduced to nitrite
(iii) Zinc dust added to (i)	A, colour not changed	nitrite not present: therefore —NO_3 in original medium has been reduced by the bacteria
	B, red colour	—NO_3 in medium reduced to —NO_2 by zinc but not by the bacteria

In uninoculated nitrate broth or cultures of organisms that do not reduce nitrate the test for nitrite is negative until zinc dust (ZoBell, 1932) or other reducing agent is added to the culture medium to reduce the nitrate contained in it. To detect small amounts of residual nitrate the amount of zinc added may be critical (Steel & Fisher, 1961). The tests are very sensitive and it is important to check the uninoculated medium for nitrite, which should not be present.

Some workers prefer to carry out the test in a semisolid medium (ZoBell, 1932); others insist that free access to oxygen is necessary for nitrate reduction by aerobes.

Conn (1936) discussed the difficulty of recording the results of the nitrate reduction test, and advised that the terms positive and negative be avoided. Instead the actual finding(s) should be recorded.

An entirely different method was described by Cook (1950) who found that when nitrate was included in blood agar base, nitrate reducing bacteria growing on the blood agar reduced the haemoglobin to methaemoglobin; this method has the advantage that the change seen is apparent even when the organism can reduce nitrite.

Nitrite reduction can be brought about by certain bacteria incapable of reducing nitrate (ZoBell, 1932). It can be shown by growing the organism in a broth containing 0·01 % $NaNO_2$ and, after sufficient time for the reduction to take place, testing for residual nitrite.

The **ONPG** (*o*-nitrophenyl-β-D-galactopyranoside) test is used to detect potential lactose fermenters which, in ordinary media, either take several days to produce acid or do not produce any acid. Lactose fermentation depends on two enzymes (i) an induced intracellular enzyme, β-galactosidase, which attacks lactose, and (ii) a permease which regulates penetration of the cell wall. Kriebel (1934) found that late-lactose-fermenters produced acid more quickly when the concentration of lactose was increased to 5 %; Chilton & Fulton (1946) recommended 10 % lactose in agar. Lederberg (1950) used ONPG for the study of β-galactosidase, and Le Minor & Ben Hamida (1962) developed a rapid ONPG test on toluene-treated bacterial cultures. Lowe (1962) found that toluene treatment was not essential to liberate the β-galactosidase and that overnight incubation of cultures in peptone water containing ONPG hydrolyzed the colourless substrate to the yellow *o*-nitrophenol.

Phenylalanine can be converted by oxidative deamination to phenylpyruvic acid (PPA) which, like many other keto acids, can be identified by adding ferric chloride (Singer & Volcani, 1955). The phenylalanine test was first used in bacteriology by Henriksen & Closs (1938) who found that *Proteus* species gave the strongest reactions but reported that *Klebsiella aerogenes* also gave some positives. Since then Henriksen (1950) and other users of the test (Buttiaux *et al.* 1954; Singer & Bar-Chey, 1954; Shaw & Clarke, 1955) have found it to be almost specific for *Proteus* and Providence. This specificity prompted Singer & Bar-Chey to put the Providence organisms into the genus *Proteus*.

Phosphatase activity was used by Barber & Kuper (1951) to aid the identification of pathogenic staphylococci; they found a high degree of correlation between phosphatase and coagulase production. By prolonging the incubation period, Baird-Parker (1963) demonstrated phosphatase production in 378 of 546 strains of staphylococci and 10 of 677 strains of micrococci. Some workers prefer a liquid medium and Lewis (1961) compared the plate and tube methods; he found that essentially similar results were obtainable in a liquid medium incubated for 6 hours and on a solid medium incubated for 18 hours with coagulase-positive staphylococci, but the tube method showed far fewer phosphatase-positive coagulase-negative strains. Among enteric bacteria, Vörös et al. (1961) found phosphatase to be produced only by strains of Proteus and Providence; using the same technique we were unable to confirm this specificity and found positives also in the Salmonella, Shigella, Klebsiella, and Escherichia groups.

This test must not be confused with the phosphatase test applied to milk as an index of efficiency of pasteurization.

Pigment formation often has considerable diagnostic value and it is an advantage to know how to encourage it. Although the pigments produced are seldom photosynthetic, most bacteria dealt with in this *Manual* form pigment better in the light; this is most noticeable in the staphylococci and serratias, but also occurs in the pseudomonads and in chromobacteria. The effect of light on pigment production by mycobacteria has become a means of distinguishing species. Temperature and medium also influence the intensity of pigmentation; most bacteria produce pigments better at temperatures below the optimum for growth. In England room temperature is usually so low that the organism may fail to grow; in such cases a 22° C incubator is useful.

Medium probably has the biggest effect on the development of pigment. In some cases the simple addition of glucose will enhance pigmentation, in other cases this will inhibit it. The old adage that 'one man's meat is another man's poison' applies to bacterial pigment production and different formulae are needed for different organisms. The elimination of all meat extracts and the addition of mannitol are beneficial for *Chromobacterium* species and may improve pigmentation of *Serratia* (Goldsworthy & Still, 1936, 1938); quite different media are needed to encourage pigmentation by pseudomonads (see Appendix A, pp. 106–7).

Survival under certain adverse conditions (usually heat) may have diagnostic significance; e.g. a streptococcus that survives heating at 60° C for 30 minutes is likely to be a group D streptococcus. The tests themselves are not easy to standardize and the methods used by different authors vary greatly. For example, after the heating test for *Streptococcus faecalis* an immediate subculture may fail to show growth, whereas if the heated broth is incubated overnight before a subculture is made, this later subculture is more likely to grow. Other factors that may affect the result are the medium or suspending fluid in which the heating is carried out, its pH value, the time allowed for the medium to heat up to the desired temperature, and the type of container, particularly the thickness of the glass, in which the sample is heated. Some authors (Abd-el-Malek & Gibson, 1948*a*) always use milk which they regard as a medium of more constant composition than man-made infusions and enzymic digests.

While the testing of vegetative bacteria for survival has its difficulties, the testing of spore-suspensions is even more full of pitfalls. The heat stability of spores varies from one species to another, but even in the same species it will vary from strain to strain, and spores of the same strain grown on different occasions do not necessarily have the same resistance to heat. For a discussion of this subject the reader is referred to papers by Kelsey (1958, 1961).

Temperature range for growth and optimal temperature are characteristic of different groups of bacteria; of those in the medical and veterinary fields the optimal temperature is usually between 35 and 40° C but the range for growth varies considerably. Some species (e.g. *Neisseria gonorrhoeae*) have only a narrow temperature range and rapidly die at temperatures outside the range; other organisms have a wide growth and an even wider survival range. In all cases the optimal temperature is near the maximum for growth.

Biochemical tests are usually made on cultures grown at the temperature optimal for growth; that this may not be optimal for the development of the product which is being tested is shown in acetoin production by hafnias which occurs at a lower temperature than the growth optimum. We have found that some salmonellas are able to grow on a medium containing an ammonium salt as nitrogen source at 30° C but will not grow on this medium at 37° C, the optimal temperature for growth on media providing organic nitrogen.

The ability of an organism to grow at 20–22, 30, and 37° C are tested in most laboratories and our diagnostic tables show, in general, the more specialized tests used by experts in different groups of bacteria; for these, easily adjusted water baths or incubators are needed. In the differentiation of species of *Mycobacterium* (Tables I*ga*, I*gb*) growth or survival is shown at twelve different temperatures.

Urease activity is tested in Christensen's (1946) urea medium which supports the growth of many bacteria. The urease activity of *Proteus* species is such that alkali can be shown in a highly buffered urea medium (Stuart, van Stratum & Rustigian, 1945) in which other enteric bacteria appear to be urease-negative; *Proteus* species can use urea nitrogen but most other urease-producing organisms need an additional nitrogen source. Urease activity is shown by alkali production from urea solutions, but, in at least two methods (Elek, 1948; Ortali & Samarani, 1955), Nessler's reagent is added to show the presence of ammonia.

RAPID METHODS

Methods have been developed by which the various characterizing tests can be made to yield their answers in minutes and hours, rather than in the day or days needed for the standard tests. These rapid techniques can be classified in three broad groups: (i) those using media in which two or more reactions can be observed at the same time, which, for want of a better name, we call *multitest media*; (ii) tests in which the volumes of reagents are reduced and, generally, the concentration of bacteria is increased; these are the *micromethods*; (iii) tests in which the reagents and sometimes the media are contained in tablets or impregnated paper, the *minitests*. Each kind of test will be discussed briefly and some references given. Those who use rapid methods like them, but there are many workers who prefer the slower standard tests.

Although these rapid methods find most use in clinical diagnostic work their accuracy depends as much as other methods on the use of pure cultures as starting material. Many of the methods are so rapid that the use of clean but not sterile glassware is permissible and plugs are not essential; but micromethods should not be made the excuse for relaxing the rigid discipline of bacteriological techniques for the carefree abandon of a biochemical laboratory. At the risk of being thought tedious, we repeat the warning given in Chapter 2 that the use of colonies directly from inhibitory media may lead to anomalous and confusing results and advise that all inoculations should be made from colonies on non-inhibitory media.

Multitest media. Russell introduced his double sugar agar slope in 1911 and since then there has been a succession of media containing multiple substrates which were intended to allow several observations to be made from one tube. Most of these media were introduced for speeding up the identification of bacteria from faeces but multiple tests can be carried out on media designed for the characterization of other organisms (Chapman, 1946; 1952). Kligler's (1917, 1918) iron agar formed the basis for TSI (triple sugar iron agar), which was apparently developed simultaneously by Sulkin & Willett (1940) and by workers in the Difco Laboratories (*Difco Manual*, 1953). Although TSI was introduced as a multipurpose medium, it has become an unofficial standard for H_2S production at a degree of sensitivity that has differential value among the enteric bacteria.

Knox (1949) described a multitest plate on which was spread a pure culture followed by coverslips and impregnated test papers. From this plate it was possible to detect H_2S production, mannitol, sucrose, and lactose fermentation, gas production, and swarming. Used in conjunction with a urea medium, the plate covered a wide range of tests some of which, when positive, suggested that the organism was not likely to be a pathogen and the culture could be discarded. Lányi & Ádám (1960) combined multiple impregnated paper disks of the Knox screening plate with a selective basal medium so

37

that colonies from a primary plate could be used as inoculum. The deoxycholate in the medium prevented interference by many organisms likely to be present in cultures of faeces.

Kohn (1954) developed media for a two-tube test for the identification of intestinal bacteria, and these media, as modified by Gillies (1956) soon became popular in England. Screw-capped containers are not suitable for multitest media (Marcus & Greaves, 1950).

Micromethods. Two different kinds of micromethods have been developed; both are rapid when compared with standard methods and, in almost all cases, the results corre-

Table 2. *References to micromethods for characterization tests*

Acetylmethylcarbinol	*Clarke & Cowan (1952)	Indole production (*cont.*)	
	*Fabrizio & Weaver (1951)		Cook & Knox (1949)
	Hoyt & Pickett (1957)		Galton, Hardy & Mitchell (1950)
	Pickett & Scott (1955)		
Catalase	Clarke & Cowan (1952)		Hoyt (1951)
	Thomas (1963)		Hoyt & Pickett (1957)
Citrate utilization	*Hargrove & Weaver (1951)		*Kaufman & Weaver (1960)
Coagulase	Cadness-Graves et al. (1943)		Kovács (1959)
	Griffith & Ostrander (1959)		Pickett, Scott & Hoyt (1955)
Decarboxylases	*Shaw & Clarke (1955)	Malonate	*Shaw & Clarke (1955)
'Fermentations'	*Bergquist & Searcy (1962)	Methylene blue reductase	Clarke & Cowan (1952)
	Bronfenbrenner & Schlesinger (1918)	MR test	Cowan (1953b)
	Clarke & Cowan (1952)	Nitrate reduction	*Bachmann & Weaver (1951)
	Cowan (1953a)		*Brough (1950)
	*Hannan & Weaver (1948)		*Clarke & Cowan (1952)
	Hoyt & Pickett (1957)	ONPG	LeMinor & Ben Hamida (1962)
	*Kaufman & Weaver (1960)		
	*McDade & Weaver (1959b)	Phenylalanine	Ben Hamida & LeMinor (1956)
	Pickett (1955)		
	Pickett & Nelson (1955)		*Henriksen (1950)
	Snyder (1954)		*Shaw & Clarke (1955)
	Tröger (1963)		Smith & Free (1962)
Gelatin hydrolysis	*Clarke & Cowan (1952)		Stewart (1961)
	*Green & Larks (1955)	Phosphatase	*White & Pickett (1953)
	Hoyt & Pickett (1957)	Starch hydrolysis	Clarke & Cowan (1952)
	*Kaufman & Weaver (1960)		Pickford & Dorris (1934)
	LeMinor & Piéchaud (1963)	Urease	Clarke & Cowan (1952)
	McDade & Weaver (1959a)		Cook (1948)
	Pickford & Dorris (1934)		Elek (1948)
	Thirst (1957b)		Galton, Hardy & Mitchell (1950)
Gluconate	*Cowan (1955b)		
	Shaw & Clarke (1955)		*Hormaeche & Munilla (1957)
Hippurate hydrolysis	Cowan (1955a)		Hoyt (1951)
H_2S production	*Clarke (1953a)		Hoyt & Pickett (1957)
	Clarke & Cowan (1952)		*NCTC method (unpublished)
	*Morse & Weaver (1950)		Ortali & Samarani (1955)
	Pickett, Scott & Hoyt (1955)		Pickett, Scott & Hoyt (1955)
Indole production	*Arnold & Weaver (1948)		*Stuart, van Stratum & Rustigian (1945)
	*Clarke & Cowan (1952)		

* The method is described briefly in Appendix E.

late well with them. The two kinds use different principles: in the first a heavy inoculum is grown in a small volume of medium, previously warmed to 37° C, and this type of test can show both preformed and induced enzymes. In the second kind, living suspensions in water, saline, or buffer are added to the test substrate; multiplication does not occur and the tests reveal only those enzymes that are preformed; for certain tests it is necessary to grow the organism on a special medium (to induce enzyme formation) before making the suspension. Several workers have developed individual microtests but Weaver and his colleagues, generally with growing cultures, produced a series which covered many of the characterizing tests of diagnostic bacteriology. Clarke & Cowan developed a series of micromethods which used non-multiplying suspensions; heavy suspensions were made from the growth on nutrient agar slopes but for the acetylmethyl-carbinol and gluconate tests suspensions were from the growth on glucose agar. In these microtests the measurement of volumes is not critical and the small volumes are measured with pipettes that deliver 50 drops of water per ml (Chick, 1908; Donald, 1913).

Those who use micromethods are continually trying to improve them particularly in regard to speed, sensitivity, and specificity. There is thus an ever-increasing number of modifications of the basic tests, and references to many of these are given in Table 2. Technical details of the methods marked with an asterisk are given in Appendix E.

Minitests. Hoyt (1951) and his colleagues pioneered a series of biochemical tests in which the substrate and, in some cases, the nutritional elements, were contained in a tablet. The objects were to reduce the storage space required for a wide variety of media, and to make possible the preparation of small batches or even individual tubes of specialized media. When tablets were placed in tubes and dissolved in a small volume of water the substrate was 'sterilized' by placing the tubes in a steamer; heavy inoculation produced rapid reactions so that the various tests could be completed within a few hours. Contaminating spores, not killed by the steaming, do not interfere with the speedy biochemical reactions; indeed it is doubtful whether multiplication occurs in these rapid tests, most of which depend on preformed enzymes.

Snyder (1954) developed tests in which impregnated filter paper was used as in the Knox (1949) screening plate. Paper sticks impregnated with reagent are sometimes used, for example Smith & Free (1962) use them for the phenylalanine test.

5

THEORY AND PRACTICE OF BACTERIAL IDENTIFICATION

In theory the identification of a bacterium consists of a comparison of the unknown with the known, the object being the ability to say that the unknown is like A (one of the knowns) and unlike B–Z (all other knowns); a subsidiary (some would say a more important) objective is to say that the unknown is A, i.e. to give it a name or identification tag. When we say that it is A we imply that it is different from the other knowns, B–Z. All identification schemes depend on knowing a great deal about the already identified (or known) units, but the human memory can cope only with a small proportion of this knowledge and memory aids make up the treasure chest of the diagnostician. In practice there are at present two distinct methods of making the identification, but a third method using a computer may soon become a practical proposition (Payne, 1963).

The first method is familiar to all biologists and is the dichotomous key. Characters are taken in turn and the keys are most successful when the feature can be expressed unequivocally as positive or negative. The only dichotomous key to deal comprehensively with bacteria is that devised by Skerman (1959). Another form, named a flow chart, was worked out by Manclark & Pickett (1961) and makes allowance for the variable reactions given by strains of some species. Thus, what we, in this *Manual*, call a 'd' character (different in different strains, positive in some, negative in others) is treated in the flow chart as both positive and negative, and the species appears in at least two places at the extremities.

Tables make up the second memory aid, and these are widely used in all laboratories. It is easier to see the essential characters in a table than in pages of descriptive matter, which is seldom precise and often made unnecessarily vague by phrases such as 'most strains are . . .', 'some strains do not . . .', 'not infrequently strains . . .', and the impossible 'strains showing no . . .'.

The construction of tables would be simplified if all strains of one species behaved alike, and if the results of all tests could be expressed as clear-cut positives and negatives. Unfortunately neither of these desiderata is likely to happen, and we are forced to use various symbols to indicate the constancy or inconstancy of characters.

The symbols now in use were developed from those used by Kauffmann, Edwards & Ewing (1956), and later adopted by the Enterobacteriaceae Subcommittee of the

International Committee on Bacteriological Nomenclature. Neither Kauffmann nor the Subcommittee fixed any numerical values to the symbols but we think that this refinement is necessary to improve the usefulness of tables. Our assessment of these values and our gradings are as follows:

$+ = 80-100\%$ of strains are positive
$d = 21-79\%$ positive
$- = 0-20\%$ positive or $80-100\%$ negative
$(\ ) =$ delayed reaction in biochemical tests.

Some characters are almost invariably positive or negative; unfortunately characters of such constancy are usually shared by similar organisms, and although they are important in characterizing an organism (and may appear in the miniature definitions given in Chapters 6 and 7), they have little value in distinguishing it from its neighbours, and seldom appear in our second-stage tables.

The tables could form the basis of a set of diagnostic punched cards to be used with similar cards on which the characters of the unknowns are punched. Sorting the cards of the unknowns with those of the knowns would be one of the quickest, most accurate and least burdensome ways of arriving at an identification (cf. Riddle *et al.* 1956).

PRACTICE OF IDENTIFICATION

So far in this *Manual* we have discussed principles and indicated how all identification is based on a comparison of the organism we wish to identify with organisms of known identity. The accuracy of the identification depends on the thoroughness of the preparatory work such as media making, preparing stains and reagents, and the degree of care taken in carrying out, observing and recording the results of the various tests.

In Chapter 2 we drew attention to the fact that bacteria isolated on inhibitory and selective media were likely to be mixed cultures, and we indicated some of the steps to be taken to purify a culture. It is not easy to be sure that the purified culture is incontrovertibly pure, and when there is any doubt whatever, it is a saving of time to repeat the purification process. To identify a culture takes a great deal of effort and to suspect at the end that the culture is impure is not only aggravating and frustrating to the clinician but is indicative that the bacteriologist has wasted much of his own time and material. Common organisms really are the commonest; when an organism cannot be identified or seems to be an exotic species, we should consider the possibility that either our culture material is impure, or that we have made some error in observation or recording. This happens to all of us and it reflects adversely on our ability and integrity when we fail to repeat observations, and go ahead believing that our results are infallible.

There are various routes by which an identification can be arrived at; the medical bacteriologist often has the advantage that he knows what he is looking for, and at an early stage directs his investigation into certain special channels. This may turn out to be a disadvantage, and the selective media used may inhibit the growth of a pathogen whose presence is unsuspected. Steel (1962a) discussed the different techniques used in making identifications of pure cultures. Basically there are three approaches to the problem; in the first, which we call the *blunderbuss* method, every conceivable test is made, and when all the results are available, the characters of the organism are compared with those listed in standard texts and *Bergey's Manual*. If all tests appropriate to the organism have been included, it will be possible to make the identification, but quite often we find that other (possibly unheard of) characters are mentioned and additional tests are needed: this is such a common experience that few bacteriologists follow the blunderbuss method. However, such a comprehensive investigation is necessary when the organism has to be characterized for its description as a new species.

The second approach is based on *probabilities* and a judicious assessment of what sort of organism is causing the particular infective process. Thus, from a boil one would expect to isolate *Staphylococcus aureus*, or from the stools of a patient with an intestinal upset, one of the Enterobacteriaceae, and it would be reasonable to put up tests that are likely to lead to as rapid an identification as is consistent with accuracy. When the most probable causal organism seems to be excluded, the investigator should continue with an open mind and follow the third approach.

The third approach is the step-by-step or *progressive* method used in this *Manual*, in which the first step aims at determining a few fundamental characters such as those used in Tables I and II. When these characters are known another set of media can be inoculated to enable the appropriate tests (to be found in a second-stage table) to be made; the number of these tests will always be less than that needed when the blunder-buss method is followed. Sometimes additional tests are needed for the better identification of a species, biotype or variety, and in Chapter 6 some of these are shown in third-stage tables.

In deciding what media to inoculate we are guided by the tests to be carried out, and we must decide for or against classical methods that are slow, e.g. gelatin stab cultures to show liquefaction or hydrolysis. Time can be saved by using multitest media in which several reactions can be observed at one time; such methods are used mainly in the preliminary screening of large numbers of cultures, and they are useful in that 'non-pathogens' or organisms thought to be of low-grade pathogenicity can be detected and discarded without more ado, and further tests restricted to those organisms that appear to fit into groups that contain potential pathogens.

Other rapid methods, described briefly in Appendix E may be considered. Not only are the methods quicker than the standard procedures, but some, at least, give more clear-cut results. We can recommend the NCTC series of microtests for acetylmethylcarbinol, H_2S, indole, urease, phenylalanine, gluconate, malonate, and nitrate reduction, but we do not recommend the micromethods for 'fermentations' or the MR test. We should warn users of these methods that the H_2S microtest is very sensitive and gives more positives than are shown in our tables.

When all the tests are completed the results are compared with the appropriate table(s); where a table is complicated by being made up of many lines or many columns it may be convenient to use a Determinator (Cowan & Steel, 1960, 1961).

In using the progressive tables in Chapters 6 and 7 we should remember that occasionally an organism of undoubted identity will have an anomalous character (such as a positive oxidase reaction in a strain of *Salmonella typhi*) so misleading that it will be impossible to make the identification by the tables. We have not made provision for exceptions such as this; neither have we made double entries for motile and non-motile variants of the same species. Asporogenous variants are common in *Clostridium welchii* and justify entry in two second-stage tables (I*d* and I*f*), and the user of Table-fig. I is reminded of the possibility of asporogenous strains of *Bacillus* species by squares surrounded by interrupted lines. The subjectiveness of reading certain tests used in the main tables has necessitated double entries for a few bacteria.

6

CHARACTERS OF GRAM-POSITIVE BACTERIA

The first-stage table is combined with a figure as Table-fig. I (p. 55) and shows how, by a small number of characters, it is possible to divide up the Gram-positive bacteria into groups that correspond to those used in orthodox classification. The characters used at this stage are both morphological and physiological. Not all the theoretical combinations of the characters are shown in Table-fig. I because many do not seem to occur in nature. The shaded areas in the figure in Table-fig. I indicate the genera that have characters shown in the different columns of the table above it, on which the figure is based. Some genera appear in more than one column, and one column may include more than one genus. *Aerococcus* is shown in the second (a_2) and third (b_1) columns, the reason being that the catalase reaction of *A. viridans* is not always easy to read. Workers expecting the production of a large volume of gas when H_2O_2 is added to the culture may record the feeble reaction with *A. viridans* as negative, whereas those who habitually work with streptococci and so are used to truly negative reactions, will take more notice of the small bubble of gas produced and will record it as positive. Reading a test such as this is subjective; therefore even the best characterizations of bacteria cannot be expressed entirely on a quantitative basis. To make provision for both readings of the catalase test on *A. viridans*, that organism is shown in two columns of Table I and in two second-stage tables, viz, Table I*a* (staphylococci and micrococci) and I*b* (streptococci). When one column includes more than one group the subdivision is made in the second-stage table. The columns of the table in Table-fig. I are headed by letters in italic with subscript numerals; further characters of organisms appearing in a column will be found in the second-stage table bearing the same italicized letter (e.g. Table I*a*). Occasionally, as with the mycobacteria, third-stage tables are needed to show the distinguishing characters (e.g. Table I*ga*).

Notes on the genera characterized in Tables I and I*a*–I*g* will be found below, and to many of these notes we add definitions which give the minimum information needed for separation (minidefinitions). These groups or genera are dealt with in alphabetical order. Some Gram-positive genera not shown in Table-fig. I, *Leuconostoc*, *Pediococcus*, and *Sporosarcina*, do not come within the field of medical bacteriology, but will be discussed briefly in Chapter 8.

NOTES ON THE GENERA

Actinomyces (Table I*d*) is restricted to the three microaerophilic species, *A. bovis* from lumpy jaw of cattle, *A. israelii* from actinomycotic infections of man, and *A. naeslundii* from the tonsils and faeces of man. Until the last few years there were no papers of value on the characterization of the actinomycetes; the information shown in the table is mainly from papers by Howell *et al.* (1959) and Pine, Howell & Watson (1960). Buchanan & Pine (1962) isolated from lachrymal canaliculitis an anaerobic actinomycete which differed from recognized *Actinomyces* spp. in cell-wall composition, pigmentation, and end-products of glucose fermentation. Grässer (1962, 1963) recognized two actinomycetes from udder actinomycosis of the pig, one almost identical with *A. israelii* and another which he called *A. suis*.

> *Minidefinition: Non-motile Gram-positive rods which may show true branching; nonsporing; not acid-fast. Microaerophilic. Catalase-negative. Attack sugars fermentatively.*

Aerococcus (Tables I*a*, I*b*) is the generic name given by Williams, Hirch & Cowan (1953) to a group of α-haemolytic Gram-positive cocci found commonly in air samples (Williams & Hirch, 1950). The catalase reaction is either weakly-positive or frankly negative, and for this reason the characters of the genus are shown in Table I*a* for staphylococci and micrococci, and also in Table I*b*, for streptococci. Deibel & Niven (1960) think that they resemble an organism named *Gaffkya homari* (Hitchner & Snieszko, 1947) from lobsters and meat (Aaronson, 1956) and that they form a single species which should be placed in the genus *Pediococcus*. We keep to our original view (Williams *et al.* 1953), shared by Günther & White (1961), that aerococci can be distinguished from pediococci, and we continue to name and identify the species *A. viridans*. In addition to producing a green zone on blood agar, the organism has many features in common with *Streptococcus faecalis*, including heat resistance and the ability to grow in alkaline media.

> *Minidefinition: Gram-positive spheres in pairs, fours, or small clusters. Non-motile; non-sporing. Facultatively anaerobic. Catalase feebly positive or negative. Attack sugars fermentatively.*

Bacillus (Table I*e*). Many of the details are from the authoritative monograph of Smith, Gordon & Clark (1952); we have included most of the species recognized by them but have excluded *B. pasteurii*, an organism that does not grow on ordinary media and which is therefore not likely to be isolated in a medical laboratory. The characters chosen are those which most readily distinguish the different species; they are based on standard tests carried out at a slightly lower temperature (28–30° C) than usual. *B. stearothermophilus* cultures will not grow at 28° C and should be incubated at 45–60° C. Except for *B. coagulans* and *B. pulvifaciens*, which prefer organic nitrogen, the sugar tests should be made in a medium with an ammonium salt as nitrogen source.

Smith *et al.* (1952) regard *B. anthracis* as a pathogenic variety of *B. cereus*, and *B. mycoides* as another variety of *B. cereus*. If they were to follow strictly the Bacteriological Code *B. anthracis* would be the species and *B. cereus* the variety as the epithet anthracis antedates cereus; they give adequate reasons for regarding *B. cereus* as the parent form. As bacteriologists working primarily with pathogens we do not follow the logical course set by Smith *et al.* and we, like Leise *et al.* (1959) and Burdon & Wende (1960), retain *B. anthracis* as a separate species. We do not show *B. mycoides* in Table I*e* for in the characters listed there, it does not differ from *B. cereus*; examination of a colony on a plate, however, would show clearly the main difference between them, namely, the rhizoid nature of the *B. mycoides* colony. Dr Gordon tells us that *B. cereus* var. *mycoides* strains and their non-rhizoid variants are usually non-motile and thus differ from *B. anthracis* only in pathogenicity. We do not include in our table the insect pathogen *B. cereus* var. *thuringiensis*.

The differences between *B. subtilis* and *B. licheniformis* do not seem great in Table I*e*, and, in the first edition of their monograph, Smith, Gordon & Clark (1946) did not recognize *B. licheniformis*. Gibson (1944) has pointed out that *B. licheniformis* colonies adhere to the medium and are difficult to pick off and in a limited experience of this genus we have found that *B. licheniformis* spores are generally more heat-resistant than those of *B. subtilis*. *B. licheniformis* is a facultative anaerobe and, in fact, was first described as an anaerobic species and was named *Clostridium licheniforme*.

Smith *et al.* (1964) have proposed neotype strains of many *Bacillus* species; one of the species, *B. badius*, is not characterized in the Smith *et al.* (1952) monograph; the details given in Table I*e* are based on Smith & Gordon in *Bergey's Manual* (1957) and on our examination of the designated type strain.

The morphological groups in Table I*e* are those described by Smith *et al.* (1952), and are as follows:

> *Group* 1. Spores oval or cylindrical; central, subterminal or terminal. Spore wall thin; bacillary body only slightly swollen or not at all.
> *Group* 2. Spores oval, rarely cylindrical; central, subterminal or terminal. Spore wall thick; bacillary body definitely swollen.
> *Group* 3. Spores spherical; terminal or subterminal. Bacillary body swollen.

Some atypical characters may be found in practice; for example the three strains of *B. stearothermophilus* that we have examined are catalase-negative at the temperature (60° C) at which we have grown the cultures.

Minidefinition: Rods typically Gram-positive in young cultures; motile (non-motile forms occur); not acid-fast. Produce spores that are usually heat resistant. Catalase-positive. Aerobic, some species facultatively anaerobic. Species differ in the way they attack sugars; some do not attack them.

Clostridium (Table I*f*). In addition to the well-established animal pathogens, other species that may be confused with them and species commonly found in dust or soil were considered. In choosing species for inclusion in Table I*f* we took into account the likelihood of isolating them; some (e.g. *C. hastiforme*) have seldom, if ever, been isolated since their original description and naming; these we regard as a burden on the literature and we do not propose to add to it by including them here. *C. difficile* and *C. innocuum* are species that are not well known but have been isolated and studied intensively in the last few years by Smith & King (1962*a*,*b*) and we think are now well enough characterized to justify inclusion. King *et al.* (1963) isolated *C. tertium* from the blood of two patients. We hesitated to put *C. fallax* in Table I*f*; Willis (1960*a*), to whom we refer readers for details on specialized anaerobic techniques and for more information on species of clostridia, says that *C. fallax* is widely distributed in nature, and that spores are rarely produced. However, the original workers (Weinberg & Séguin, 1915) who characterized the species (as *Bacillus fallax*, at a time when all rod-shaped bacteria, whether sporing or not, were labelled Bacillus) reported that it did not produce spores in media with or without glucose, and that old cultures did not resist boiling for 1 minute. It seems possible that *B. fallax* W & S was a non-sporing anaerobe, and should not be in the genus *Clostridium*, and our inclusion of the species in Table I*f* is made with considerable reserve.

Table I*f* is based on data from Reed & Orr (1941), Memorandum (1943), Smith (1955), Willis (1960*a*), and the results obtained by Miss H. E. Ross in her long experience with anaerobes in our Collection and elsewhere. We follow Brooks & Epps (1959) in keeping separate *Clostridium bifermentans* from *C. sordellii*; in showing nitrate reduction our results appear to contrast with those of Brooks & Epps, but they did not test the medium for residual nitrate and thus wrongly assumed that nitrate had not been reduced. Unlike Moussa (1959), we do not combine *C. chauvoei* (*C. feseri*) with *C. septicum*. The only significant difference between proteolytic *C. botulinum* and *C. sporogenes* is toxin production which is not shown in the table. It is a well-known fact that *Clostridium welchii* (*C. perfringens*) does not spore readily either in culture or in the animal body. Indeed, Willis (1960*a*) goes so far as to say that the absence of spores is one of the characteristic features of the species; as a consequence he advises that in trying to make the primary isolation, heating at 80° C for 10 minutes is to be avoided as it is likely to kill any *C. welchii* present. Because this species may not produce spores in culture and does not need strict anaerobic conditions for growth, we have also included it in Table I*d*, which characterizes other Gram-positive bacteria that are favoured by anaerobic conditions. Many species of clostridia can be subdivided into subspecies (e.g. *C. welchii* subsp. *agni*) or toxin types by the different toxins produced. However, few bacteriologists have the specific antitoxins available, or the experience to carry out these tests, and we have not thought it necessary or advisable to draw up third-stage

47

tables to show these toxin types. Those interested in these finer subdivisions we refer to papers by Brooks, Sterne & Warrack (1957) for *C. welchii*, and by Oakley, Warrack & Clarke (1947), Oakley & Warrack (1959) for *C. oedematiens*.

Some comment on the tests used in Table I*f* is needed. The motility of anaerobes is not easy to detect and only a positive result has any significance. The shape and position of spores, when present, calls for subjective judgement and it may well be making too fine a distinction to describe one spore as subterminal and another as central. In our earlier tables (Cowan & Steel, 1961) we avoided this issue by indicating only those strains that produced terminal spores, and assumed that all others produced central or subterminal spores. A few clostridia are microaerophilic but even these species grow better under anaerobic conditions.

Minidefinition: Rods, Gram-positive in young cultures; typically motile (non-motile forms occur). Not acid-fast. Produce spores that are usually heat resistant. Catalase-negative. Anaerobic, some species facultatively microaerophilic. Some species attack sugars fermentatively, others not at all.

Corynebacterium (Table I*c*) is a genus in which have been included animal pathogens and commensals, plant pathogens and soil bacteria. The cell-wall composition and antigens of the plant pathogenic corynebacteria are unlike those of the animal strains (Cummins, 1962). Conn (1947) and others (e.g. Clark, 1952) have protested against the inclusion of motile, or branched, Gram-positive rods in the genus. In the non-medical field the confusion was so great that Conn & Dimmick (1947) stated that Krassilnikov's *Mycobacterium* was the same as Jensen's *Corynebacterium*. For a review of the coryneform bacteria in fields other than medicine see Jensen (1952); Abd-el-Malek & Gibson (1952) describe the corynebacteria of milk, with which they include *Microbacterium*, a thermoduric organism (Doetsch & Pelczar, 1948).

In the medical field there are bacteria in the genus *Corynebacterium* that should be excluded. One such is *C. acnes* (discussed in Chapter 8) which produces propionic acid from carbohydrates and according to Douglas & Gunter (1946) should be classified in the genus *Propionibacterium*.

Cummins & Harris (1956) showed that the cell-wall composition of *Corynebacterium pyogenes* differed from that of other corynebacteria and was similar to that of streptococci. Barksdale *et al.* (1957) reported that extracts of S forms of the species reacted with several group G streptococcus antisera. They also showed that *C. pyogenes* gave rise to mutants indistinguishable from *C. haemolyticum* (Maclean, Liebow & Rosenberg, 1946). We show *C. pyogenes* both in Table I*b* and in Table I*c* not because we are undecided about its taxonomic position, but so that it shall not escape identification.

Corynebacterium ulcerans (Gilbert & Stewart, 1926–7) is a starch-fermenting corynebacterium that in some respects resembles *C. diphtheriae* var. *gravis*. It can, however, be distinguished by gelatin liquefaction, urease production and its inability to reduce nitrates (Cook & Jebb, 1952; Henriksen & Grelland, 1952).

C. equi is unusual in producing a pink-pigmented colony. Under appropriate conditions, *C. bovis* has been found to attack sugars (Cobb, 1963). The basal medium for carbohydrate tests may be more important with corynebacteria than with other organisms; Lovell (1946) found that in peptone water sugars, glucose was the only sugar regularly attacked by *C. renale*.

Minidefinition: Gram-positive rods which, under most conditions of growth, do not branch; typically non-motile (certain plant pathogens are motile); non-sporing; not acid-fast. Catalase-positive. Aerobic or facultatively anaerobic. Attack sugars fermentatively or do not attack them.

Erysipelothrix (Table I*d*) was surveyed by Langford & Hansen (1954) who came to the conclusion that only one species, *E. insidiosa* was justified; we accept their findings and therefore do not show *E. rhusiopathiae* and *E. muriseptica*. White & Shuman (1961) showed that the fermentation patterns of erysipelothrix strains varied with the medium and indicator, but most strains had a constant pattern under the same growth conditions; they recommended a basal medium containing serum.

Minidefinition: Gram-positive rods; non-branching; non-motile; non-sporing; not acid-fast. Catalase-negative. Facultatively anaerobic. Attack sugars by fermentation.

Kurthia (Table I*c*) is not normally regarded as pathogenic but Elston (1961) isolated strains from clinical material. Gelatin liquefaction distinguishes *K. zopfii* (negative) from *K. bessonii* (positive).

Minidefinition: Gram-positive rods; motile; non-sporing; not acid-fast. Catalase-positive. Facultatively anaerobic. Do not attack sugars.

Lactobacillus (Tables I*d*, I*da*) is divided into three subgenera, *Thermobacterium, Streptobacterium* and *Betabacterium* (Orla-Jensen, 1919) and the characters of these are shown in Table I*d*. *Betabacterium* species are heterofermentative and, under suitable conditions (Gibson & Abd-el-Malek, 1945) produce gas from glucose. This gas production is not likely to be confused with gas produced by clostridia and their non-sporing variants, which occurs readily in a variety of media when the cultures are incubated under anaerobic conditions. Another test for heterofermentation is described by Williams & Campbell (1951). The division of *Lactobacillus* into species is shown in Table I*da*. Heterofermentative lactobacilli and *L. delbrueckii* and *L. leichmannii* produce ammonia from arginine when grown in a tomato juice basal medium containing glucose, yeast extract and Tween 80 (Briggs, 1953*a, b*). Man, Rogosa & Sharpe (1960) recommend a special basal medium (p. 110) for the sugar reactions of lactobacilli.

Döderlein's bacillus is not a bacteriological entity; most lactobacilli from the human vagina seem to be *L. acidophilus* (Rogosa & Sharpe, 1960). The acidophilic bacteria isolated by McIntosh, James & Lazarus-Barlow (1922) from carious teeth are not adequately characterized and are not shown in Table I*da*. *L. bifidus* is not now regarded as a lactobacillus and will be considered in Chapter 8.

Motile lactobacilli were described by Harrison & Hansen (1950) but seem to be rare. Another abnormal form is catalase-positive (Dacre & Sharpe, 1956).

Both *L. plantarum* and *L. casei* may be divided into varieties which are not included in Table I*da*. On the basis of tests shown it is not possible to distinguish *L. jugurti* from *L. bulgaricus*; they differ serologically, by the molecular configuration and the optical rotation of the lactic acid produced, and by the total acidity produced in litmus milk. These are highly specialized characteristics and for more information about them and on the classification and identification of lactobacilli the reader is referred to G. H. G. Davis (1955, 1960), Sharpe (1955), Rogosa & Sharpe (1959, 1960), J. G. Davis (1960), and Rogosa, Franklin & Perry (1961).

Minidefinition: Gram-positive rods, typically non-motile; non-sporing; not acid-fast. Anaerobic and facultatively aerobic. Catalase-negative. Grow best at about pH 6. Attack sugars fermentatively.

Listeria (Table I*c*) was first described by Murray, Webb & Swann (1926). Since then it has been isolated from a variety of animals, including man. Characteristic of the organism is its ability to grow at 5° C and to produce acetylmethylcarbinol. For a review see Seeliger (1961).

Minidefinition: Gram-positive rods; motile; non-sporing; not acid-fast. Catalase-positive. Aerobic. Attack sugars by fermentation.

Micrococcus (Table I*a*). Until a few years ago the view was held that micrococci could not be distinguished from staphylococci; Hucker (1924*b*) thought that the combined genus should be *Micrococcus*; Shaw, Stitt & Cowan (1951) that it should be *Staphylococcus*. Gradually opinion is changing (Symposium, 1962), and with the development of new techniques, characters are being found by which the two groups of organisms may be separated. Various proposals have been made with such distinguishing criteria as the ability to utilize glucose anaerobically in a complex medium (Evans, Bradford & Niven, 1955), the utilization of mannitol anaerobically (Mossel, 1962), the oxidation or fermentation of glucose (Baird-Parker, 1963), and the ability to produce acetylmethylcarbinol (Kocur & Martinec, 1962; Kocur, personal communication). An international subcommittee has been set up to study the problem and recommend a suitable classification; we show in Table I*a* a provisional scheme suggested by us which embodies features of the schemes proposed by Evans, Baird-Parker, and by Kocur & Martinec.

In our classification of the catalase-positive, Gram-positive aerobic cocci, we regard those that ferment glucose as staphylococci, and those that oxidize the sugar, or do not attack it, as micrococci. Packet-forming cocci are included in micrococci; in our view

Gaffkya is not identifiable, and the generic name *Sarcina* should be reserved for the anaerobic packet-forming Gram-positive cocci (Shaw *et al.* 1951). Among the staphylococci pigmentation is not important (and is not necessarily reflected in the name), but in the micrococci it is a more constant and stable character; it is the only character by which *M. roseus* can be distinguished from certain other micrococci. The characterization of *M. luteus* is based on the neotype strain (ATCC 398) suggested by Evans *et al.* (1955); ATCC 398 is biochemically inert and differs significantly from the characterization published in *Bergey's Manual* from the third to the seventh editions, in which *M. luteus* was said to produce acid from glucose, sucrose, and mannitol.

Micrococcus roseus consists of strains with a common feature in producing a pink pigment, but may differ in biochemical characters. Hill (1959) thought that these pink pigment producers formed a natural group. To avoid anticipating the recommendations of the international subcommittee, the other micrococci, which Baird-Parker (1963) divided into 6 groups, we bring together in Table I*a* as *Micrococcus* sp(p).

Minidefinition: Gram-positive spheres in pairs, fours or small clusters, the cocci being of uniform size in each cluster. Typically non-motile and non-sporing (occasionally motile and so-called sporing forms occur). Catalase-positive. Aerobic. Attack sugars oxidatively or not at all.

Mycobacterium and **Nocardia** are considered together in Table I*g*, which is intended to provide a further subdivision before considering species in third-stage tables. The heading 'warm-blooded tubercle bacilli' refers to tubercle bacilli from warm-blooded animals, and in Table I*ga* it is convenient to show these as separate species with the name *Mycobacterium tuberculosis* for the human type, *M. bovis* for the bovine, and *M. avium* for the avian. The vole bacillus (*M. murium*, *M. microti*) does not appear in the tables as too little is known of its characters. Johne's bacillus (*M. johnei*, *M. paratuberculosis*) is also not included; it needs media containing killed acid-fast bacilli or extracts of them. Details of suitable media will be found in papers by Taylor (1950) and Smith (1953).

Gordon & Smith (1955) identified the so-called cold-blooded tubercle bacilli with *M. fortuitum* and these are included with the saprophytic acid-fast bacilli in Table I*g* under the heading 'rapidly-growing acid-fast bacilli'. In Table I*ga M. ulcerans* (MacCallum *et al.* 1948) and *M. balnei* (Linell & Nordén, 1952) are separated from the so-called 'anonymous' acid-fast bacilli, but both groups are compared with the slowly-growing warm-blooded tubercle bacilli. The characterizations given are not sufficient to distinguish conclusively between the human and bovine tubercle bacilli, but this distinction is one for the expert, for whom this table is not intended.

There are several classifications of the anonymous acid-fast bacteria (Runyon, 1959; Collins, 1962; Marks & Richards, 1962) which include some rapidly-growing species; thus Runyon's group IV, Collins' assembly D, and Marks & Richards' groups 6 and 7 are included in the species shown in Table I*gb*. There seems general agreement that Runyon's group I, Collins' assembly A, and Marks & Richards' group I can be equated with *M. kansasii* (Table I*ga*). Although we have seen a compromise provisional scheme for identifying mycobacteria (prepared for members of the Acid-Fast Club by C. H. Collins), we have combined the remaining 'anonymous' acid-fast bacilli into three columns of Table I*ga*; these may well be subdivided but we are not competent to do so. We have shown the catalase reaction as it occurs in strains isolated from untreated patients; this reaction may change *in vivo* during the course of intensive chemotherapy. In addition to the characters shown in Table I*ga*, other characters not suitable for tabulation may be important, such as colonial consistency, emulsifiability, and texture; bacillary length and 'cord' formation (tendency to parallel alignment).

In classifying the mycobacteria use is made of the temperatures at which the different organisms will grow. The tests for growth or survival at several different temperatures involve the use of several water baths, so that these and some of the other tests used to distinguish between the species of *Mycobacterium* and *Nocardia* are outside the range of tests done in most routine laboratories. We show the results of these tests in Table I*gb* to indicate how the species may be determined if the facilities are available. *M. phlei* is unique in being able to grow at 52° C, *M. balnei* in having a narrow temperature range for growth when first isolated; after it has been in subculture for some time this organism may be able to grow at 37° C but in Table I*ga* we have shown growth only at 30–33° C, the temperature range that this organism demands when first isolated, and when it has to be identified. *M. marinum* appears to be closely related to *M. balnei* and these species may be identical.

M. fortuitum and other rapidly growing acid-fast bacilli are shown in detail with the nocardias in Table I*gb*, which is compiled mainly from Gordon & Mihm (1959, 1962*a, b*) and many personal communications from Dr R. E. Gordon. We do not stress the pigment formation of mycobacteria which may show great variability (Gordon & Rynearson, 1963).

Some textbooks convey the impression that a useful distinction can be made between those bacilli that are acid-fast and those that are acid- and alcohol-fast; this distinction cannot be substantiated in practice and most workers in this field use, as the decolorizing agent, a mixture of acid and alcohol as this gives the most reliable and consistent results. We use and recommend such a mixture (Appendix C), and consequently in Table I*g* we do not have a line for alcohol-fastness.

Minidefinitions: Mycobacterium. Non-motile Gram-positive rods which do not branch. Typically they are acid-fast. Non-sporing, and do not produce aerial hyphae. Aerobic. Attack sugars by oxidation.

Nocardia. Non-motile Gram-positive rods which sometimes show branching. May be feebly acid-fast. Produce aerial hyphae. Aerobic. Attack sugars by oxidation.

Staphylococcus (Table I*a*). The differentiation of this genus from *Micrococcus* is discussed on p. 50. The most satisfactory method of detecting the ability of staphylococci to ferment glucose anaerobically needs the use of an anaerobic jar (Cowan & Steel, 1964); paraffin seals do not ensure complete anaerobiosis and test methods in which they are used are not always sufficiently exacting to exclude the oxidative organism from attacking glucose. In Table I*a* we show *Staphylococcus* as consisting of *S. aureus*, the coagulase-positive species, and *S. epidermidis*, the name used for all other staphylococci. In this we differ from our earlier classification in which we followed Shaw *et al.* (1951).

There is much overlapping between *S. saprophyticus* and *S. epidermidis* as characterized by Evans in *Bergey's Manual* (1957) but Jones, Deibel & Niven (1963) have shown that they do not correspond exactly. They are alike in being skin commensals and in being regarded as non-pathogens, although under certain circumstances, for example in the urinary tract, they may be low-grade pathogens. The majority of pathogenic strains are *S. aureus* and these are the only ones typable by bacteriophage (Wilson & Atkinson, 1945; Williams & Rippon, 1952) or by serology (Cowan, 1939; Christie & Keogh, 1940; Hobbs, 1948; Oeding, 1952, 1960).

Minidefinition: Gram-positive spheres in pairs and clusters, the cells showing variation in size and Gram-retaining power. Non-motile, non-sporing. Facultatively anaerobic. Catalase-positive. Attack sugars by fermentation.

Streptococcus species are shown in Table I*b*; additional groups labelled with letters of the alphabet and mainly identified by precipitin reactions are not shown; these additional groups may be heterogeneous in the biochemical reactions, for example, Skadhauge & Perch (1959) and Rifkind & Cole (1962) recognize three biotypes of group M. Included in the table are *Corynebacterium pyogenes*, which has the cell-wall composition of a streptococcus and extracts react with streptococcal grouping sera (Cummins & Harris, 1956; Barksdale *et al.* 1957), and *Aerococcus viridans*, which has some resemblance to the group D streptococci and to pediococci. *Streptococcus salivarius* is not shown under that name in Table I*b* where it appears, with its earlier epithet, as *S. hominis* (Williams, 1956).

Exceptions to the many characters shown in Table I*b* must be expected; on suitable media dextrans may be produced by some strains of *S. bovis* (Niven, Smiley & Sherman, 1941). Some of the dextran-producing strains of *S. sanguis* may fail to yield group H antigen in extracts prepared from them (Porterfield, 1950); not all group H strains produce a dextran or all group K strains a levan. *S. sanguis* produces a dextran only in sucrose broth (Niven, Kiziuta & White, 1946), *S. hominis* produces its levan on sucrose agar. A few strains of *S. bovis* will survive heating at 60° C for 30 minutes. Most group D streptococci will grow at 45° C but some strains of *S. durans* fail to grow at this temperature.

The precipitin reactions of streptococci are not always easy to determine; this difficulty applies particularly to strains of group D (Shattock, 1949), some extracts of which will not react with otherwise satisfactory antisera unless the cell is broken up mechanically (Smith & Shattock, 1962). Some strains of *S. equinus*, *S. uberis*, *S. sanguis*, and *S. hominis* do not react with any of the grouping sera and their identification must be made on other characters.

Group A strains are unusual in being sensitive to bacitracin (Maxted, 1953). We confirmed Pownall's (1935) observation that many group D streptococci are motile; hence the necessity for column b_2 in Table I. In addition to the characters shown in Table I*b*, *S. faecium* and *S. durans* may be distinguished from the other enterococci by their failure to grow on medium containing $0 \cdot 03$–$0 \cdot 04 \%$ potassium tellurite (p. 105) and by their inability to reduce $2:3:5$-triphenyltetrazolium chloride (Barnes, 1956). Deibel, Lake & Niven (1963) regard *S. durans* as a variety of *S. faecium*.

α-haemolytic streptococci consist of the pneumococcus (*S. pneumoniae*) and ill-defined species collectively designated the greening streptococci. The term *S. viridans* is now seldom used and the greening streptococci are shown under the name *Streptococcus mitis*; at present these appear to be serologically heterogeneous.

The laboratory diagnosis of streptococcal infections is discussed in detail by Williams (1958).

Minidefinition: *Gram-positive spheres in pairs or chains; typically non-motile (motile strains occur); non-sporing. Facultatively anaerobic. Catalase-negative. Attack sugars fermentatively.*

Table-fig. I.—*First-stage diagnostic table for Gram-positive bacteria*

	a		b		c				d	e	f	g	
	a_1	a_2	b_1	b_2	c_1	c_2	c_3	c_4				g_1	g_2
SHAPE	S	S	S	S	R	R	R	R	R	R	R	R	R
ACID-FAST	−	−	−	−	−	−	−	−	−	−	−	+	−
SPORES	−	−	−	−	−	−	−	−	−	+	+	−	−
MOTILITY	−	−	−	+	+	−	−	+	−	d	d	−	−
GROWTH IN AIR	+	+	+	+	+	+	+	+	d	+	−	+	+
CATALASE	+	+	−	−	+	+	+	+	−	+	−	d	+
OXIDASE	−	−	−	−	−	−	−	−	−	d	−	−	−
GLUCOSE (acid)	d	+	+	+	+	+	−	−	+	d	d	+	+
O–F test	O/-	F	F	F	F	F	−	−	F	F/O/-	F/-	O/NT	O

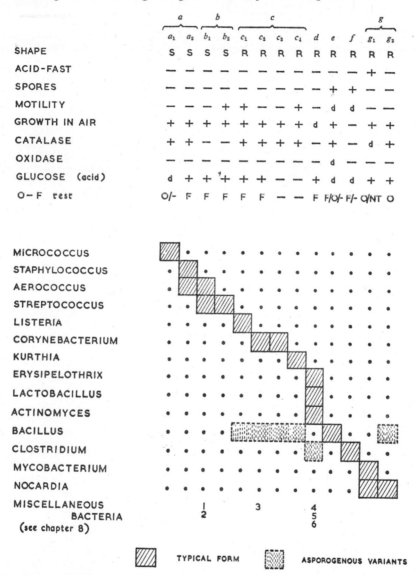

MICROCOCCUS
STAPHYLOCOCCUS
AEROCOCCUS
STREPTOCOCCUS
LISTERIA
CORYNEBACTERIUM
KURTHIA
ERYSIPELOTHRIX
LACTOBACILLUS
ACTINOMYCES
BACILLUS
CLOSTRIDIUM
MYCOBACTERIUM
NOCARDIA
MISCELLANEOUS BACTERIA (see chapter 8)

1
2   3   4
5
6

TYPICAL FORM   ASPOROGENOUS VARIANTS

Symbols common to all tables:

    + = 100–80% strains positive; d = 79–21% strains positive; − = 20–0% strains positive; F = fermentation; O = oxidation; (•) = delayed reaction; NT = not testable.

Symbols special to Table I:

    S = sphere; R = rod.

Table I*a*. Second-stage table for Micrococcus, Staphylococcus, *and* Aerococcus

	Micrococcus luteus	M. sp(p).	M. roseus	Staphylococcus aureus	S. epidermidis	Aerococcus viridans
Catalase	+	+	+	+	+	W
Glucose (acid)	−	d	d	+	+	+
O–F test	−	O/-	O/-	F	F	F
V–P	−	−	−	+	d	−
Nitrate reduction	−	d	d	+	d	−
Pink pigment	−	−	+	−	−	−
Phosphatase	−	−	−	+	d	−
Coagulase	−	−	−	+	−	−

W = weak reaction.

Table I*b*. Second-stage table for Streptococcus *species*, Corynebacterium pyogenes, *and* Aerococcus

	S. pyogenes	S. agalactiae	S. dysgalactiae	S. equisimilis	S. equi	S. zooepidemicus	S. bovis	S. equinus	S. durans	S. faecalis	S. faecium	S. sanguis	S. hominis	S. lactis	S. cremoris	S. mitis	S. uberis	S. pneumoniae	Corynebacterium pyogenes	Aerococcus viridans
Antigenic group	A	B	C	C	C	C	D	D*	D	D	D	H*	K*	N	N	−	−	−	−	−
Growth at 45° C	−	−	−	−	−	−	+	+	d	+	+	d	+	−	−	d	+	−	−	−
Survives 60° C–30′	−	−	−	−	−	−	−	−	+	+	+	d	−	d	d	−	+	−	..	+
Growth in 6·5 % NaCl	−	−	−	−	−	−	−	−	+	+	+	−	−	−	−	−	−	−	..	+
Growth at pH 9·6	−	−	−	−	−	−	−	−	d	+	+	−	−	−	−	−	−	−	..	+
Growth on 10 % bile	−	+	−	+	d	−	+	+	+	+	+	+	+	+	+	−	+	−	..	+
Growth on 40 % bile	−	+	−	−	−	+	+	+	+	+	+	+	+	−	+	−	d	−	−	+
Aesculin hydrolysis	−	−	d	−	+	+	+	+	+	+	+	+	+	d	d	−	+	..	−	d
Arginine hydrolysis	+	+	+	+	+	+	−	−	+	+	+	+	−	+	−	d	+	..	−	−
Hippurate hydrolysis	−	+	d	−	−	−	−	−	d	d	d	−	−	d	−	−	+	−	..	+
Gelatin liquefaction	−	−	−	−	−	−	−	−	−	−†	−	−	−	−	−	−	−	−	+	−
Litmus milk	A	AC	B	B	−	A	A	−	A	RAC	A	AC	RAC	RAC	RAC	RAC	RAC	AC	AC	A
Arabinose (acid)	−	−	−	−	−	−	d	−	−	−	+	−	−	d	−	−	−	−	+	d
Maltose (acid)	+	+	+	+	+	d	+	+	+	+	+	+	+	+	−	+	+	+	+	+
Trehalose (acid)	+	+	+	+	−	−	d	−	d	+	.+	+	+	d	d	−	+	−	−	+
Raffinose (acid)	−	−	−	−	−	+	−	−	−	−	−	d	+	−	−	−	−	+	−	d
Salicin (acid)	+	d	d	d	+	+	+	+	d	+	+	+	+	d	d	+	+	d	−	+
Glycerol (acid)	−	+	−	+	−	−	−	−	+	+	+	−	−	−	−	−	+	+	+	+
Mannitol (acid)	−	−	−	−	−	d	−	+	+	d	−	−	d	−	d	−	+	d	−	d
Sorbitol (acid)	−	−	d	−	−	+	−	−	−	+	−	−	−	−	−	−	+	−	−	d
EHC or bile solubility	−	−	−	−	−	−	−	−	−	−	−	−	−	−	−	−	−	+	−	−
Haemolysis	β	α/β	α	β	β	β	α/-	α	β/-	β/-	α/β	α	−	α	α	α	α	α	β	α
Sucrose media	..	..	..	..	..	..	..	..	..	..	..	D	L	..	..	..	..	..	..	..

* = in the precipitin test, extracts of some strains do not react with antisera.
Litmus milk: A = acid; B = acid produced but clotting variable; C = clot; R = reduction.
Sucrose media: D = dextran produced; L = levan produced.
† = liquefying strains occur and form var. *liquefaciens*.

Table I*c*. *Second-stage table for* Listeria, Corynebacterium, *and* Kurthia

	Listeria monocytogenes	*C. diphtheriae v. gravis*	*C. diphtheriae v. mitis*	*C. diphtheriae v. intermedius*	*C. ulcerans*	*C. xerosis*	*C. murium*	*C. renale*	*C. ovis*	*C. bovis*	*C. equi*	*C. hofmannii*	*C. haemolyticum*	*C. pyogenes*	*Kurthia spp.*
Catalase	+	+	+	+	+	+	+	+	+	+	+	+	+	−	+
Motility	+	−	−	−	−	−	−	−	−	−	+	−	−	−	+
Arginine hydrolysis	..	−	−	−	−	−	−	+	+	−	−	−	..	..	..
Gelatin liquefaction	−	−	−	−	+	−	−	−	−	−	−	−	+	+	d
Glucose (acid)	+	+	+	+	+	+	+	+	+	−	−	−	+	+	−
Lactose (acid)	d	−	−	−	−	−	−	d	d	−	−	−	+	+	.
Maltose (acid)	+	+	+	+	d	+	+	d	+	−	−	−	+	+	.
Sucrose (acid)	d	−	−	−					−	d	−	−	−	+	d	−
Trehalose (acid)	+	−	−	−	+	−	+	−	−	−	−	−	−	−	−
Starch (acid)	d	+	−	−	+	−	+	d	+	−	−	−	d	+	−
Salicin (acid)	+	−	−	−	−	−	d	−	−	−	−	−	−	−	−
Nitrate reduction	−	+	+	+	−	+	+	+	d	−	+	+	−	−	−
Urease	−	−	−	−	+	−	d	+	+	−	+	+	−	−	−
Pink pigment	−	−	−	−	−	−	−	−	−	−	+	−	−	−	−
Haemolysis	+	−	+	−	.+	−	−	d	d	−	−	−	+	+	−

Table I*d*. *Second-stage table for* Lactobacillus, Erysipelothrix, Actinomyces, *and non-sporing* Clostridium welchii

	Thermobacterium	*Streptobacterium*	*Betabacterium*	*E. insidiosa*	*A. bovis*	*A. israelii*	*A. naeslundii*	*Non-sporing C. welchii*
	Lactobacillus							
Growth at 45° C	+	d	d	−	−	−	−	+
Growth at 15° C	−	+	d	−	−	−	−	+
Growth in air	W	W	W	+	−	−	−	−
Tomato juice favours growth	+	+	+	−	−	−	−	−
Starch hydrolysis	−	−	−	−	+	d	d	+
Litmus milk: acid and clot within 24 h	−	−	−	−	−	−	−	+
Xylose (acid)	−	−	d	d	−	+	−	−
Lactose (acid)	d	d	d	+	+	+	d	+
Sucrose (acid)	d	d	d	−	+	+	+	+
Raffinose (acid)	d	d	d	−	−	d	+	+
Mannitol (acid)	d	+	d	−	−	+	−	−
Nitrate reduction	−	−	−	−	−	+	+	+
Gas in cooked meat	−	−	−	−	−	−	−	+

W = feeble growth.

Table I*da.* Third-stage table for Lactobacillus *species*

	L. helveticus	L. jugurti	L. bulgaricus	L. lactis	L. acidophilus	L. leichmannii	L. delbrueckii	L. salivarius	L. plantarum	L. casei	L. fermenti	L. buchneri	L. brevis	L. cellobiosus	L. viridescens
Growth at 45° C	+	+	+	+	+	+	+	+	d	d	+	−	−	−	−
Growth at 15° C	−	−	−	−	−	−	−	+	+	−	+	+	+	d	+
NH₃ from arginine*	−	−	−	−	−	d	d	−	−	−	+	+	+	+	−
Arabinose (acid)	−	−	−	−	−	−	−	−	d	−	d	+	d	+	−
Xylose (acid)	−	−	−	−	−	−	−	−	−	−	d	−	+	d	−
Galactose (acid)	+	+	+	+	+	−	−	+	+	+	+	+	+	+	−
Sorbose (acid)	−	−	−	−	−	−	−	−	−	+	−	−	−	−	−
Cellobiose (acid)	−	−	−	−	+	+	−	−	+	+	+	−	−	+	−
Lactose (acid)	+	+	+	+	+	d	−	+	+	d	+	+	d	d	−
Maltose (acid)	+	−	−	+	+	+	d	+	+	+	+	+	+	+	+
Melibiose (acid)	−	−	−	−	−	−	−	−	+	−	+	+	+	+	−
Sucrose (acid)	−	−	−	−	+	+	+	+	+	d	d	+	+	+	d
Trehalose (acid)	−	−	−	+	+	+	−	+	+	+	+	−	+	+	−
Melezitose (acid)	−	−	−	−	−	−	−	−	+	+	−	+	−	−	−
Raffinose (acid)	−	−	−	−	−	−	−	−	+	d	−	+	d	+	−
Glycogen (acid)	−	−	−	−	d	−	−	−	−	−	−	−	−	−	−
Amygdalin (acid)	−	−	−	−	+	+	+	+	+	+	−	−	−	−	−
Salicin (acid)	−	−	−	+	+	+	−	d	+	+	−	−	d	d	−
Mannitol (acid)	−	−	−	−	−	−	−	−	+	+	+	−	d	d	−
Sorbitol (acid)	−	−	−	−	−	−	−	−	+	+	+	−	−	−	−

*see text, p. 49.

Table I*e.* Second-stage table for Bacillus *species*
(sugar reactions in medium with ammonium salt base)

	B. anthracis	B. cereus	B. badius	B. firmus	B. lentus	B. licheniformis	B. megaterium	B. pumilus	B. subtilis	B. coagulans	B. pulvifaciens	B. pantothenticus	B. alvei	B. brevis	B. circulans	B. laterosporus	B. macerans	B. polymyxa	B. stearothermophilus	B. sphaericus
Gram reaction	+	+	+	+	+	+	+	+	+	+	+	+	v	v	v	v	v	v	v	v
Morphological group	1	1	1	1	1	1	1	1	1	1 or 2	2	3	2	2	2	2	2	2	2	3
Motility	−	+*	+	+	+	+	+	+	+	+	+	+	+	+	+	+	+	+	+	+
Growth at 65° C	−	−	−	−	−	−	−	−	−	−	−	−	−	−	−	−	−	−	+	+
Anaerobic growth in glucose broth	+	+	−	−	−	+†	−	−	−	+	+	−	+†	−	d	+	+†	+†	+	−
Citrate utilization	+	+	−	−	−	+	+	+	+	−	d	−	d	−	−	−	−	−	−	.
Gelatin hydrolysis	+	+	−	+	+	+	+	+	+	−	+	+	+	+	+	+	+	+	+	+
Casein hydrolysis	+	+	−	+	+	+	+	+	+	−	+	+	+	+	+	−	+	−	+	d
Starch hydrolysis	+	−	+	−	+	+	+	+	+	−	+	+	+	−	+	−	+	−	+	−
Glucose (acid)	+	+	−	−	+	+	+	+	+	+	NG	+	+	+	+	+	+	+	+	+
Arabinose (acid)	−	−	−	−	−	+	+	+	+	d	NG	d	−	−	+	−	+	+	d	−
Mannitol (acid)	−	−	−	−	−	+	+	+	+	d	NG	−	−	d	+	+	+	−	−	−
Indole	−	−	−	−	−	−	−	−	−	−	−	+	−	−	d	−	−	−	−	−
V–P	+	+	−	−	−	+	+	+	+	d	−	+	−	+	−	−	+	−	−	−
Nitrate reduction	+	+	−	+	−	+	−	+	+	d	+	d	−	d	d	+	+	+	+	−
Urease	−	d	−	−	+	d	d	−	d	−	−	−	−	−	−	−	−	−	d	d
LV	+	+	−	−	−	−	−	−	−	−	−	−	−	−	+	−	−	d	−	−

* *B. cereus* v. *mycoides* and non-rhizoid variants are usually non-motile.
† Gas may be produced.
NG = no growth on ammonium salt basal medium.
v = variable; generally positive in young cultures.
Morphological groups 1–3; for definitions see text, p. 46.

Table I*f*. *Second-stage table for* Clostridium *species*

	C. welchii	*C. butyricum*	*C. tertium*	*C. carnis*	*C. septicum*	*C. chauvoei*	*C. oedematiens*	*C. tetanomorphum*	*C. botulinum* (non-proteolytic)	*C. botulinum* (proteolytic)	*C. bifermentans*	*C. sordellii*	*C. sporogenes*	*C. difficile*	*C. innocuum*	*C. histolyticum*	*C. putrefaciens*	*C. tetani*	*C. fallax*
Motility	−	+	+	+	+	+	+	+	+	+	+	+	+	+	−	+	−	+	+
Spore	Co	Co	To	So	So	So	So	Tr	Co	Co	C/So	C/So	So	To	To	So	Tr	Tr	?So
Microaerophilic	−	−	+	+	−	−	−	−	−	−	−	−	−	−	−	+	−	−	−
Gelatin hydrolysis	+	−	−	−	+	+	+	−	−	+	+	+	+	−	−	+	−	+	−
Meat digestion	−	−	−	−	−	−	−	−	−	+	+	+	+	.	−	+	−	−	−
Serum digestion	−	−	−	−	−	−	−	−	−	+	+	+	+	−	−	+	−	d	−
Milk	AGC	AGC	AC	AC	A(C)	AGC	GC	−	A	D	CD	CD	D	−	Z	D	−	Z	A(C)
Glucose (acid)	+	+	+	+	+	+	+	+	+	+	+	+	+	+	+	−	−	−	+
Lactose (acid)	+	+	+	+	+	+	−	−	−	−	−	−	−	−	+	−	−	−	+
Sucrose (acid)	+	+	+	+	−	+	−	−	−	−	−	−	−	−	+	+	−	−	+
Salicin (acid)	−	+	+	+	+	−	−	−	−	−	−	+	−	+	+	−	−	−	+
Indole*	−	−	−	−	−	−	d	+	−	−	+	+	−	−	−	−	−	+	−
Nitrate reduction	+	+	+	−	+	+	+	+	−	−	+	+	+	−	−	−	−	+	+
H₂S	+	−	−	−	+	+	+	+	+	+	+	+	+	+	..	+	+	−	−
LV	+	−	−	−	−	−	d	−	+	+	+	+	+	+	..	−	−	−	−
Haemolysis	+	−	−	+	+	+	+	d	+	+	+	+	−	−	−	+	−	+	+
Urease	−	−	−	..	−	..	−	−	−	d	−	+	−	..	..	+	..	d	..

* Reed (1942) found that some species could break down indole so that cultures might give a negative result in tests for residual indole.

Spores: Capital letter=position of spore (T=terminal; S=subterminal; C=central).
  Lower case letter=shape of spore (o=oval; r=round).
Milk: A=acid; c=clot; (c)=slow formation of clot;
  D=digestion; G=gas; z=some strains give a soft clot.

Table I*g*. *Second-stage table for* Mycobacterium *and* Nocardia

	Warm-blooded tubercle bacilli	Temperature-sensitive (30–33° C) acid-fast bacilli	Slowly growing (anonymous) acid-fast bacilli	Rapidly growing acid-fast bacilli	*Nocardia* spp.
Catalase	d	+	d	+	+
Growth in 3 days	−	−	−	+	+
Growth at 37° C	+	−	+	+	+
Growth at 25° C	−	−	+	+	+
Pigmentation	−	d	d	d	d

Temperature-sensitive acid-fast bacilli are *M. balnei* and *M. ulcerans*.

Table I*ga. Third-stage table for slowly-growing acid-fast bacilli*

	M. tuberculosis	M. bovis	M. avium	M. ulcerans	M. balnei	M. marinum	M. kansasii	Scotochromogens*	Thermophils†	Non-chromogens‡
Catalase	+§	+§	w	+	+	+	+	+	d	d
Growth at 44° C	−	−	+	−	−	−	−	·	+	−
Growth at 37° C	+	+	+	−	−	+	+	+	+	+
Growth at 33° C	+	+	+	+	+	+	+	+	+	+
Growth at 30° C	−	−	+	+	+	+	+	+	+	+
Growth at 25° C	−	−	+	+	+	+	+	+	+	+
Growth at 20° C	−	−	+	−	−	+	−	−	−	−
Thiosemicarbazone	s	s	R	R	R	R	s	R	R	R
Pigment in light	−‖	−	−	−	+	+	+	+	−	−
Pigment in dark	−‖	−	−	−	−	−	−	+	−	−
Niacin	+	−	−	−	−	−	−	−	−	−

  * Runyon's group 2; Collins' assembly B (in part); Marks & Richards' group 2.
  † Runyon's group 3; Collins' assembly C; Marks & Richards' groups 3 and 4.
  ‡ Collins' assembly B (in part); Marks & Richards' group 5.
  § May be catalase-negative in strains from treated patients.
  ‖ May be pigmented on serum-containing media.
  w = weak reaction by most strains.
  s = sensitive.
  R = resistant.

Table I*gb. Third-stage table for rapidly-growing mycobacteria and* Nocardia *species*
(sugar reactions in ammonium salt base)

	M. phlei	M. smegmatis	M. fortuitum	M. rhodochrous	N. asteroides	N. brasiliensis	N. caviae	N. madurae
Growth at 52° C	+	−	−	−	−	−	−	−
Growth at 50° C	+	d	−	−	d	−	−	−
Growth at 45° C	+	+	−	d	d	−	d	d
Growth at 40° C	+	+	d	d	+	d	+	+
Growth at 10° C	−	d	d	+	−	d	−	−
Survives 60° C for 4 h	+	−	−	d	..	..	..	..
Survives 50° C for 8 h	+	..	..	..	+	−	+	d
Benzoate utilization	−	+	−	+	−	−	−	−
Mucate utilization	−	+	−	−	−	−	−	−
Starch hydrolysis	+	+	+	+	d	d	d	d
Casein digestion	−	−	−	−	−	+	−	+
Tyrosine decomposition	−	−	−	d	−	+	−	+
Xanthine decomposition	..	..	..	−	−	−	+	−
Arabinose (acid)	+	+	−	−	−	−	−	+
Maltose (acid)	−	−	−	d	−	−	+	d
Dulcitol (acid)	−	+	−	−	−	−	−	−
Mannitol (acid)	+	+	d	+	−	+	+	+
Sorbitol (acid)	+	+	−	+	−	−	−	−
Inositol (acid)	−	+	−	−	−	+	+	d
Urease	+	+	+	d	+	+	+	d
MacConkey (indicator change)	−	d	+	−	−	−	−	−

7

CHARACTERS OF GRAM-NEGATIVE BACTERIA

The first step in the identification of Gram-negative bacteria is shown in Table-fig. II (p. 76). Columns a_1 and a_2 cover the Gram-negative cocci except the anaerobic species (*Veillonella*) which will be discussed briefly in Chapter 8. Because of its morphological similarity to *Neisseria*, especially on first isolation, the organism named *Bacterium anitratum* (*Acinetobacter anitratus* in this *Manual*) is shown for comparison in Table IIa, the second-stage table which characterizes the neisseria, as well as in Table IIe. The Mimeae, described as neisseria-like in smears, are discussed briefly in Chapter 8. *Diplococcus mucosus* (von Lingelsheim, 1906) is shown in Table IIa under the name *Neisseria mucosa* proposed by Cowan (1938a). The motile Gram-negative rods that are catalase-positive and ferment carbohydrates are shown in Table IIb and the non-motile in Table IIc. Included in Table IIb for comparison with *Chromobacterium violaceum* is an oxidizing organism *Chromobacterium lividum*; this is psychrophilic and does not grow at 37° C. It is also shown in Table IIe. *Pasteurella pseudotuberculosis* (Table IIb) is motile at 22° C but not at 37° C.

Notes and minidefinitions of the Gram-negative genera shown in Tables II and IIa–IIh are given below.

NOTES ON THE GENERA

Acinetobacter (Tables IIa,e,f). A genus proposed by Brisou & Prévot (1954) for non-motile species that would otherwise fit in *Achromobacter*; they included in it, as *Acinetobacter anitratum* (sic), two species, *Bacterium anitratum* (Schaub & Hauber, 1948) syn. B5W (Stuart, Formal & McGann, 1949) and *Moraxella lwoffii* var. *glucidolytica*, which had previously been shown to be identical (Brisou & Morichau-Beauchant, 1952). *Acinetobacter anitratus* (*Bacterium anitratum*) is often found in human clinical material; it is frequently misidentified as *Diplococcus mucosus*, which we discuss with the neisseria on p. 69. One of the characteristics of *A. anitratus* is its ability to attack monosaccharides but not higher saccharides in peptone water sugars. When the sugar concentration is raised to 5 or 10 % it can attack lactose. Biotypes occur which vary in soap tolerance (Billing, 1955), gelatin liquefaction, growth at 44° C (Ashley & Kwantes, 1961), and urease activity.

We proposed (Steel & Cowan, 1964) that the generic definition of *Acinetobacter* be

61

modified to allow the inclusion of bacteria that do not produce acid from carbohydrates, and that the glanders and the parapertussis bacilli, both misfits in the genera in which they were included, should be translated to it. This modification permits *M. lwoffii* to be included in the genus. Prévot (1961) includes seventeen species in the genus.

Minidefinition: Non-motile Gram-negative rods. Aerobic. Catalase-positive; oxidase-negative. Attack sugars by oxidation or not at all. Do not produce pigment.

Actinobacillus (Tables IIc,d). In this group we include *A. lignieresii* and *A. equuli* (*B. viscosum equi, Shigella equirulis*). Our experience of *A. lignieresii* is limited to a few strains, all catalase-positive, which puts them in column c_1 of Table II; Phillips (1960, 1961) studied more than 200 strains and found some to be catalase-negative, so that some isolates may also correspond with the reactions of column c_2. As the catalase and oxidase reactions of strains of *A. equuli* may also be positive or negative, the hatching for the genus in Table-fig. II extends over columns c_1, c_2, and d_1; the detailed characterizations are found in Table IIc. The paper by Vallée, Thibault & Second (1963) provided us with some information on the relatively unknown species, *A. equuli*.

Haupt, in *Bergey's Manual* (1957, p. 417), put the glanders bacillus in *Actinobacillus*, but as the type species of that genus, *A. lignieresii*, attacks glucose by fermentation and the glanders bacillus attacks it oxidatively, we think that this move was misguided. The taxonomic position of the glanders bacillus is difficult to decide and we place it in *Acinetobacter*.

Minidefinition: Gram-negative rods; non-motile. Facultatively anaerobic. Catalase positive or negative; oxidase positive or negative. Attack sugars fermentatively without gas production.

A–D group (Table IIc) is the term given to organisms named *B. alkalescens* and *B. dispar* by Andrewes (1918); they are non-motile and are now regarded as anaerogenic biotypes of *Escherichia*, with which they show much antigenic overlap. *B. alkalescens* is lactose-negative, *B. dispar* is a late lactose fermenter. Szturm-Rubinsten & Piéchaud (1962) recognize two biotypes on the basis of the ONPG test. Biochemically these organisms may be confused with shigellas.

Minidefinition: Gram-negative rods; non-motile. Catalase-positive; oxidase-negative. Facultatively anaerobic. Attack sugars by fermentation; gas not produced. Lactose fermented slowly or not at all. Citrate-negative; KCN-negative.

Aeromonas (Table IId). The subdivision of this group presents difficulties because those workers who have studied the problem most intensively are not agreed on the solution. Eddy (1960, 1962) distinguished between the aerogenic, V–P-positive, gluconate-positive species (*A. liquefaciens*) and the anaerogenic, V–P-negative, gluconate-negative *A. formicans*; Ewing, Hugh & Johnson (1961) combined them under the name *A. hydrophila*. We do not propose to enter the discussion on the nomenclature of these species (see Eddy, 1962) but, as we follow the division made by Eddy (1960) we adopt the names he used at that time. Ewing *et al.* (1961) include C27 (Ferguson & Henderson, 1947), a motile organism sharing an antigen with phase I *Shigella sonnei*, in the genus *Aeromonas* as *A. shigelloides*, but Eddy & Carpenter (1964) agree with Habs & Schubert (1962) and place it in a new genus *Plesiomonas*. We combine the classifications proposed by Eddy (1960, 1962) and by Ewing *et al.* (1961), and in Table II*d* show four species.

In the characterizations given by Eddy (1962) and by Ewing *et al.* (1961) there is a major discrepancy in *A. salmonicida*; Ewing found only 5 % of strains hydrolyzed arginine whereas Eddy found that 100 % were positive in the test; this forces us to temporize and to show the character as variable. It is questionable whether this non-motile fish pathogen (*A. salmonicida*), which needs a lower temperature (25° C) for incubation, should be included in the group and Smith (1963) has created a new genus, *Necromonas*, for it.

The optimal temperature for *Aeromonas* species is between 25 and 30° C; many strains will grow at 1° C and may spoil food kept in domestic refrigerators. *A. salmonicida* will not grow at 37° C.

Minidefinition: Gram-negative rods; generally motile. Catalase-positive; oxidase-positive. Facultatively anaerobic. Sugars attacked fermentatively; gas may be produced. Arginine usually hydrolyzed.

Alcaligenes (Table II*f*). Nyberg (1934–5) divided the Gram-negative rods that did not produce acid from carbohydrates into two subgroups: (i) *B. faecalis alcaligenes* was a short thick rod, non-motile or feebly motile by peritrichate flagella, and (ii) *Vibrio alcaligenes*, a long thin rod, actively motile by a polar flagellum; the second subgroup would probably now be classified as *Pseudomonas alcaligenes* (Ikari & Hugh, 1963) or *Comamonas percolans* (Davis & Park, 1962).

Conn (1942) reviewed the changes that had occurred in our ideas on the genus and pointed out that the 'non-fermenting' bacteria may be of two kinds: (i) those unable to use carbohydrate, and (ii) those that break it up so completely that the end-products do not give an acid reaction in ordinary media, CO_2 being so feeble an acid that it can not be detected in media of even a low buffer content. Moore & Pickett (1960) pointed out that strains that fail to show acid production in conventional sugar media may do so in tests designed to show oxidation of sugar, or in rapid tests in which alkali production is kept to a minimum (see Chapter 4 and Appendix E).

We include in *Alcaligenes* motile strains of Gram-negative rods that fail to produce acid in conventional media, and since we do not take notice of the type of flagellation, do not distinguish between Nyberg's first and second subgroups. In this genus we place *Alcaligenes bronchisepticus* (*Bordetella bronchiseptica*), which is distinguished from *A. faecalis* by its ability to break down urea.

Minidefinition: Gram-negative rods; motile. Aerobic. Catalase-positive; oxidase-positive. Do not produce acid from sugars in peptone-containing media.

Bacterium is not a valid generic name (Opinion no. 4, revised, 1954). Unlike *Bacillus*, which is valid for aerobic spore-forming rods, *Bacterium* is not attached to any generic group, and those organisms that were named Bacterium this-and-that have had to be allocated to genera that are now recognized: in Chapter 8 we have left *Bacterium typhiflavum* with that name as, in the absence of authentic cultures, we are unable to make up our minds on its correct taxonomic position. One organism that has been a taxonomic puzzle for a long time has kept *Bacterium anitratum* as its name; we have followed the lead of French workers and, in this *Manual*, it will be found under the name *Acinetobacter anitratus* (Tables II*a*,*e*).

Bacteroides (Table II*h*). We use this generic name for the anaerobic Gram-negative non-spore-forming rods, and show the characters of four species. As they are more difficult than aerobes to isolate, these organisms are less often studied; consequently their classification is not well established (see, for example, Dack, 1940; Beerens, 1953–4; Smith, 1955; Rentsch, 1963). In making Table II*h* we drew on the experience of Prévot (1961) and Willis (1960*a*); where this was contradictory we sought other sources. Beveridge (1934) found that *B. necrophorus* was catalase-positive, and we found *B. fragilis* also positive; consequently, in Table II*h* we record the catalase reaction of these two species as variable (d).

Minidefinition: Gram-negative rods; non-sporing. Anaerobic. Attack sugars by fermentation.

Bordetella (Table II*g*). As used in this *Manual* the name *Bordetella* is restricted to one species, the pertussis or whooping-cough bacillus. This organism does not grow on ordinary medium until it has been in artificial culture for some time, and a medium rich in blood (Bordet-Gengou, see p. 105) has always been used for isolation. The characteristic nutritional requirements seemed to justify the creation of a special genus for the organism. However, Turner (1961) has shown that it is not an organism that demands a rich medium but it is nutritionally exacting; peptones contain substances that are inhibitory to *B. pertussis* but a meat extract agar without peptone is suitable for the isolation of the organism. The nutritional requirements and metabolism of the species were reviewed by Rowatt (1957); its isolation and identification by Lautrop (1960).

64

Minidefinition: Gram-negative rods; non-motile. Aerobic. Catalase-variable; oxidase-positive. Do not grow on simple media containing peptone; grow on Bordet-Gengou medium. Do not attack sugars in peptone-containing media

Brucella (Table IIf) is a group of organisms whose cultural and serological characters blend into each other so that some workers regard the whole as one species, and other workers as three not well-defined species. The international *Brucella* subcommittee (Stableforth & Jones, 1963) decided in favour of three species, each subdivided into biotypes, and a distinct new species, *B. neotomae*, only a few strains of which have been isolated. We do not share the view of the subcommittee about this new species and from our experience of it we are not prepared to accept *B. neotomae* in the genus *Brucella*. We shall consider it among the bacteria of uncertain taxonomic position in Chapter 8, together with *B. ovis*, which the subcommittee does not accept as a brucella. In peptone-water sugars brucellas (except *B. neotomae*) do not produce detectable acid but, by using special techniques in media without peptone, acid can be shown (Pickett & Nelson, 1955).

The tests used to separate the species *Brucella melitensis*, *B. abortus*, and *B. suis* are specialized, their performance must be adequately controlled at all stages, and their interpretation is subjective. Modern views on the group are given in the report of the international subcommittee (Stableforth & Jones, 1963), and in Biberstein & Cameron (1961); Castañeda (1961) discusses the diagnosis of brucella infections.

Minidefinition: Gram-negative rods; non-motile. Aerobic or carboxyphilic. Catalase-positive; oxidase-positive or negative. Do not show acid production from sugars in peptone-containing media. Urease-positive.

Chromobacterium (Tables IIb,e) raises several problems for the systematist and consequently for the diagnostician. The generic name is reserved for Gram-negative rods that produce blue, violet or black colonies on appropriate media; those producing other pigments will be found in this *Manual* under other genera; red in *Serratia*, and yellow in *Flavobacterium*, *Enterobacter*, and *Pseudomonas*.

The old descriptions of *Chromobacterium violaceum* are quite inadequate, and three workers independently set out to identify the organism and to redescribe it in modern terms. They found that several distinct Gram-negative rods produced violet pigment; unfortunately the name *C. violaceum* was applied by Sneath (1956) to a mesophilic organism, and by Leifson (1956) and Eltinger (1956, 1957) to a psychrophil. The problem was referred to the Judicial Commission of the International Committee on Bacteriological Nomenclature which ruled (Opinion no. 16, 1958) that the mesophilic species should be *C. violaceum*. Apart from differing in temperature range, *C. lividum* (the psychrophilic species) oxidizes sugars and is represented by the hatched square under column e_2

in Table-fig. II, whereas *C. violaceum*, which ferments sugars, is in column *b*. The oxidase reaction of these bacteria cannot be determined by methods that depend on the production of a violet colour. A comprehensive monograph on the violet pigmented organisms by Sneath (1960) should be read by those who would know more of the group. *C. violaceum* seems to be a pathogen for humans (Sneath *et al.* 1953). The two species appear in the same genus only because both produce a violet pigment, and our definition has to be qualified (see also Chapter 9).

Minidefinition: Gram-negative rods; motile. Catalase-positive. Produce violet pigment.

Violaceum subgroup: Facultatively anaerobic; mesophilic. Attack sugars by fermentation.

Lividum subgroup: Aerobic; psychrophilic. Attack sugars by oxidation.

Citrobacter (Table II*b*). The common water and soil forms are rapid lactose-fermenters and form *Citrobacter freundii*. A less common variety produces indole (this is the Intermediate II coliform of the water bacteriologists, or *C. freundii* II, see Report, 1956*b*). The Ballerup and Bethesda groups are non-lactose or late-lactose fermenters of the Citrobacter group, and when growing in plate cultures may be recognized by the characteristically foul odour they produce.

Minidefinition: Gram-negative rods; motile. Catalase-positive; oxidase-negative. Facultatively anaerobic. Attack sugars fermentatively; gas is produced. Citrate-positive; KCN-positive.

Enterobacter (Table II*b*) is the name proposed by Hormaeche & Edwards (1960) for a group of motile organisms with IMViC reactions $- - + +$; *Enterobacter cloacae* (synonyms *B. cloacae* Jordan, 1890; *Cloaca cloacae* Castellani & Chalmers, 1919) was designated type species. Some strains produce a non-diffusible yellow pigment. Two other species have been described, *Enterobacter aerogenes*, and a psychrophil, *E. liquefaciens*. The biochemical reactions of *E. liquefaciens* vary according to the temperature of growth; for example, about two-thirds of strains are V–P-positive in cultures grown at 25° C, but only about one-third are positive in 37° C cultures.

Minidefinition: Gram-negative rods; motile. Catalase-positive; oxidase-negative. Facultatively anaerobic. Attack sugars fermentatively; gas produced. V–P-positive. Gelatin may be liquefied slowly; gluconate-positive. Produce ornithine decarboxylase. (*Compare with* Serratia *and* Hafnia.)

Escherichia (Table II*b*), like many other enteric bacteria, is subdivided into numerous serotypes some of which seem to cause infections in man, particularly O groups 26, 55, 111, 119, 127, and 128, which are associated with gastro-enteritis of infants (Taylor, 1961). Biochemical varieties of *E. coli* (e.g. *commune*, *communior*) formed on the basis of different sugar reactions, are no longer regarded as significant, and an important change in approach to *Escherichia* is the modern view that lactose-negative strains are acceptable in the group. Water bacteriologists use a classification based on indole, and gas production from lactose at 44° C (Report, 1956*b,c*). Many strains are non-motile or only feebly motile on first isolation, and permanently non-motile and anaerogenic strains (A–D group, p. 62) may have major antigens in the Escherichia series (Ewing, 1949*b*).

    Minidefinition: Gram-negative rods; motile. Catalase-positive; oxidase-negative. Facultatively anaerobic. Attack sugars fermentatively; gas normally produced. Citrate-negative; KCN-negative.

Flavobacterium (Table II*e*) is included in this *Manual* because several strains of this genus from pathological material have been collected at the Communicable Disease Center, Atlanta, Georgia, by King (1959); these strains appear to form a homogeneous group, divisible into several serotypes, which has been named *Flavobacterium meningosepticum*. Indole production was positive in King's strains and negative in those isolated by Cabrera & Davis (1961). It seems to us that when it is better known this bacterium will be isolated more frequently and we must urge readers not to discard cultures producing bright yellow colonies without further investigation.

    Minidefinition: Gram-negative rods; non-motile. Catalase-positive; oxidase-positive. Aerobic. Colonies have a yellow pigment. Sugars attacked slowly by oxidation.

Gemella (Table II*a*) is a genus for neisseria-like cocci that are catalase-negative, oxidase-negative and attack sugars by fermentation (Berger, 1960*a*, 1961). The only species we show in Table II*a* was first described by Thjötta & Böe (1938) as *Neisseria haemolysans*.

    Minidefinition: Gram-negative cocci. Facultatively anaerobic. Catalase-negative; oxidase-negative. Attack sugars by fermentation.

Haemophilus (Table II*g*) as we define it, is restricted to organisms that need one or both of the two factors *X* (haemin or haematin) and *V* (coenzyme I; diphosphopyridine nucleotide) for growth. These species will not grow on the media used in the biochemical tests shown in the main Table II, and media with *X* and *V* factors are needed for the indole and nitrate tests shown in Table II*g*. A re-examination of the original cultures of *H. suis* (Lewis & Shope, 1931) by Matthews & Pattison (1961) showed that they are no longer dependent on *X* factor; we have shown this *X* requirement in Table II*g*.

    In addition to the species shown in Table II*g*, Pittman & Davis (1950) distinguish *H. aegyptius* (the Koch-Weeks bacillus) from *H. influenzae* by differences in xylose and indole. Two so-called *Haemophilus* species, *H. aphrophilus* and *H. vaginalis* are discussed briefly in Chapter 8 (pp. 84–5).

For a review of the genus and its pathogenicity the reader is referred to Zinnemann (1960).

Minidefinition: Gram-negative rods, non-motile. Facultatively anaerobic. Do not grow on ordinary medium unless it is supplemented by X *and/or* V *factors.*

Hafnia (Table II*b*). The Hafnia group is the non-lactose fermenting counterpart of the *Enterobacter* group, and Ewing (1963) has suggested that these groups should be combined (see Chapter 9). As with *Enterobacter*, the biochemical characters are subject to temperature variations, and the most typical results are given at 25–30° C.

Minidefinition: As Enterobacter *except for the following: lactose is not attacked; gelatin is not liquefied.*

Klebsiella (Table II*c*). For many years the main problem in identifying Friedländer's bacillus was to distinguish it from *Aerobacter aerogenes* (Beijerinck, 1900), a non-motile bacterium; much less difficult was its separation from the motile organism we now know as *Enterobacter aerogenes*, but for some years also known as *Aerobacter aerogenes* (Hormaeche & Edwards, 1958). The classification used in this *Manual* and the reactions shown in Table II*c* are from Cowan, Steel, Shaw & Duguid (1960), with minor changes dictated by the examination of more strains. The correlation between the species and the capsule serotypes is not shown in the table but is as follows: *K. aerogenes*, all serotypes; *K. pneumoniae*, serotype 3; *K. edwardsii* v. *edwardsii*, serotypes 1 and 2; *K. edwardsii* v. *atlantae*, serotype 1; *K. rhinoscleromatis*, serotype 3; *K. ozaenae*, serotypes 3, 4, 5, and 6. The classification recommended by the Enterobacteriaceae Subcommittee is based mainly on serology and takes little account of the great range of biochemical reactions within the group. Like most Enterobacteriaceae, the reactivity of klebsiella antigens extends beyond the Klebsiella group. Indole-positive forms of *K. aerogenes* are not uncommon; strains that produce indole and liquefy gelatin have been named *K. oxytoca* but Lautrop (1956*b*) and Hugh (1959) think that they should be excluded from *Klebsiella*; Ewing (1963) prefers to keep them in the genus. Cowan *et al.* (1960) excluded both motile forms and strains that liquefied gelatin.

Minidefinition: Gram-negative rods; non-motile. Catalase-positive; oxidase-negative. Facultatively anaerobic. Attack sugars fermentatively, usually with production of gas. KCN and V–P-positive (important exceptions). Ornithine decarboxylase not produced. Urea generally hydrolyzed. Phenylalanine-negative.

Moraxella (Table II*f*) was created by Lwoff (1939) for non-haemophilic bacteria that did not attack carbohydrates, which had previously been placed in *Haemophilus*. Most of the bacteria placed by Lwoff in the genus were from the conjunctiva, but other workers added strains from other sources (*M. lwoffii* from soil), and strains that attacked carbohydrates; the last were later shown to be *Bacterium anitratum* (Brisou & Morichau-Beauchant, 1952). Brisou (1953), Floch (1953) and others excluded *M. lwoffii* and the sugar-attacking organisms from the genus *Moraxella*. Henriksen (1960) restricts the genus to oxidase-positive organisms and so excludes *M. lwoffii*. In defining the genus *Moraxella* we follow both the French workers and Henriksen.

Cultures of *Moraxella* species are very sensitive to drying and some strains will not grow at 37° C except in a moist atmosphere; they grow best when plates are put in a closed jar (Henriksen, 1952).

Minidefinition: *Gram-negative rods; non-motile. Aerobic. Catalase-positive; oxidase-positive. Do not attack sugars. Growth improved by addition of serum or blood.*

Neisseria (Table II *a*). In addition to the two well-known human pathogens, the gonococcus and the meningococcus, the genus contains *N. flavescens*, a species that caused a limited epidemic of meningitis in Chicago (Branham, 1930) and has not with certainty been isolated since (personal communication from the late Dr Sara Branham) though Prentice (1957) thought that the organism he isolated from a patient with meningitis might be *N. flavescens*. At first none of the strains isolated in Chicago attacked any sugars but after many years in artificial culture our strains, and those kept by Dr Branham, acquired the ability to produce acid from glucose, maltose, and sucrose. We include *N. flavescens* in our table and record its original characters in the hope that someone will isolate it again and will send a subculture to us. For somewhat similar reasons we include *N. mucosa* which was originally isolated by von Lingelsheim (1906, 1908), and re-isolated by Sir Philip Panton from the cerebrospinal fluid of two patients operated upon by the same neurosurgeon in the same operating theatre; these cultures were identified and described by one of us (Cowan, 1938*a*) but the cultures were lost during the 1939–45 war. From a patient with meningitis Reimann & Koucky (1939) isolated a similar organism but did not identify it conclusively. Other cultures isolated as *Diplococcus mucosus* (McFarlan, 1941; Bray & Cruickshank, 1943) have rather different characters and resemble *Bacterium anitratum*; most cultures sent to us as *D. mucosus* have, on repeated subculture, become bacillary in form and were undoubtedly strains of *B. anitratum*. The strains we had in 1938 reduced nitrates, were highly virulent for mice, and produced filtrates which also were toxic for mice in quite small doses; in all these characters they differed from *B. anitratum* and we cannot accept Seeliger's (1952–3) view that *B. anitratum* is a synonym for *D. mucosus*. Nitrate-reducing strains were described by Véron, Thibault & Second (1959).

Newly described species of *Neisseria*, *N. caviae* (Pelczar, 1953) and *N. animalis* (Berger, 1960*b*) are included in Table II *a*, the data being taken from papers of the original authors. In Table II *a* the species *N. sicca*, *N. flava*, and *N. perflava*, listed by Branham & Pelczar in *Bergey's Manual* (1957, p. 483–5) are combined as *N. pharyngis*

Wilson & Smith (1928). For details of other newly described species the reader is referred to the monograph by Berger (1963).

Minidefinition: Gram-negative spheres. Catalase-positive; oxidase-positive. Aerobic. Attack sugars by oxidation or not at all.

Pasteurella (Tables II*b,c,d*). The group is not homogeneous and strains labelled Pasteurella may fall in one of three columns of Table II. *P. pseudotuberculosis* is usually motile at 22° C but is always non-motile at 37° C (Preston & Maitland, 1952); it attacks sugars by fermentation, is catalase-positive and oxidase-negative. As Sneath & Cowan (1958) found in a computer analysis of data from our Collection, the species has many affinities with the Enterobacteriaceae and we characterize it in Table II*b* with the motile members of that group (family).

P. pestis, the plague bacillus, grows slowly in Hugh & Leifson's medium and acid first appears in the open tube and only later in the closed tube. We now think that this reaction should be interpreted as fermentation, and show *P. pestis* in Table II*c* with the non-motile Enterobacteriaceae. In this table the characters are very similar to those of *Shigella flexneri*; at the bench no difficulty arises as the shigella grows much more vigorously than the pasteurella and produces a larger colony. For a review of the diagnosis of plague see Pollitzer (1954, 1960) and also Girard (1953) who discussed the subdivision of *P. pestis* into three varieties on the production of acid from glycerol and the reduction of nitrate. The two species *P. pestis* and *P. pseudotuberculosis* make up the genus *Yersinia* proposed by van Loghem (1944–5).

P. multocida (*P. septica*) is a gathering together of many so-called species that produce haemorrhagic septicaemia in various animals and infections in man in close contact with them. There is now a tendency to split off segments of this all-embracing species as *P. pneumotropica* (Jawetz, 1950; Henriksen, 1962), *P. haemolytica* (Newsom & Cross 1932; Biberstein, Gills & Knight, 1960; Smith, 1961) and its variety *ureae* (Henriksen & Jyssum, 1960; Jones, 1962). These oxidase-positive species are shown in Table II*d*; however, not all strains of *P. multocida* are oxidase-positive by Kovács' test and the oxidase-negative strains are shown in Table II*c*. Some *P. haemolytica* strains are catalase-negative (Biberstein *et al.* 1960).

Two minidefinitions are given, the first for *P. pestis* and *P. pseudotuberculosis* (*Yersinia* of van Loghem), the second for the *P. multocida* group.

Minidefinitions: Yersinia group. Gram-negative rods; motile or non-motile. Catalase-positive; oxidase-negative. Facultatively anaerobic. Attack sugars fermentatively without gas production; do not attack sucrose. Grow on MacConkey agar.

Multocida group. Gram-negative rods; non-motile. Catalase-positive; oxidase-positive or negative. Facultatively anaerobic. Attack sugars fermentatively without gas production; ferment sucrose. Do not grow on MacConkey agar (few exceptions).

Proteus (Table II*b*). The present classification of the genus is based on proposals made by Rustigian & Stuart (1945) in which four species were recognized. A breakdown into other genera, *Morganella* (Fulton, 1943) and *Rettgerella* (Kauffmann, 1953) has not gained wide acceptance, in spite of support by Rauss & Vörös (1959). Kauffmann combines *P. vulgaris* and *P. mirabilis* as *P. hauseri*. The four species *P. vulgaris*, *P. mirabilis*, *P. morganii*, and *P. rettgeri* are all urease-positive and deaminate phenylalanine to phenylpyruvic acid. On soft agar all may show swarming.

Minidefinition: Gram-negative rods; motile. Catalase-positive; oxidase-negative. Facultatively anaerobic. Attack sugars fermentatively, usually with gas production. Urease-positive; phenylalanine-positive.

Providence (Table II*b*) organisms were first recognized as an entity by Stuart *et al.* (1946) as the 29911 group. They had been isolated before as *B. inconstans* and later as *B. alcalifaciens*. Because they are phenylalanine-positive, a character shared only with the *Proteus* species, Singer & Bar-Chay (1954) and Shaw & Clarke (1955) proposed that they should be included in *Proteus*. Edwards & Ewing (1962) prefer to keep them separate and divide them into two biotypes, *A* and *B*; we have adopted this device in Table II*b* rather than give them the species names proposed by Ewing (1962), the validity of which is doubtful.

Minidefinition: Gram-negative rods; motile. Catalase-positive; oxidase-negative. Facultatively anaerobic. Attack sugars fermentatively, usually with the production of gas. Urease-negative; phenylalanine-positive.

Pseudomonas (Table II*e*) is a group which includes pathogens for animals and plants, and as these groups are studied in different laboratories the characterizations are based on different tests and techniques. It seems possible that strains pathogenic for plants are also pathogenic for animals. The two species studied by both groups of workers are *Pseudomonas aeruginosa* (*P. pyocyanea*) and *P. fluorescens*; these species have much in common with *P. pseudomallei* (Whitmore's bacillus). Wetmore & Gochenour (1956) found that a comparison of the temperature range for growth is a means of distinguishing the species, and *P. pseudomallei* is inhibited by media such as SS agar (Difco), deoxycholate agar, and CTAB agar on which the other two species will grow. The flagella of Whitmore's bacillus were described as peritrichate by Legroux & Genevray (1933), and as polar by Brindle & Cowan (1951) and by Wetmore & Gochenour (1956), all of whom showed that it had many characters in common with pseudomonads; it was included in the genus *Pseudomonas* by Haynes in *Bergey's Manual* (1957, p. 100) and by Lysenko (1961).

P. aeruginosa produces alkali on Christensen's urea medium and, rather more slowly,

6

on the base without urea; in Stuart, van Stratum & Rustigian's urea medium alkali is not produced.

In characterizing *P. fluorescens* we follow Rhodes (1959) who regards the group in a wide sense; on the other hand Lysenko (1961) names several other species within Rhodes' fluorescens group, and restricts *P. fluorescens* to a closely-defined subgroup. Klinge (1960) distinguishes *P. fluorescens*, which liquefies gelatin, from *P. putida*, which does not liquefy it. *P. alcaligenes* (Ikari & Hugh, 1963) can only be distinguished from *Alcaligenes faecalis* by the mode of the flagellar attachment.

Many pseudomonads break down arginine but Møller's method is not satisfactory with these organisms. Sherris *et al.* (1959) and Thornley (1960) have described suitable methods.

Minidefinition: *Gram-negative rods; motile. Catalase-positive; oxidase-positive. Aerobic. Attack sugars by oxidation; do not produce gas. Diffusible yellow or green pigment(s) may be produced.*

Salmonella (Table II*b*), which Kauffmann (1963*a*) now divides into three subgenera, consists of several hundreds of different serotypes. The antigenic analysis is not a routine procedure but a task for a specialized reference laboratory. However, simplified diagnostic schemes, using a limited number of sera, have been suggested (Edwards & Kauffmann, 1952; Spicer, 1956), and their use makes possible the presumptive serotyping of the majority of salmonellas isolated. One serotype, *Salmonella typhi*, is quite distinct both serologically and biochemically and warrants separate description; it differs from almost all the other salmonellas in its inability to produce gas in the breakdown of carbohydrates, and in being citrate-negative. *S. gallinarum*, which causes disease in poultry, also does not produce gas. Other serotypes may produce anaerogenic variants (this is particularly common in *S. paratyphi*-A isolated in Egypt and Syria) but the normal forms produce gas. The type species of the genus, *S. choleraesuis*, is biochemically atypical and does not ferment arabinose or trehalose. The Arizona group, originally named *S. arizonae* and so named in Table II*b*, often ferment lactose, liquefy gelatin slowly and are usually malonate-positive (Shaw, 1956). Most other serotypes are biochemical variants on a fairly stable pattern; Borman, Stuart & Wheeler (1944) proposed that they should be named *S. kauffmannii*, Kauffmann & Edwards (1952) suggested *S. enterica*, while Ewing (1963) proposed *S. enteritidis* for them.

Many strains which produce indole, hydrolyze gelatin, or are malonate-positive are now recognized as salmonella serotypes. The typically non-motile salmonellas (*S. gallinarum* and *S. pullorum*) are shown in Table II*c*; the distinction between these two organisms is described in detail by Trabulsi & Edwards (1962).

Minidefinition: *Gram-negative rods; motile. Catalase-positive; oxidase-negative. Facultatively anaerobic. Attack sugars by fermentation with production of gas (important* *exception does not produce gas and is citrate-negative). Citrate usually positive; KCN-negative.*

Serratia (Table II*b*). Characteristically the organisms produce a bright red pigment but in culture non-pigmented variants are constantly thrown off and also seem to occur in nature. Meat extract inhibits pigment formation but this may be restored by transfer to a medium without meat (Goldsworthy & Still, 1936). Kharasch, Conway & Bloom (1936) thought that glucose was necessary for pigment production by *S. marcescens*; on the other hand Goldsworthy & Still (1936, 1938) found that glucose inhibited and mannitol stimulated pigmentation. Our experience confirms all these findings and indicates that different strains vary in the way in which they respond to glucose in the medium. Medium A of King, Ward & Raney (1954) is one of the most satisfactory media for showing pigment production.

Sometimes the organisms are found in human secretions and, by growth in sputum after expectoration, may suggest that the patient has haemoptysis (Robinson & Woolley, 1957). They are suspected of being the cause of infections in man and, with their recognition in the non-pigmented form, reports of their occurrence are becoming more frequent. The V–P negative variety, *S. marcescens* var. *kiliensis*, has also been isolated in the non-pigmented form from sputum (Bövre & Tönjum, 1963).

Serratia marcescens liquefies gelatin very rapidly and in this and many other characters it closely resembles *Enterobacter liquefaciens* (Pederson & Breed, 1928). Fulton, Forney & Leifson (1959) distinguished two biochemical patterns in strains isolated from man and animals; pattern 2 might be regarded as pigmented coliforms.

Reviews of the group by Ewing, Davis & Reavis (1959) and Martinec & Kocur (1961) should be consulted by those who want more information.

***Minidefinition:** Gram-negative rods; motile. Catalase-positive; oxidase-negative. Facultatively anaerobic. Attack sugars fermentatively, often with gas production. V–P usually positive. Gelatin liquefied. Gluconate-positive. Produce ornithine decarboxylase. Often produce a red pigment when grown on suitable media.*

Shigella (Table II*c*). Modern ideas on the classification of shigellas are largely due to Ewing who built on foundations laid by Murray (1918), Andrewes & Inman (1919), and by Boyd (1938) whose recognition of group and specific antigens introduced some system into the antigenic analysis of the group. Ewing is also largely responsible for showing that many so-called shigellas are non-motile, anaerogenic members of the Escherichia group. The two groups are closely related and may be interfertile, the progeny resembling the A–D group (Luria & Burrows, 1957).

Biochemically the Shigella group is divided into the mannitol fermenters and the mannitol non-fermenters but Ewing (personal communication) has found exceptions with regard to mannitol fermentation in nearly all the serotypes. The mannitol non-fermenting subgroup (*S. dysenteriae*) differs from the others in that serotype 1 (Shiga's bacillus) is catalase-negative; among other shigellas catalase-negative strains are occasionally found (Carpenter & Lachowicz, 1959) but this is not a constant character of any serotype except *S. dysenteriae* 1. *S. dysenteriae* 2 (Schmitz's bacillus) always produces indole; some strains of *S. flexneri* 6 (Newcastle and Manchester varieties) produce a small bubble of gas in glucose peptone water (but see Orr Ewing & Taylor, 1945 for the influence of the peptone), and other serotypes may have certain biochemical characteristics which we do not show in Table II*c*. Details of the biochemical characters of the serotypes can be found in Edwards & Ewing (1962). Serotypes of *S. flexneri* are ONPG negative; *S. boydii* 9 strains are ONPG positive, but other serotypes of *S. boydii* vary in this test.

S. sonnei is typically a late fermenter of lactose but not all strains ferment the sugar, and Szturm-Rubinsten (1963) recognizes different biotypes. A rapid test (ONPG) which shows the inherent ability of the late lactose fermenters to ferment lactose has recently been described (Le Minor & Ben Hamida, 1962) and tests of other shigellas show that strains of many serotypes may be potential lactose fermenters (Szturm-Rubinsten & Piéchaud, 1963).

Minidefinition: Gram-negative rods; non-motile. Catalase-positive (important exception is negative); oxidase-negative. Facultatively anaerobic. Attack sugars by fermentation without gas production (a few exceptions produce a little gas). Citrate-negative; KCN-negative.

Vibrio (Table II*d*). The disease and diagnosis of cholera are discussed by Pollitzer (1959). We characterize only *Vibrio cholerae* in our table and regard *V. eltor* as a biochemical variant (or biotype) which is V–P-positive and haemolytic for human cells (De *et al.* 1954). De found that calcium salts were necessary to show certain haemolysins but they inhibited others. In subculture true cholera vibrios may acquire haemolytic properties (de Moor, 1949) but this may be delayed in fresh isolates of the el Tor variety. Feeley & Pittman (1963) showed that when the methods were standardized, the haemolytic test was a reliable tool in distinguishing between *V. cholerae* and *V. eltor*. The so-called non-agglutinable (NAG) vibrios are not, in themselves, important; they can be distinguished by serological methods but a medical laboratory needs to test cultures against only one antiserum which will agglutinate true cholera vibrios and the el Tor variety (Gardner & Venkatraman, 1935). We do not think any advantage is gained by subdividing vibrios by fermentation reactions, although both the cholera and el Tor vibrios ferment mannose and sucrose, but not arabinose (Heiberg, 1936). Wahba & Takla (1962) recommend a chemical flocculation test for distinguishing the cholera from the el Tor vibrios, but the test is not suitable for rough strains.

74

For the microaerophilic *V. fetus* see Chapter 8.

Minidefinition: Gram-negative rods; motile. Catalase-positive; oxidase-positive. Aerobic or facultatively anaerobic. Attack sugars by fermentation; gas not produced. Do not hydrolyze arginine.

Much more systematic work is being done on the Gram-negative rods than on all the Gram-positive bacteria and in Table-fig. II, which follows on p. 76, we show a diagnostic scheme that is based on ideas that are at present acceptable to most workers. But it is obvious that in this very active field ideas on classification are changing, and some of the possibilities will be discussed in Chapter 9. Recent work indicates that the applications of the principles of numerical taxonomy will enable us to create groups that can be characterised in a statistical manner; this will be more informative than the +, d and − characters recorded in our tables.

Table-fig. II.—*First-stage diagnostic table for Gram-negative bacteria*

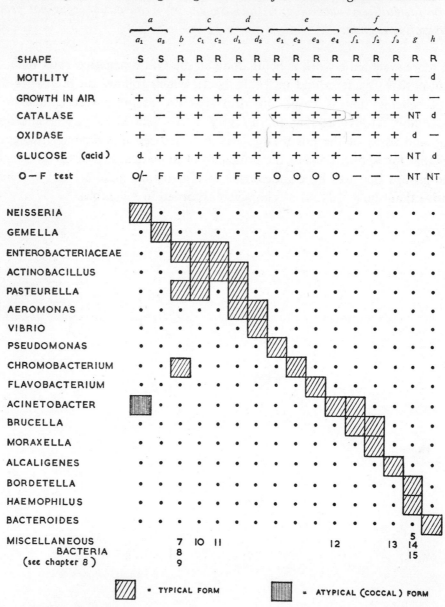

| | = TYPICAL FORM | | = ATYPICAL (COCCAL) FORM |

Symbols common to all tables:

$+$ = 100–80% strains positive; d = 79–21% strains positive; $-$ = 20–0% strains positive; F = fermentation; O = oxidation; ($\cdot$) = delayed reaction; NT = not testable.

Symbols special to Table II:

S = sphere; R = rod.

Table II*a*. *Second-stage table for* Neisseria, Gemella, *and* Acinetobacter anitratus

	N. gonorrhoeae	N. meningitidis	N. catarrhalis	N. flavescens	N. pharyngis	N. animalis	N. caviae	N. mucosa	Acinetobacter anitratus ('Bacterium anitratum')	Gemella haemolysans
Catalase	+	+	+	+	+	+	+	+	+	−
Oxidase	+	+	+	+	+	+	+	+	−	−
Growth at 22° C	−	−	+	+	+	+	+	+	+	+
Growth on nutrient agar	−	−	+	+	+	+	+	+	+	+
Glucose (acid)	+	+	−	−	+	d	−	+	+	+
Lactose (acid)	−	−	−	−	−	−	−	(+)	−*	−
Maltose (acid)	−	+	−	−	+	−	−	−	−	+
Sucrose (acid)	−	−	−	−	d	+	−	−	−	+
Nitrate reduction	−	−	d	−	−	−	+	+	−	−
Pigment	−	−	−	+	+	−	+	−	−	−
Haemolysis	−	−	−	−	−	−	d	−	−	+

* Negative on 1 % lactose, positive on 10 % (see p. 61).

Table II*b*. *Second-stage table for motile Enterobacteriaceae and similar organisms*

	Salmonella typhi	S. arizonae	Other Salmonella	Escherichia coli	Citrobacter freundii	Ballerup-Bethesda	Hafnia alvei	Enterobacter aerogenes	E. cloacae	E. liquefaciens	Serratia marcescens	Proteus vulgaris	P. mirabilis	P. morganii	P. rettgeri	Providence A	Providence B	Pasteurella pseudotuberculosis	Chromobacterium violaceum	C. lividum*
Citrate utilization†	−	+	+	−	+	+	+	+	+	+	+	d	d	−	+	+	+	−	d	+
KCN	−	−	−	−	+	+	+	+	+	+	+	+	+	+	+	+	+	−	+	d
Gelatin hydrolysis‡	−	(+)	−	−	−	−	−	d	(+)	+	+	+	+	−	−	−	−	−	+	−
Glucose (gas)	−	+	+	+	+	+	+	+	+	+	d	+	+	+	−	−	+	−	−	−
Arabinose (acid)	−	+	d	+	+	+	+	+	+	+	−	−	−	−	+	−	−	−	+	−
Lactose (acid)	−	d	−	+	+	d	−	+	+	d	d	−	−	−	−	−	−	−	d	−
Sucrose (acid)	−	−	d	d	d	d	d	+	+	+	+	+	+	−	d	d	d	−	d	−
Adonitol (acid)	−	−	−	−	−	−	−	+	d	−	d	−	−	+	+	−	−	−	−	−
Dulcitol (acid)	d	−	+	d	d	d	−	d	d	−	−	−	−	−	−	−	−	−	−	−
Mannitol (acid)	+	+	+	+	+	+	+	+	+	+	+	−	−	+	−	d	+	−	−	−
Inositol (acid)	−	−	d	−	−	−	−	+	−	+	d	−	−	+	−	+	−	−	−	−
Indole	−	−	−	+	−	−	−	−	−	−	−	+	−	+	+	+	+	−	−	−
V–P	−	−	−	−	−	−	−	d	+	+	d	+	−	d	−	−	−	−	−	−
H₂S (in TSI)	+	+	+	−	+	+	+	−	−	−	−	+	−	−	−	−	−	+	−	−
Urease	−	−	−	−	d	d	−	−	d	d	−	+	+	+	+	−	+	−	+	−
Lysine decarboxylase	+	+	+	d	−	−	+	+	−	d	+	−	−	−	−	−	−	−	−	−
Arginine dihydrolase	+	+	+	d	+	−	−	+	−	+	−	−	−	−	−	−	−	−	+	d
Ornithine decarboxylase	−	+	+	d	d	d	+	+	+	+	+	−	+	+	−	−	−	−	−	−
Gluconate	−	−	−	−	−	+	+	+	+	+	−	d	−	−	−	−	−	−	−	d
Malonate	−	+	−	−	d	−	+	+	d	−	d	−	−	−	−	−	−	−	d	−
Phenylalanine	−	−	−	−	−	−	−	−	−	−	−	+	+	+	+	+	+	−	−	−
Pigment	−	−	−	−	−	−	−	−	d	−	d	−	−	−	−	−	−	−	+	+
ONPG	−	+	−	+	+	d	+	+	+	+	−	−	−	−	−	−	−	+	−	d

* Included only for comparison; its attack on carbohydrates is oxidative.
† Citrate utilization in Koser's or Simmons' medium.
‡ Gelatin hydrolysis: + = positive within 7 days at 22° C;
  (+) = positive after 7 days.

Table II*c*. *Second-stage table for* Shigella, Klebsiella, Pasteurella, *and* Actinobacillus

	Shigella dysenteriae 1	S. dysenteriae 2 +	S. flexneri & S. boydii	S. sonnei	A–D group	Klebsiella aerogenes	K. pneumoniae	K. edwardsii v. edwardsii	K. edwardsii v. atlantae	K. ozaenae	K. rhinoscleromatis	Salmonella gallinarum	S. pullorum	Pasteurella multocida	P. pestis	P. pseudotuberculosis	Actinobacillus lignieresii	A. equuli
Catalase	−	+	+	+	+	+	+	+	+	+	+	+	+	+	+	+	d	d
Citrate utilization*	−	−	−	−	−	+	+	d	+	d	−	−	d	−	−	−	−	−
Growth on MacConkey	+	+	+	+	+	+	+	+	+	+	+	+	d	−	+	+	+	d
KCN	−	−	−	−	−	+	−	+	+	+	+	−	−	+	−	−	−	−
Gelatin hydrolysis	−	−	−	−	−	−	−	−	−	−	−	−	−	−	−	−	−	−
Glucose (gas)	−	−	−	−	−	+	+	−	+	d	−	−	−	+	−	−	−	−
Lactose (acid)	−	−	−	(+)	d	+	+	(+)	(+)	(+)	−	−	−	−	−	−	d	+
Sucrose (acid)	−	−	−	(+)	d	+	+	+	+	d	+	−	−	(+)	−	−	+	+
Dulcitol (acid)	−	−	−	−	d	d	+	−	−	−	−	−	+	−	d	−	−	−
Mannitol (acid)	−	−	+	+	+	+	+	+	+	+	+	+	+	+	+	+	+	+
Indole	−	d	d	−	d	−	−	−	−	−	−	−	−	+	−	−	−	−
MR	+	+	+	+	+	−	+	d	+	+	+	+	+	−	+	+	−	−
V–P	−	−	+	−	−	+	−	+	d	−	−	−	−	−	−	−	d	−
H₂S (in TSI)	−	−	−	−	−	−	−	−	−	−	−	+	+	d	−	−	+	−
Urease	−	−	−	−	−	+	+	+	+	d	−	−	−	−	−	+	d	+
Lysine decarboxylase	−	−	−	d	+	+	+	+	d	−	+	−	+	−	−	−	−	−
Arginine dihydrolase	−	−	−	d	d	−	−	−	−	−	−	d	+	−	−	−	−	−
Ornithine decarboxylase	−	−	−	+	d	−	−	−	−	−	−	+	+	−	−	−	−	−
Gluconate	−	−	−	−	−	+	d	+	d	−	−	−	−	−	−	−	−	−
Malonate	−	−	−	−	−	+	+	d	−	−	+	−	−	−	−	−	−	−
ONPG	+	d	d	d	d	+	+	+	+	+	−	−	−	−	+	+	+	+
Christensen's citrate	..	..	..	−	+	..	..	..	..	..	..	..	..	..	..	..	..	..

* Citrate utilization in Koser's or Simmons' medium.

Table II*d.* *Second-stage table for* Aeromonas, Vibrio, Pasteurella, *and* Actinobacillus

	Aeromonas liquefaciens	A. formicans	A. shigelloides	A. salmonicida	Vibrio cholerae	Pasteurella multocida	P. pneumotropica	P. haemolytica v. haemolytica	P. haemolytica v. ureae	Actinobacillus lignieresii	A. equuli
Motility	+	+	+	−	+	−	−	−	−	−	−
Growth at 37° C	+	+	+	−	+	+	+	+	+	+	+
Growth on MacConkey	+	+	+	+	+	−	−	d	−	+	d
KCN	+	d	−	−	d	+	d	d	−	−	−
Gelatin hydrolysis	+	+	−	+	+	−	−	−	−	−	−
Glucose (gas)	+	−	−	+	−	−	−	−	−	−	−
Xylose (acid)	−	−	−	−	d	d	d	+	−	+	+
Lactose (acid)	d	d	+	−	(+)	−	d	d	−	d	+
Sucrose (acid)	+	+	−	−	+	(+)	+	+	+	+	+
Glycerol (acid)	+	+	+	+	d	−	+	d	−	d	−
Mannitol (acid)	+	+	−	+	+	+	−	+	+	+	+
Sorbitol (acid)	+	−	−	−	d	d	−	d	+	−	−
Indole	+	+	+	−	+	+	+	−	−	−	−
V–P	+	−	−	−	d	−	−	−	−	d	−
H₂S	d	−	−	−	−	d	−	d	−	+	−
Urease	−	−	−	−	−	−	+	−	+	d	+
Lysine decarboxylase	−	−	+	−	+	−	−	−	−	−	−
Arginine dihydrolase	+	+	+	d	−	−	−	−	−	−	−
Ornithine decarboxylase	−	−	d	−	+	+	d	d	−	−	−
Gluconate	+	−	−	−	−	−	−	−	−	−	−
Haemolysis	+	d	−	+	d	−	−	+	+	−	−

Table II*e*. *Second-stage table for* Pseudomonas, Chromobacterium, Flavobacterium, *and* Acinetobacter *species*

	Pseudomonas aeruginosa	P. fluorescens	P. pseudomallei	Chromobacterium lividum	Flavobacterium meningosepticum	Acinetobacter mallei	A. anitratus
Motility	+	+	+	+	−	−	−
Oxidase	+	+	+	−	+	−	−
Growth at 42° C	+	−	+	−	−	−	d
Growth at 37° C	+	d	+	−	+	+	+
Growth at 5° C	−	+	−	+	−	−	−
Citrate utilization	+	+	+	+	−	d	+
Growth on MacConkey	+	+	+	d	d	−	+
KCN	+	d	+	d	−	d	+
Gelatin hydrolysis	+	d	+	−	+	∓	d
Starch hydrolysis	−	−	+	−	−	−	−
Mannitol (acid)	d	d	+	−	(+)	d	−
Indole	−	−	−	−	d	−	−
Nitrate reduction	+	d	+	+	−	+	−
Urease	+	d	d	−	−	d	d
Gluconate	+	d	−	d	−	−	−
Pigment	+	+	d	+	+	−	−
Diffusion of pigment	+	+	−	−	−	−	−
Arginine dihydrolase	+	+	+	d	−	+	−

Table II*f*. *Second-stage table for* Alcaligenes, Acinetobacter, Brucella, *and* Moraxella *species*

	Alcaligenes faecalis	Alcaligenes bronchisepticus	Acinetobacter lwoffii	Acinetobacter parapertussis	Brucella spp.	Moraxella spp.
Motility	+	+	−	−	−	−
Oxidase	+	+	−	−	d	+
Growth on nutrient agar	+	+	+	+	+	d
Citrate utilization	d	d	+	d	−	−
Growth on MacConkey	+	+	+	−	d	−
KCN	+	+	−	−	−	−
Gelatin hydrolysis	−	−	−	−	−	d
Nitrate reduction	d	+	−	−	+	d
H$_2$S	d	d	−	−	d	−
Urease	−	+	−	+	+	−

Table II*g*. *Second-stage table for* Bordetella *and* Haemophilus

	Bordetella pertussis	Haemophilus influenzae	H. haemolyticus	H. para-influenzae	H. para-haemolyticus	H. suis	H. canis
Growth on Bordet-Gengou	+	—	—	—	—	—	—
Growth on Fildes' digest agar	—	÷	+	+	+	+	+
X factor needed	—	+	+	—	—	+	+
V factor needed	—	+	+	+	+	+	—
Indole	—	d	d	d	—	—	+
Nitrate reduction	—	+	+	+	+	+	+
Haemolysis on blood agar	NG	—	+	—	+	—	—

NG = no growth.

Table II*h*. *Second-stage table for* Bacteroides

	Bacteroides necrophorus	B. fragilis	B. melaninogenicum	B. serpens
Motility	—	—	—	+
Catalase	d	d	—	—
Gelatin hydrolysis	—	—	d	(+)
Glucose (acid)	+	+	+	+
Lactose (acid)	d	—	+	+
Maltose (acid)	+	—	+	+
Sucrose (acid)	+	+	+	—
Mannitol (acid)	d	—	+	—
Indole	+	—	+	—
H$_2$S	d	—	+	—
Black pigment	—	—	+	—
Haemolysis	+	—	+	—

8

MISCELLANEOUS BACTERIA AND BACTERIA OF UNCERTAIN TAXONOMIC POSITION

In this chapter we give brief notes on bacteria which are not included in the main chapters for one or more of the following reasons:

 (i) their taxonomic position is uncertain,
 (ii) they are infrequently isolated or identified, and therefore are not well characterized,
 (iii) they are rare in this country and we have no personal experience of their isolation; in most cases we have only handled old laboratory strains,
 (iv) they are not normally isolated from clinical specimens and would seem to fall outside the scope of this *Manual* but for the fact that they may be found in foodstuffs, water or soil.

A lead to some of the organisms appears as a number at the foot of Table-figs. I (p. 55) and II (p. 76), and these are given corresponding numbers in this chapter.

1. **Leuconostoc** species are heterofermentative and, when tested under suitable conditions of medium, pH, temperature of incubation and a heavy inoculum, will produce CO_2 from glucose (Gibson & Abdel-Malek, 1945). A review of these dairy organisms by Garvie (1960) will be useful to those who wish to subdivide them into species.

2. **Pediococcus cerevisiae** produces sarcina sickness of beer and pediococci have also been found in material such as meat-curing brines. On ordinary media catalase is not produced but variable amounts are formed in the presence of glucose (Felton, Evans & Niven, 1953); with a low glucose content Gutekunst, Delwiche & Seeley (1957) obtained poor growth but catalase was demonstrable; in high (1 %) glucose growth was better but catalase could not be shown unless the pH was adjusted to neutrality. Details of the characters and different approaches to the classification of the pediococci will be found in papers by Pederson (1949), Nakagawa & Kitahara (1959), Deibel & Niven (1960), and Günther & White (1961).

3. **Corynebacterium minutissimum** is the combination proposed by Sarkany, Taplin & Blank (1962) for the organism isolated from erythrasma. Characteristically the organism fluoresces under ultra-violet light when grown on a solid medium containing autoclaved

serum. It has metachromatic granules, is not haemolytic, grows in air and under microaerophilic conditions, and does not reduce nitrates. It is catalase-positive, oxidase-negative, indole-negative, MR and V–P-negative. Urease is not produced, gelatin is not liquefied. It produces acid from fructose, glucose, mannose, and maltose. Sucrose may be positive, but the following sugars are negative: lactose, trehalose, raffinose, dulcitol, and mannitol. Partridge & Jackson (1962) think that this organism might be a member of the genus *Bacillus*.

4. Corynebacterium acnes is an anaerobic diphtheroid isolated from the human skin and is alleged to cause acne. Characterization of the acne organism is poor but Douglas & Gunter (1946) suggest that it is one of the propionibacteria, a view supported by Moore & Cato (1963) but not shared by Sundman, Björksten & Gyllenberg (1959). Fleming (1909) found that the addition of oleic acid encouraged growth of *C. acnes* which suggests that Corynebacterium Q of Pollock, Howard & Boughton (1949) may be related to this species. *C. acnes* is said to be catalase-positive.

5. Haemophilus vaginalis. Several different organisms from the vagina have been named *Haemophilus vaginalis*; some appear to be *Haemophilus influenzae* (Lapage, 1961; Zinnemann & Turner, 1962), others are either Gram-variable or, in young cultures are frankly Gram-positive (Zinnemann & Turner, 1963). These two groups differ in their dependence on *X* and *V* factors and in many cultural characters; the non-haemophilic, Gram-variable group are catalase-negative, oxidase-negative, do not reduce nitrate, and grow on McLeod's chocolate tellurite medium. Because of their negative catalase reaction Lapage (1961) thought that it would be interesting to grow them on media containing tomato juice. Zinnemann & Turner (1963) did not regard the negative catalase test as important and transferred the organisms to *Corynebacterium* as *C. vaginale*, and would amend the definition of the genus from 'catalase-positive' to 'usually catalase-positive'. Amies & Garabedian (1963) think that these vaginal bacteria are dissociated forms of lactobacilli.

6. Lactobacillus bifidus is an anaerobic bacterium isolated from the stools of breast-fed infants; taxonomically it is not correctly placed in *Lactobacillus* (Rogosa & Sharpe, 1959), and Sundman *et al.* (1959) suggest that it may be related to the genus *Butyribacterium*. It is not a pathogen but a curiosity of medical bacteriology.

7. Bacterium typhiflavum was originally isolated from water, soil, and faeces of typhoid contacts. The characters described by Cruickshank (1935) were: yellow-colony-forming Gram-negative rods, motile at 22° C but not at 37° C. Catalase-positive, produce acid without gas from arabinose, xylose, rhamnose, glucose, sucrose, salicin, and mannitol. Acid is not produced from lactose, dulcitol, and inositol. Gelatin liquefied in 6–15 days. Indole-negative, MR-positive, V–P-negative; nitrates reduced. Cruickshank's strains have not been preserved and strains sent to us by other workers as *B. typhiflavum* were found to be pigmented strains of *Enterobacter cloacae*.

8. **Erwinia** is a genus originally created for the coliforms that are plant pathogens. They are typical members of the Enterobacteriaceae and apart from plant pathogenicity they do not differ significantly from the intestinal coliforms of vertebrates. Some species do not reduce nitrates. Those strains that cause dry necroses, galls or wilts are *Erwinia*, but those producing soft rot are now known as pectobacteria.

9. **Pectobacterium.** A genus of coliforms that cause soft rot in plants; it differs from *Erwinia* in producing a pectinase.

10. **Actinobacillus actinomycetemcomitans** is often associated with *Actinomyces israelii* in material from patients with actinomycosis, but King & Tatum (1962) had many strains from sources in which actinomycosis was improbable. They compared 33 strains isolated over a period of 10 years and a strain from our Collection with more than thirty strains of *Haemophilus aphrophilus* (q.v. below). Although the generic names suggest that these organisms are quite different, King & Tatum found that they had many characters in common, and thought that they were more like each other than like the genera into which they had hitherto been placed.

In morphology both organisms are small Gram-negative coccobacilli; in broth they grow as granules which stick to the sides of the tubes. The actinobacillus colonies are the smaller and are more adherent to the medium. Growth of both organisms is improved in CO_2. King & Tatum found that most strains produced a small amount of gas in carbohydrate-containing media; this was shown most easily by using the technique of Hormaeche & Munilla (1957) of plunging a red-hot wire into the medium. In the O–F test, sugars are fermented. A comparison of the characters of these organisms is shown in Table 3.

Although they made a detailed comparison of these two species and showed that they had much in common, King & Tatum (1962) did not make any recommendations about their taxonomic position.

11. **Haemophilus aphrophilus** was originally isolated by Khairat (1940) from a blood culture and so named because it needed X factor and CO_2 for growth. King & Tatum (1962) could not confirm the requirement for X factor on the strains sent to them for identification but they pointed out that these strains had been subcultured an unknown number of times and might have lost the X factor dependence. Some strains could have come from undiagnosed cases of actinomycosis and one was found in the same specimen as *Actinomyces israelii*. The strains had much in common with strains of *Actinobacillus actinomycetemcomitans* (Table 3), but had few characters of the genera *Haemophilus* or *Actinobacillus*.

85

Table 3. *Characters of* Actinobacillus actinomycetemcomitans (A.a.) *and* Haemophilus aphrophilus (H.a.)

	A.a.	H.a.
Motility	–	–
Catalase	+	–
CO_2 improves growth	+	+
Gelatin hydrolyzed	–	–
Glucose (gas)	d	+
Xylose (acid)	–	d
Lactose (acid)	+	–
Sucrose (acid)	+	–
Mannitol (acid)	–	d
Indole	–	–
Nitrate reduced	+	+
Urease	–	–
H_2S (Pb acetate paper)	+	+

12. **Brucella neotomae** is an organism isolated from desert wood rats; it is accepted as a *Brucella* species by the international subcommittee (Stableforth & Jones, 1963) but we include it in this chapter because, from our examination of four of the eight strains so far isolated, we are uncertain of its correct taxonomic position. It produces acid in ordinary carbohydrate-containing media, in which other *Brucella* species do not show acid production.

13. **Vibrio fetus** is microaerophilic and grows better in an atmosphere of CO_2; growth is feeble under anaerobic conditions. It is catalase-positive, oxidase-positive and reduces nitrate; it does not attack carbohydrates. Although normally a pathogen of cattle and sheep, it has been isolated from human sources (King, 1962). Veterinary workers recognize two biotypes of *V. fetus* (Park *et al.* 1962); in addition there is a similar organism, *V. bubulus*, which differs only by being catalase-negative.

14. **Brucella ovis** is the name given to an organism causing a disease of sheep; it is not accepted by the international subcommittee as a *Brucella* species because it bears little antigenic relation to other members of the genus (Stableforth & Jones, 1963). Our grounds for rejecting this organism are based on its inability to grow on media suitable for *Brucella* species, but it grows on rich media such as blood agar and very well on Bordet-Gengou medium; it might be considered for inclusion in *Bordetella* (Biberstein & Cameron, 1961). Ovine brucellosis and the causal organism are reviewed by Lawrence (1961).

15. **Pasteurella tularensis** is an organism that has not been isolated in the British Isles but is not uncommon in other parts of the world. Its systematic position is doubtful but as it is the cause of a septicaemic disease similar to those caused by the pasteurellas

it is usually classified with those organisms. Russian workers (Olsufiev, Emelyanova & Dunayeva, 1959) put it in the genus *Francisella* and divide the species into two varieties. It will not grow on simple media and is unlikely to be isolated unless it is specifically looked for; the addition of blood and cysteine to media increase the probability of isolating it. Blood may be replaced by plasma and catalase (Hood, 1961). Snyder *et al.* (1946) regard it as a microaerophilic organism.

BACTERIA NOT INCLUDED IN TABLE-FIGS. I AND II

The tribe Mimeae was named by De Bord for organisms from the genital tract morphologically similar to gonococci and which, in his opinion, invalidated the smear as a means of diagnosing gonorrhoea (De Bord, 1939, 1943). It was composed of three genera, *Mima, Herellea,* and *Colloides* (De Bord, 1942; Deacon, 1945). The descriptions were inadequate for recognition of these organisms which have remained bacteriological puzzles. Cultures sent to us bearing these names have been found to be members of well recognized genera. Henriksen (1963) equated *Colloides* with coliforms, *Mima polymorpha* with *Moraxella lwoffii* (*Acinetobacter lwoffii* in this *Manual*) and *Mima polymorpha* var. *oxydans* with *Moraxella nonliquefaciens*; he thought that the species *H. vaginocola* was not identical with *B. anitratum*, although Ewing (1949a) had found that *Herellea* strains were agglutinated by *Bacterium anitratum* antiserum. Henriksen's conclusions were confirmed by Mitchell & Burrell (1964) in a serological study of cell-free extracts; they thought that the true identity and relations of this group of bacteria must await the purification and identification of the different antigenic fractions.

Pseudomonas maltophilia was described by Hugh & Ryschenkow (1961) as a motile Gram-negative rod which produced acid from maltose and mannose by oxidation but not from glucose. It is catalase-positive and oxidase-variable, grows on nutrient agar, and liquefies gelatin; H_2S and urease are not produced; citrate utilization, KCN resistance, and nitrate reduction may be positive or negative. In our medium, the organism shows lysine decarboxylase activity (Steel & Midgley, 1962). Hugh & Ryschenkow isolated the organism from a variety of sources including clinical specimens.

Sporosarcina. Kluyver & van Niel (1936) resurrected this genus for the oxidative and spore-forming, packet-forming cocci. Although the term spore is used, the heat resistance is not comparable to that of spore-forming rods in the genera *Bacillus* and *Clostridium*. These organisms are not likely to be found in medical material as they do not grow at 37° C. The type species, *S. ureae*, is motile. The physiology of this species was reviewed by MacDonald & MacDonald (1962) and by Kocur & Martinec (1963).

Streptomyces. The genus is ill-defined and Gordon & Mihm (1962a) believe that it cannot be separated from *Nocardia* on morphological characters. Streptomycetes are not acid-fast but this feature is variable in nocardias. Bradley & Anderson (1958) consider that separation of the genera is not justified on differences in morphology and bacteriophage sensitivity, but Cummins & Harris (1958) found differences in the cell-wall composition of strains of the two genera. Many *Streptomyces* species have been named or described, the majority were isolated from soil during investigations for new antibiotic-producing organisms; a few strains were isolated in circumstances which suggested a pathogenic role. Gordon & Mihm (1962*b*) found that tests for decomposition of casein, tyrosine, and xanthine may be of value in distinguishing some streptomycetes from recognized species of *Nocardia*.

Veillonella are anaerobic Gram-negative cocci. For a discussion on anaerobic cocci the reader is referred to Hare *et al.* (1952) and Thomas & Hare (1954). In spite of a great deal of work by Prévot the systematics of these bacteria have not been worked out satisfactorily. Two technical difficulties stultify progress; the first is that these cocci appear to be difficult to purify; either they mutate with great rapidity, or more likely, they exist mostly as mixed cultures, perhaps in symbiosis. The second difficulty in working with these organisms is that they tend to die out quickly in artificial culture, especially when plates are left for more than a few hours in an ordinary atmosphere.

9

TAXONOMIC IMPLICATIONS
(FOR THOSE INTERESTED)

Although we did not set out to write a book on bacterial systematics, the preparation and revision of the tables drew our attention to certain apparent similarities that had not occurred to us before. For example, it was while discussing what to do with the glanders bacillus that we noticed how neatly it fitted into the genus *Acinetobacter* (Brisou & Prévot, 1954), and how by extending the definition of that genus we could include *Moraxella lwoffii* and the parapertussis bacillus (Steel & Cowan, 1964).

Other problems we had to think out concerned *Micrococcus, Staphylococcus, Gaffkya,* and *Sarcina*; we decided that we could no longer support the classification we proposed earlier (Shaw *et al.* 1951). A clear alternative has not yet emerged, and our difficulty is increased by our knowledge that an international subcommittee is trying to solve the same problem and to reconcile the different proposals made by Evans and his colleagues (Evans, 1948; Evans *et al.* 1955), Mossel (1962), Baird-Parker (1962, 1963), and Pohja & Gyllenberg (1962). At the risk of arriving at conclusions differing in some ways from those likely to be made by the international subcommittee under the chairmanship of Dr J. B. Evans, we decided to make the division on the results of methods described in this *Manual*. It seemed logical for us to make the primary division on the method by which the cocci attack glucose, but a few experiments convinced us that the O–F method used by us, the modification by Baird-Parker, and the different technique used by Evans *et al.* do not give the same results with all strains. We decided, therefore, to base the division on the results of the O–F test: the fermentative cocci are regarded as staphylococci; the oxidizers and those that do not attack carbohydrates are the micrococci. The next problem was what to do with *Staphylococcus afermentans* named by Shaw *et al.* on the results of tests in peptone water sugars. Evans *et al.* (1955) showed that the type strain of this species could, in a basal medium without sugar, produce alkali. Apparently this was sufficient to neutralize any acid produced from the breakdown of sugar, for when we grew it in sugar media with an inorganic base it oxidized the carbohydrate and produced detectable acid.

These examples indicate the types of problem we faced in preparing the tables. When the tables were finished we noticed how slight were some of the differences between the characters in different columns such as those between *Corynebacterium hofmannii* and *C. equi*, and between *Shigella flexneri* and *Pasteurella pestis*. In cultural and bio-chemical characters the plague and pseudotuberculosis bacilli differ considerably from the multocida group of *Pasteurella*. In a computer analysis by Sneath & Cowan (1958) the plague organism appeared to be allied to the enteric bacteria; this was confirmed by the similarity of characters shown in Table IIc by *P. pestis* and *Shigella flexneri*. *P. pseudotuberculosis* is similar but is motile at 22° C and splits urea. van Loghem (1944–5) suggested that a new genus *Yersina* should be created for *P. pestis* and *P. pseudotuberculosis*; we have seen little authoritative comment on this proposal and hesitate to follow him as our experience of plague bacilli is limited to old stock cultures and only a few recent isolates. Mollaret & Le Minor (1962) found that β-galactosidase was possessed by both species but not by *P. multocida*.

Five adjacent columns in Table IIb are very similar; they comprise *Hafnia alvei*, *Enterobacter aerogenes*, *E. cloacae*, *E. liquefaciens*, and *Serratia marcescens*. The similarity between the last two is remarkably close and was noticed by Pederson & Breed as long ago as 1928. Sakazaki (1961) and Ewing (1963) suggest that *Hafnia alvei* should be put into the genus *Enterobacter*; we think that if a combination is to be made, all these five organisms should be placed in one genus. Of the generic names, *Serratia* is the oldest; it was given by Bizio in 1823 to 'small, stemless fungi; hemispherical capsules occurring in clusters' (Merlino 1924) that were found on bleeding polenta. These capsules were almost certainly yeast cells (Cowan, 1956) but by the advocacy of Breed & Breed (1924) and repeated use in successive editions of *Bergey's Manual* the name has become firmly attached to the bacterium once well known as *B. prodigiosus*. The type species, *Serratia marcescens*, differs in Table IIb only slightly from both *E. aerogenes* and *E. liquefaciens*, and these might be considered to be varieties of *S. marcescens*.

The differences between the fermentative *Chromobacterium violaceum* and the oxidative *C. lividum* are most obvious in Table-fig. II where the hatched squares representing them are widely separated; the difference in temperature range is not shown by the tables because they are only directly compared in Table IIb, in which this feature is not recorded. However, the whole picture is one of two distinct groups that are as dissimilar as *Pseudomonas* and *Aeromonas* and the many d characters of *C. lividum* in Tables IIb and IIe suggest that a further subdivision of that species should be made, either into two varieties or better as two species of a new genus.

Bordetella and *Haemophilus* present difficulty because they will not grow in the media normally used for the characterization tests. We think that our translation of the parapertussis bacillus to *Acinetobacter* (Steel & Cowan, 1964) helps to define *Bordetella* more precisely, as does the return of the bronchisepticus organism to *Alcaligenes*.

Moraxella is tidied up by Henriksen's (1960) exclusion of *M. lwoffii*, and this organism fits neatly into *Acinetobacter* as redefined to include organisms that do not attack carbohydrates. Lautrop (1961) has shown gliding movements by strains of *Moraxella lwoffii* and *B. anitratum*, and this has been confirmed by Piéchaud (1963) and by Halvorsen (1963) who also showed motility in true *Moraxella* species. Lautrop transferred *M. lwoffii* and *B. anitratum* to the genus *Cytophaga*, but as the techniques used to show these gliding movements do not lend themselves to routine diagnostic work we have not followed him, and prefer to put them into *Acinetobacter*, without prejudice to a reconsideration of their systematic position when more information is available.

In preparing the tables we tried to do the minimum of injury to existing classifications and to avoid the creation of any new names. Our literature searches showed us how little good work has been done on some groups of organisms, and how much on others. Among the deficiencies one of the most neglected groups seems to be *Actinomyces*, and we do not think that the separation into the three species shown in Table I*d* is even as clear as it seems in that table. We have not placed much weight on colony appearance, a feature that only experience can make useful but if, by some means, we could make it less subjective, it might be helpful in separating some of the more difficult organisms.

Having prepared the tables we feel entitled to ask whether our groupings are natural (not in a phylogenetic sense), and whether we have chosen the best criteria for making easily separable groupings. The answers to these questions can come from those who use the tables, or perhaps better by using the tables for feeding into a computer programmed to advise on the identification of bacteria (Payne, 1963).

PREPARATION OF CULTURE MEDIA

GENERAL CONSIDERATIONS

This *Manual* does not cover the isolation of bacteria from clinical material, and therefore we do not include enrichment media. Special properties, such as the ability of certain streptococci to grow on bile-containing media, find a place in the characterization of unknown isolates and justify the inclusion of a few differential and selective media.

In this appendix, media are listed under the following headings:

Basic nutrient media
Enriched media
Differential and selective media
Media for enhancement of pigmentation
Media for carbohydrate studies
Miscellaneous

CLEANING AND STERILIZATION OF GLASSWARE

Glassware to contain media such as Koser's citrate, in which there is a single source of an element, must be chemically clean to be free from that element. A satisfactory cleaning solution consists of 10 % sodium dichromate in 25 % (v/v) sulphuric acid.

Glassware such as Petri dishes and test tubes (metal and cotton stoppered) are sterilized in a hot air oven, preferably with a fan, at 160–170° C for one hour. The efficiency of the oven and the even distribution of heat should be controlled each day by placing Browne's type III* tubes on each shelf (see Darmady, Hughes & Jones, 1958; Brown & Ridout, 1960). Overheating of cotton-plugged tubes must be avoided; several workers (Wright, 1934a; Drea, 1942; Pollock, 1948) have drawn attention to the inhibitory effect of substances volatilized from cotton during dry heat sterilization. Tubes and flasks capped with polypropylene covers (Varney, 1961) and screw-capped bottles (caps loose) are sterilized by autoclaving.

INDICATORS

The pH indicators used in bacteriology are shown in Table 4; some are not readily soluble in water and are dissolved in dilute alkali or ethanol. The preparation of Andrade's indicator and litmus solution are more complex and details are given below.

*Albert Browne Ltd., Chancery Street, Leicester.

Table 4. *Indicators and their characteristics*

Indicator	Usual concentration %	ml 0·05 N-NaOH per g indicator	Solvent	pH range	Colour change (acid to alkaline)
Methyl red	0·2	—	50% ethanol	4·2–6·3	red-yellow
Chlorphenol red	0·2	47	water or 50% ethanol	4·8–6·4	yellow-purple
Andrade's			water	5–8	pink-yellow
Litmus			40% ethanol	5–8	red-blue
Bromcresol purple	0·2	37	water or 50%	5·2–6·8	yellow-purple
Bromthymol blue	0·2	32	ethanol	6·0–7·6	yellow-blue
Neutral red	0·1	—	50% ethanol	6·8–8·0	red-yellow
Phenol red	0·2	57	water	6·8–8·4	yellow-red
Cresol red	0·2	53	or 50%	7·2–8·8	yellow-red
Thymol blue	0·2	43	ethanol	8·0–9·6	yellow-blue
Phenolphthalein	0·1	—	50% ethanol	8·3–10·0	colourless-red

Andrade's indicator (modified from Andrade, 1906)

Acid fuchsin	5 g
Distilled water	1000 ml
N-NaOH	150–180 ml

Dissolve the acid fuchsin in the distilled water and add 150 ml of alkali solution. Mix and allow the mixture to stand at room temperature with frequent shaking for 24 h, the colour should change from red to brown. If the dye has not been sufficiently decolorized add a further 10 ml of alkali, mix thoroughly and leave for another 24 h. Subsequent additions of alkali may have to be made. The ultimate colour desired is a straw-yellow and the aim is to attain this with the minimum of alkali.

Test: add 1% of the indicator to peptone water pH 7·2, mix thoroughly and determine pH; note the rise in pH due to the alkalinity of the indicator and label accordingly. Should the increase in pH be 0·2 all batches of medium to which this indicator is to be added must have an initial pH value 0·2 lower than the desired final reaction.

Litmus solution (modified from McIntosh, 1920)

Litmus, granular	250 g
Ethanol (40%)	1000 ml

Grind the litmus and place in a flask with 500 ml of the ethanol; boil for 1 min, decant the liquid and add the remainder of the ethanol to the residue; boil for 1 min, decant and add the liquid to the first decoction. Centrifuge and adjust the volume of the supernatant to 1000 ml with ethanol (40 %); add N-HCl drop by drop until the solution becomes purple.

Test for correct reaction: boil 10 ml of distilled water, cool, and add one drop of litmus solution; after mixing the water becomes mauve.

This indicator solution is used at a concentration of about 2·5 %.

CARBOHYDRATES

'Sugars' used in bacteriology are shown in Table 5 where they are grouped by their chemical structure.

Table 5. *Carbohydrates used in bacteriology*

Class	Carbohydrate	Convenient concentration in water (w/v) at 20° C
Pentoses	Arabinose (L+)	40
	Xylose	50
Methyl pentose	Rhamnose (isodulcitol)	40
Hexoses	Fructose (laevulose)	50
	Galactose	30
	Glucose (dextrose)	50
	Mannose	50
	Sorbose	40
Disaccharides	Cellobiose	10
	Lactose	15
	Maltose	50
	Melibiose	10
	Sucrose (saccharose)	50
	Trehalose	25
Trisaccharides	Melezitose	10
	Raffinose	10
Polysaccharides	Glycogen	5; dissolves to produce an opalescent solution
	Inulin	20 at 70° C; solution may be slightly opalescent
	Starch, soluble	soluble in hot water
Glycosides	Aesculin (esculin)	0·1; 7·5 on heating
	Amygdalin	7·5
	Arbutin	10
	Salicin	3
Alcohols	Adonitol	40
	Dulcitol	5; readily soluble on heating
	Erythritol	40
	Glycerol	miscible in all proportions
	Mannitol	15
	Sorbitol	50
Non-carbohydrate	Inositol	15

CLARIFICATION OF MEDIA

Liquid media may be clarified by filtration through paper, sintered glass, or asbestos fibre (Seitz filtration). To prevent adsorption the use of a filter aid such as kieselguhr or talc is best avoided. Wright (1934b) found that filtration of broth through a thick filtering layer resulted in marked reduction in its growth-promoting capacity.

The grades of material suitable for clarification of media are shown in Table 6.

Table 6. *Materials, and grades, suitable for clarifying media*

		Agar-containing media	
	Liquid media	Simple funnel	Buchner funnel
Papers:			
Green's	$798\frac{1}{2}$; $904\frac{1}{2}$	$500\frac{1}{2}$; $904\frac{1}{2}$	960; 993
Whatman	1; 30; 52	15	52
Postlip	633E	agar-agar	agar-agar
Schleicher & Schüll	$520B\frac{1}{2}$; $598\frac{1}{2}$	$520A\frac{1}{2}$; $520B\frac{1}{2}$	520B
Delta	$317\frac{3}{4}$		376
Munktell	5		0
Sintered glass:			
Jena }	1; 2		
Pyrex }			
Asbestos pads:			
Seitz	K3; K4; K5		
Sterimats	FCB		
Carlson	K3; K5		

Agar-containing media must be clarified while in the molten state; paper pulp is often used or a grade of filter paper especially designed for the filtration of agar sols. To prevent solidification during filtration, a steam or hot water jacketed funnel is used; alternatively, filter rapidly through a Buchner funnel, in which case, a paper of greater wet strength should be used. A method for the filtration of agar-containing media during sterilization in an autoclave was described by Brown (1961).

Gelatin-containing media were in the past clarified with the aid of egg white or horse serum; gelatin for bacteriological use is now of such quality that this step is unnecessary and gelatin media may be clarified as those containing agar.

STERILIZATION OF MEDIA

The method of sterilization recommended for each medium is included with the details of preparation.

STORAGE OF MEDIA

Freshly prepared medium is desirable although with some (e.g. Wilson & Blair's bismuth sulphite agar) maturation is necessary. Many media can be safely kept at room temperature or in a refrigerator for several weeks, or even months, before use. Stability varies with the individual medium and it is not possible to fix a useful storage life. The important point is that moisture should be retained. To prevent evaporation and concentration of the constituents when media are to be stored, they should be kept in screw-capped rather than in cotton-plugged containers. Appreciable evaporation can occur in a refrigerator but this can be prevented by putting tubed media in polythene bags. If nutrient agar slopes appear to be dry, they should be melted and re-solidified.

Strong light is detrimental to most media and storage in the dark is preferable, especially for those containing dyes or indicators.

Egg media should be kept for a long period before use in order that contaminants that grow only at room-temperature have the opportunity to develop into visible colonies.

Cotton-plugged tubes are a potential source of contamination; the moisture absorbed by the cotton is sufficient to permit development of fungi, and hyphae may penetrate a cotton plug.

Media which have been kept in a refrigerator should be allowed to attain room temperature before use. Because the solubility of gases in liquids decreases with increase in temperature it is essential to check that gas bubbles do not appear in the Durham's tubes of carbohydrate media as they warm up from storage to room temperature. Fluid media to be used for anaerobic cultivation (particularly those containing thioglycollate) should be heated in a boiling water bath to remove dissolved air and allowed to cool undisturbed before use.

Poured plates may be kept at 4–15° C, but they should not be put close to the cooling unit of a domestic type refrigerator. Excess water of condensation can be avoided by allowing the medium to cool before pouring it into Petri dishes. If plates are to be stored in an exposed position they should be stacked with the lid uppermost; in canisters they should be inverted.

Higher forms of life can also be troublesome in a laboratory and we must be on the look-out for insects (beetles) and arachnids (mites). They are potentially dangerous in a medical laboratory, when plates are kept on the bench or incubated at 22° C, and we have observed the 'footprints' left by mites crossing Petri dishes inoculated with cultures. Dehydrated media are particularly liable to insect attack; the eggs laid by the adult hatching into larvae which can feed upon carbohydrate material.

VOLUMES OF MEDIA

The volume to be put in Petri dishes will vary with the size of the dish. In the United Kingdom, there is a British Standard specification (B.S. 611:1952) for glass Petri dishes but not for polystyrene dishes.

Petri dishes: $3\frac{1}{2}''$ (90 mm) dia. 15–20 ml of medium
$4''$ (100 mm) dia. 20–25 ml of medium

Volumes of media for tubes are shown in Table 7; the metric sizes are not exact equivalents but the nearest commercially available.

Table 7. *Usual volumes of media (in ml) for tubes of various sizes*

Medium	Tube size			
	$3 \times \frac{1}{2}$ in 75×12 mm	$4 \times \frac{1}{2}$ in 100×12 mm or 100×13 mm	$5 \times \frac{1}{2}$ in 125×12 mm or 125×15 mm	$6 \times \frac{5}{8}$ in 150×16 mm
Liquids	1–2	2–2·5	3	4–5
Slopes (slants)	1	1·5–2	2·5–3	5
Slopes with butts	2·5	2·5	3·5–4	7
Stabs	2·5	2·5	4	7

Marcus & Greaves (1950) found that screw-capped tubes were unsuitable for differential media unless the caps were loose, or replaced by cotton plugs, as atypical reactions were obtained.

COMMERCIALLY AVAILABLE MEDIA

When comparable media are commercially available, the manufacturer is indicated. Manufacturers of dehydrated and ready prepared media include:

Oxoid Division of Oxo Ltd.   (Oxoid)
    Southwark Bridge Road, London, S.E.1.
    U.S.A. agents:
        Consolidated Laboratories Inc.
          P.O. Box 234, Chicago Heights, Illinois.

Baltimore Biological Laboratory, Inc.   (BBL)
    2201 Aisquith Street, Baltimore 18, Maryland, U.S.A.
    Agents in the British Isles:
        Becton, Dickinson & Co. Ltd.
          Donore Road,
          Drogheda, Co. Meath, Eire.

Difco Laboratories Inc.   (Difco)
    920 Henry Street, Detroit 1, Michigan, U.S.A.
    U.K. agents:
        Baird & Tatlock (London) Ltd.
        Freshwater Road, Chadwell Heath, Essex.

Fisher Scientific Company,   (Fisher)
    (International Division), 633 Greenwich Street, New York 14, N.Y.
    U.K. agents:
    Shandon Scientific Co. Ltd.
        65 Pound Lane, Willesden, London, N.W.10.

FORMULAE OF MEDIA

Agar. In this appendix the agar concentration relates to Japanese agar; when New Zealand agar is to be used, the amount stated in the formula should be multiplied by 0·6 to give the approximately equivalent gel strength. Concentrations for different types of gel are shown in Table 8.

Table 8. *Concentration of agar for different purposes*

Type of medium	Origin of agar	
	Japan	New Zealand
Solid (normal)	1·5–2 %	1·0–1·2%
Solid (to inhibit 'spreaders')	7 %	4 %
Semi-solid	0·1–0·5 %	0·05–0·3 %

Water. The term water, used in many formulae, implies potable tap water. When distilled water is specified in a formula, de-ionized water may be substituted.

BASIC NUTRIENT MEDIA

Nutrient broth

Beef extract	10 g
Peptone	10 g
NaCl	5 g
Water	1000 ml

Dissolve the ingredients by heating in the water. Adjust to pH 8·0–8·4 with 10 N-NaOH and boil for 10 min. Filter, adjust to pH 7·2–7·4, and sterilize at 115° C for 20 min. Commercial: Oxoid.

Nutrient agar is nutrient broth gelled by the addition of 2 % agar.

Semi-solid nutrient agar (synonyms: Craigie agar, sloppy agar, slush agar) is nutrient broth containing 0·4 % shred agar.

Double-strength nutrient agar follows the same formula as nutrient agar, but the volume of water is reduced to 500 ml.

Peptone water

Peptone	10 g
NaCl	5 g
Water	1000 ml

Dissolve the solids by heating in the water. Adjust to pH 8·0–8·4 and boil for 10 min. Filter, adjust to pH 7·2–7·4, and sterilize at 115° C for 20 min. Commercial: Oxoid.

Peptone water agar is peptone water gelled by the addition of 2 % agar.

Robertson's cooked meat medium (modified from Lepper & Martin, 1929)

Minced meat	1000 g
0·05 N-NaOH	1000 ml

Add the minced meat to the alkali solution, mix well and heat to boiling, simmer for 20 min with frequent stirring. Skim off the fat and check pH, which should be about 7·5. Strain through gauze or muslin, squeeze out excess liquor, and dry the meat particles at a temperature below 50° C. For use, place sufficient dried meat in a screw-capped container to a depth of about 2·5 cm and add sufficient nutrient broth to give a depth of about 5 cm. Sterilize at 115° C for 20 min; avoid rapid release of pressure in the autoclave after sterilization.

Note. Although called Robertson's cooked meat, the method of preparation differs considerably from the original method (Robertson, 1916).

Cooked meat medium (alternative formula)

Horse meat, fat-free and minced	450 g
Distilled water	1000 ml

Boil the meat in the water for 1 h. Filter through muslin and press the meat dry.

NaCl	5 g
Peptone	10 g

Add the NaCl and peptone to the filtrate, adjust to pH 8·4 with 10 N-NaOH and bring to the boil.

Sodium thioglycollate, 45 % soln.	1 ml

Filter and add the thioglycollate solution.

Distribute the dry meat particles to a depth of 2·5 cm into screw-capped bottles, add the broth to a level of 5 cm. Sterilize at 115° C for 20 min; allow the pressure to fall slowly after sterilization.

Digest broth (modified from Hartley, 1922, and Pope & Smith, 1932)

Meat, finely minced	600 g
Na_2CO_3, anhyd.	8 g
Water	1000 ml

Add the alkali and the meat to the water, heat to 80° C, stir well and cool.

Pancreatic extract, Cole & Onslow's	20 ml
$CHCl_3$	20 ml

Heat the infused mixture to 45–50° C, add the pancreatic extract (below) and chloroform, and maintain at 45–50° C for 4–6 h with frequent stirring. Follow the course of digestion by the biuret test (p. 130).

HCl, conc.   16 ml

Add the acid, boil for 30 min and filter. Adjust to pH 8, boil for 30 min and filter. Adjust to pH 7·6, determine the amino acid nitrogen content (see p. 131) and dilute the broth to contain 700–750 mg amino acid N_2 per l. Sterilize at 115° C for 20 min.

Notes. Cole & Onslow's pancreatic extract may be replaced by a commercial trypsin extract or powder.

Pope & Smith recommend the fractional addition of the enzyme during the digestion process.

Commercial: Oxoid.

Digest agar is digest broth gelled by the addition of 2 % agar.

Pancreatic extract (Cole & Onslow, 1916)

Fresh pig pancreas	250 g
Distilled water	750 ml
Industrial methylated spirit	250 ml

Add the water and spirit to the fat-free and minced pancreas in a 2-litre flask and stopper tightly. Shake thoroughly and leave at room temperature for 3 days with frequent shaking. Filter, add 0·1 % conc. HCl to the filtrate and mix well. Store at 4° C. The cloudy precipitate which settles in a few days may be filtered off. The extract may be expected to retain its activity for several months when stored at 4° C.

Note. A satisfactory extract should have a tryptic content of at least 50 units per ml (see p. 129).

Infusion broth (modified from Wright, 1933)

Meat, minced	450 g
Water	1000 ml

Infuse the meat in the water overnight at 4° C.

Peptone	10 g
NaCl	5 g

Skim the fat from the infused mixture, add the peptone and salt and boil for 30 min. Filter, adjust to pH 8·4 and boil for 20 min. Filter, adjust to pH 7·6, and sterilize at 115° C for 20 min.

Commercial: BBL, Difco, Fisher.

Infusion agar is infusion broth gelled by the addition of 2 % agar.

CYLG broth (Marshall & Kelsey, 1960)

Casein digest	10 g
Marmite*	5 g
Sodium glycerophosphate	10 g
Potassium lactate, 50 % w/w	10 ml
Glucose	2 g
Inorganic salts soln.	5 ml
Distilled water	1000 ml

Dissolve the ingredients by heating, mix, filter, and sterilize at 115° C for 20 min.

Inorganic salts solution:

10 N-H_2SO_4	0·1 ml
$MgSO_4.7H_2O$	4 g
$MnSO_4.4H_2O$	0·4 g
$FeSO_4.7H_2O$	0·4 g
Water	100 ml

Add the acid to the water and dissolve the salts without heating.

Note. This basal medium may be supplemented by the addition of blood or serum, gelled by the addition of agar, and can form the basis of many standard media. It is reproducible, does not require pH adjustment, and can be prepared and stored in concentrated form.

Thioglycollate broth (modified from Brewer, 1940)

Peptone	15 g
Yeast extract	5 g
NaCl	5 g
Agar	1 g
Thioglycollic acid	1 g
Water	1000 ml

Dissolve the solids in the water with the aid of gentle heat. Add the thioglycollic acid and adjust to pH 8·5 with N-NaOH. Autoclave at 115° C for 10 min. To prevent darkening of the medium screw-caps should be loosened during autoclaving.

Glucose	5 g
Methylene blue, 1 % aq. soln.	0·2 ml

Adjust to pH 7·2, add the glucose and dye soln., mix well and sterilize at 115° C for 10 min.

*Marmite Ltd., Seething Lane, London, E.C.3.

Notes. This medium should be stored in screw-capped containers in the dark at 4° C (Cook & Steel, 1959 *b*).

If more than 20 % of the medium shows a green colour before use, it should be heated in a boiling water bath or steamer for 5–10 min and allowed to cool undisturbed; this treatment must not be repeated.

Dorset egg medium

Egg yolk and white	800 ml (about 16 hen eggs)
NaCl, 0·9 % sterile aq. soln.	200 ml

Wash the eggs in 70 % ethanol and lay on a sterile surface. Break the shells with a sterile knife and let the contents fall into a sterile flask; add the saline aseptically. Shake thoroughly to break up the yolks and produce a homogeneous mixture. Distribute 2 ml volumes into sterile 5 ml screw-capped (bijou) bottles or 5 ml volumes into sterile 30 ml screw-capped (1 oz McCartney) bottles. Slope the containers in an inspissator and heat slowly to 75° C. Maintain at this temperature for 1 h and repeat the process on each of the following two days.

Note. As an alternative to inspissation for egg and serum media, several workers have described methods of autoclaving which result in uniform slopes free from air bubbles. The following procedure may be used: place the tubes in the autoclave in an inclined position and close the door and all valves of the autoclave; allow steam to enter the chamber rapidly until the pressure reaches 15 lb/in². Maintain this pressure for 10 min; as the air has not been expelled, the temperature will rise slowly, preventing the formation of air bubbles during coagulation. After 10 min, open the air exhaust valve very slowly ensuring that a pressure of 15 lb/in² is maintained until the valve is fully open; rapid pressure changes will cause disruption of the slopes. Maintain the steam pressure for 15 min and then close both the steam supply and air exhaust valves. Allow the autoclave to cool slowly and do not open it until 5 min after the pressure has fallen to atmospheric.

ENRICHED MEDIA

Blood agar

Defibrinated blood	50 ml
Nutrient agar	950 ml

Melt the nutrient agar, cool to 50° C and add the blood aseptically. Mix and distribute in tubes or plates.

Notes. Haemolysis can be seen better in layered blood agar plates. For such plates, a layer of peptone water agar is poured into the Petri dish, allowed to set, and the blood-containing medium is poured on top. Alternatively, a simple agar solution without nutrients may be used as the lower layer; it must however be made isotonic to prevent haemolysis of the blood in the upper layer.

The inclusion of glucose in the basal medium for blood agar is not recommended as its presence inhibits haemolysin production by streptococci (Fuller & Maxted, 1939).

Blood broth is prepared by the aseptic addition of 5 % sterile defibrinated blood to the appropriate volume of nutrient broth.

Chocolate agar

Place a blood agar plate (medium down) in a 65° C incubator for 1–1½ h until the medium assumes a uniform 'chocolate' colour.

Alternatively, melt nutrient agar and cool to 50° C. Add 5 % sterile blood, mix and heat in a water bath to 80° C with frequent mixing. Maintain at 80° C until the medium has a 'chocolate' colour. Distribute.

Fildes' peptic digest of blood (Fildes, 1920)

Defibrinated sheep blood	25 ml
NaCl, 0·9 % sterile aq. soln.	75 ml
HCl, conc.	3 ml
Pepsin	0·5 g

Mix the blood and saline in a glass-stoppered bottle and add the pepsin and acid. Shake thoroughly and place in a water bath at 55° C for 4 h with occasional shaking. Add 6 ml 5 N-NaOH and check that pH is 7·0. Add 0·25 ml $CHCl_3$ as preservative and shake thoroughly. The digest will keep at least 12 months but should be stored at 4° C. It is better to leave it too acid rather than too alkaline.

Notes. Before use the chloroform must be removed by heating gently in a water bath.

Preliminary results suggest that the digest may be sterilized by filtration but insufficient comparative work has been carried out to recommend this in place of adding $CHCl_3$.

Commercial: Difco, Oxoid.

Fildes' digest agar

Fildes' peptic digest of blood	50 ml
Nutrient agar	950 ml

Maintain the Fildes' digest at 55° C for 30 min to volatilize the chloroform. Then aseptically add it to the base, previously melted and cooled to 55° C. Mix and distribute.

Serum agar

Sterile serum	50 ml
Nutrient agar	950 ml

Melt the nutrient agar, cool to 50–55; C and aseptically add the serum. Mix and distribute.

Serum broth is prepared by the aseptic addition of 5 % sterile serum to the nutrient broth.

Serum glucose agar (Jones & Morgan, 1958)

Peptone	10 g
Beef extract	5 g
NaCl	5 g
Agar	20 g
Water	1000 ml

Prepare the base as for nutrient agar (p. 98) and sterilize.

Sterile horse serum	50 ml
Glucose, 20 % aq. soln.	50 ml
Nutrient base	1000 ml

Add the serum and sterile glucose soln. to the base, previously melted and cooled to 50–55° C. Mix and distribute aseptically.

Commercial (base): Oxoid.

Glucose broth

Glucose, 20 % aq. soln.	50 ml
Nutrient broth	950 ml

Sterilize the glucose solution by filtration and add aseptically to the nutrient broth. Mix and distribute aseptically.

Glycerol agar

Glycerol	50 ml
Nutrient agar	1000 ml

Melt the nutrient agar, add the glycerol, mix, and sterilize at 115° C for 20 min.

Note. Gordon & Smith (1953) use 7 % glycerol in soil extract agar (p. 123).

Tomato juice agar (modified from Kulp & White, 1932)

Tomatoes	250 g
Distilled water	500 ml

Cut up the tomatoes and steam in the water for an hour or until they are pulped. Clarify through gauze and filter through paper.

Peptone	10 g
Peptonized milk	10 g
Agar	20 g
Tomato juice	400 ml
Distilled water	600 ml

Dissolve the solids in the water by heating. Add the tomato juice, mix, and sterilize at 115° C for 20 min. The final pH value of the medium should be 6–6·2.

Commercial: BBL, Difco, Oxoid.

DIFFERENTIAL AND SELECTIVE MEDIA

Bile agar (equivalent to 10 % bile)

Ox bile, dehydrated	10 g
Serum, sterile	50 ml
Nutrient agar	1000 ml

Melt the nutrient agar, add the bile, mix and dissolve. Sterilize at 115° C for 20 min. Cool to about 55° C and aseptically add the serum. Mix and distribute.

Notes. For 40 % bile agar, use 40 g dehydrated ox bile per litre. Bile agar can be used as whole plates, or ditches in plates of blood or serum agar.

Blood-tellurite agar

K_2TeO_3, 2 % aq. soln.	16 ml
Sterile blood	50 ml
Infusion agar	1000 ml

Melt the agar medium, cool to 50° C and aseptically add the blood and sterile tellurite soln. The medium must not be heated after addition of the tellurite. Mix and distribute.

Notes. Sterilize the tellurite soln. by filtration, not by heat. K_2TeO_3 concentration in this medium is approx. 0·03 % (1/3333).

Several tellurite media have been described; Anderson *et al.* (1931) used a 'chocolate' (heated blood) agar base, and laked blood was used by Wilson (1934) and Hoyle (1941).

Bordet-Gengou agar (modified from Bordet & Gengou, 1906)

Peptone	10 g
NaCl	5 g
Glycerol	10 ml
Soluble starch	2·5 g
Water	1000 ml
Agar	30 g

Make a smooth paste of the soluble starch with a few ml of the water. Dissolve the peptone, NaCl, and glycerol in the remaining water, heat, and add the starch suspension. Adjust to pH 7·5, add the agar and dissolve by heating. Sterilize at 115° C for 20 min.

For use, aseptically add 500 ml horse blood (warmed to 45° C) to 1000 ml of base melted and cooled to 55–60° C. Mix and distribute.

Notes. Medium in plates should be thick, at least 5 mm in depth, and must not be over-dried; it should be bright red in colour (Bailey, 1933); a dark medium indicates old or overheated blood.

Some brands of peptone are markedly inhibitory to the growth of *Bordetella pertussis* and the original formula of Bordet & Gengou did not include peptone. Dawson *et al.* (1951) consider that 30 % blood is the minimum for a satisfactory product; however, haemolysis is not usually seen when the blood concentration exceeds 30 %; the original medium contained 50 %.

MacConkey agar (modified from MacConkey, 1908; Report, 1956*c*)

Peptone	20 g
NaCl	5 g
Sodium taurocholate	5 g
Water	1000 ml

Dissolve the peptone, NaCl and bile salt in the water by heating. Adjust to pH 8·0, boil for 20 min, cool and filter.

Agar	20 g
Lactose	10 g
Neutral red, 1 % aq. soln.	10 ml

Add and dissolve the agar by boiling and adjust to pH 7·4. Add the lactose and indicator soln., mix and sterilize at 115° C for 20 min.

Notes. The exact quantity of indicator depends on the depth of colour preferred.

Sodium taurocholate, sodium tauroglycocholate or other satisfactory bile salt may be used (see Appendix B, p. 129).

The use of 0·1 % Teepol (an anionic detergent) in place of bile salt in MacConkey agar has been recommended by Jameson & Emberley (1956).

Commercial: Oxoid.

MacConkey broth see p. 110.

MEDIA FOR ENHANCING PIGMENT PRODUCTION
Potato slopes

Take several large potatoes and scrub them thoroughly under running water. Cut cylinders with an 18–20 mm cork borer, rejecting any that are bruised or diseased. Cut each cylinder obliquely into two and place each half in a 30 ml screw-capped bottle or 25 mm diameter tube with the thick end resting on a small plug of absorbent cotton. Fill the containers with water and steam for 30 min. Pour off the water and sterilize at 115° C for 20 min.

Mannitol yeast-extract agar

Peptone	2·5 g
NaCl	2·5 g
Agar	20 g
Water	1000 ml

Dissolve the solids by heating in the water. Adjust to pH 8·0, boil for 30 min and filter.

Mannitol	5 g
Yeast extract	2·5 g

Adjust to pH 7·0, add the mannitol and yeast extract. Mix, dissolve, and sterilize at 115° C for 20 min.

King, Ward & Raney's media (King *et al.* 1954)

Medium A—for pyocyanin

Peptone	20 g
Glycerol	10 g
K_2SO_4, anhyd.	10 g
$MgCl_2$, anhyd.	1·4 g
Water	1000 ml

Dissolve the constituents by heating in the water. Adjust to pH 7·2 if necessary. Add 20 g agar and dissolve by autoclaving at 115° C for 10 min. Filter, and sterilize at 115° C for 10 min.

Medium B—for fluorescin

Proteose peptone	20 g
Glycerol	10 g
K_2HPO_4	1·5 g
$MgSO_4.7H_2O$	1·5 g
Water	1000 ml

Proceed as for medium A above.

MEDIA FOR CARBOHYDRATE STUDIES

Hugh & Leifson's O–F medium (Hugh & Leifson, 1953)

Peptone	2 g
NaCl	5 g
K_2HPO_4	0·3 g
Agar	3 g
Distilled water	1000 ml
Bromthymol blue, 0·2 % aq. soln.	15 ml

Dissolve the solids by heating in the water. Adjust to pH 7·1, filter, and add the indicator. Sterilize at 115° C for 20 min.

Add a sterile solution of the appropriate carbohydrate aseptically to give a final concentration of 1 %. Mix and distribute aseptically in 10 ml volumes into sterile tubes of not more than 16 mm diameter.

Commercial: Difco.

Peptone water sugars

The method of preparation will depend on the indicator:

Andrade's. Adjust the reaction of 900 ml peptone water to pH 7·1–7·3 so that the addition of 10 ml Andrade's indicator will bring it to pH 7·5. Sterilize at 115° C for 20 min; this medium is pink when hot but the colour fades on cooling. Dissolve 10 g of the appropriate sugar in 90 ml of water and steam for 30 min or sterilize by filtration. Aseptically add this to the sterile peptone water + indicator and distribute into sterile test tubes with inverted Durham's tubes and steam for 30 min.

Other indicators. To 900 ml peptone water add 10 ml indicator solution (bromcresol purple, bromthymol blue, or phenol red) and sterilize at 115° C for 20 min. Dissolve 10 g of the appropriate sugar in 90 ml water and steam for 30 min or sterilize by filtration. Add this to the sterile base, distribute into sterile tubes with inverted Durham's tubes and steam for 30 min.

Notes. The addition of some carbohydrates may cause an acid reaction; in these instances add sufficient 0·1 N-NaOH to restore the original colour.

Where the solubility of a carbohydrate is low (Table 5, p. 94), the required amount of solid material may be added to the base and, when solution is complete, the medium sterilized.

Commercial: Andrade's—Oxoid; bromcresol purple—BBL, Fisher; phenol red—BBL, Fisher, Oxoid.

Broth sugars

This formula is included here because broth-based sugars are used extensively in the U.S.A. and are recommended by the international subcommittee on Enterobacteriaceae (Report, 1958).

Peptone	10 g
Meat extract	3 g
NaCl	5 g
Distilled water	1000 ml
Andrade's indicator	10 ml

Dissolve the solids in the water, add the indicator and adjust to pH 7·1–7·2. Sterilize at 115° C for 20 min. Aseptically add 1 % of the appropriate carbohydrate, mix, distribute into sterile tubes containing inverted Durham's tubes, and steam for 30 min.

Serum water sugars

Peptone	4 g
Na$_2$HPO$_4$	0·8 g
Distilled water	800 ml
Sterile serum	200 ml
Bromcresol purple, 0·2 % soln.	10 ml

Dissolve the peptone and phosphate in the water, steam at 100° C for 15 min and filter. Add the serum and steam for a further 15 min. Check pH to 7·6–7·8 and add the indicator. Sterilize at 115° C for 10 min.

Aseptically add 1 % of the appropriate sugar as a sterile solution and distribute into sterile tubes.

Note. It is an advantage to have perfectly clear media. Different batches of serum differ in their coagulability by heat, and occasionally the medium is cloudy when serum in the amount given above is used. It is a good plan to add varying amounts of each batch of serum (e.g. in concentrations of 10–25 %) to tubes of the basal medium, to autoclave them, and to choose the highest concentration that does not show marked cloudiness after sterilization.

Ammonium salt sugars (Smith, Gordon & Clark, 1952)

(NH$_4$)$_2$HPO$_4$	1 g
KCl	0·2 g
MgSO$_4$.7H$_2$O	0·2 g
Yeast extract	0·2 g
Agar	20 g
Distilled water	1000 ml
Bromcresol purple, 0·2 % soln.	4 ml

Add the solids to the water and dissolve by steaming. Add the indicator and sterilize at 115° C for 20 min. Allow the basal medium to cool to about 60° C and add the appropriate carbohydrate as a sterile solution to give a final concentration of 1 %. Mix and distribute aseptically into sterile tubes which are inclined so that the medium sets as a slope.

Sugars for neisserias (Thompson & Knudsen, 1958)

Digest broth	1000 ml
Agar	3 g
Phenol red, 0·2 % soln.	10 ml
Sterile rabbit serum	50 ml
Sugar, sterile 10 % soln.	100 ml

Dissolve the agar in the broth by heating, add the indicator solution and sterilize at 115° C for 20 min. Cool to about 55° C and aseptically add the serum and sugar solution. Distribute into sterile tubes.

Notes. The four sugars used to differentiate *Neisseria* spp. are glucose, lactose, maltose, and sucrose.

Wilkinson (1962) recommends a solid medium containing hydrocele fluid for detecting acid production by *Neisseria* spp.

Sugars for lactobacilli (Man *et al.* 1960)

MRS broth, modified	1000 ml
Carbohydrate	20 g
Chlorphenol red, 0·2 % soln.	20 ml

Prepare the basal broth as on p. 121, omitting the beef extract and glucose; adjust to pH 6·2–6·5, add the indicator, and sterilize at 115° C for 20 min. Add the carbohydrate, mix, and distribute; steam for 30 min.

Lactose (10 %) agar

Peptone	5 g
Beef extract	3 g
Lactose	100 g
Agar	20 g
Distilled water	1000 ml
Bromcresol purple, 0·2 % soln.	10 ml

Dissolve the solids in the water by heating, adjust to pH 6·8 with 10 N-NaOH, filter, and add the indicator solution. Sterilize at 115° C for 20 min and distribute as plates or slopes.

MacConkey broth (Report, 1956c)

Peptone	20 g
NaCl	5 g
Sodium taurocholate	5 g
Water	1000 ml
Bromcresol purple, 0·2 % soln.	5 ml
Lactose	10 g

Dissolve the peptone, NaCl and bile salt in the water by heating. Adjust to pH 8·0 and boil for 20 min. Cool, filter, and adjust to pH 7·4. Add the lactose and indicator solution, mix and distribute into tubes containing inverted Durham's tubes. Sterilize at 115° C for 15 min.

Note. See MacConkey agar (p. 106) for remarks on bile salts.

Commercial: Oxoid.

MR and V–P media

Glucose-phosphate medium

Peptone	5 g
K₂HPO₄	5 g
Distilled water	1000 ml

Steam until the solids are dissolved, filter, and adjust to pH 7·5.

Glucose	5 g

Add the glucose, mix and distribute 1·5 ml volumes into tubes. Sterilize at 115° C for 10 min.

Notes. For sterilization, the tubes must be placed in a solid-bottomed container to protect them from contact with the boiling water; if this is neglected, the medium becomes straw-yellow in colour.

Workers in the U.S.A. generally use 7 g peptone in the above formula.

Commercial: BBL, Difco, Fisher, Oxoid.

Glucose-peptone medium (Abd-el-Malek & Gibson, 1948*b*)

Peptone	10 g
Glucose	5 g
Distilled water	1000 ml

Mix and dissolve by gentle heating. Filter, adjust to pH 7·6, and distribute into tubes. Sterilize at 115° C for 10 min in a solid-bottomed container.

Glucose-salt medium (Smith, Gordon & Clark, 1946)

Proteose peptone	7 g
NaCl	5 g
Glucose	5 g
Distilled water	1000 ml

Dissolve the solids in the water, tube, and sterilize at 115° C for 20 min in a solid-bottomed container.

Starch agar

Potato starch	10 g
Distilled water	50 ml
Nutrient agar	1000 ml

Triturate the starch with the water to a smooth cream, and add to the molten nutrient agar. Mix, and sterilize at 115° C for 10 min. Distribute into Petri dishes.

Notes. This medium should not be filtered after adding the starch suspension. Overheating may hydrolyze the starch.

Media for dextran and levan production
Sucrose agar

Sterile serum	50 ml
Sucrose	50 g
Digest agar	1000 ml

Melt the digest agar, add the sucrose, and steam for 30 min. Cool to 55° C, aseptically add the serum, and distribute into Petri dishes.

Sucrose broth

Sucrose	50 g
Infusion broth	1000 ml

Dissolve the sucrose in the broth and steam for 1 h.

MISCELLANEOUS MEDIA

Aesculin broth

Aesculin	1 g
Ferric citrate	0·5 g
Peptone water	1000 ml

Dissolve the aesculin and iron salt in the peptone water, and sterilize at 115° C for 10 min.

Aesculin agar is aesculin broth gelled by the addition of 2 % agar.

Aesculin bile agar (Williams & Hirch, 1950; Swan, 1954) can be prepared by the addition of aesculin and iron salt to bile agar (p. 105).

Arginine broth (Niven *et al.* 1942)

Peptone (tryptone)	5 g
Yeast extract	5 g
K_2HPO_4	2 g
Glucose	0·5 g
Arginine monohydrochloride	3 g
Distilled water	1000 ml

Dissolve by heating, adjust to pH 7·0, boil, filter, and sterilize at 115° C for 20 min.

Note. The original formula of Niven *et al.* specified D-arginine monohydrochloride; we use the L-isomer and find it satisfactory.

Casein agar (milk agar) (modified from Hastings, 1903)

Milk, skim	500 ml
Nutrient agar, double-strength	500 ml

Prepare the skim-milk as on p. 120 and sterilize by heating at 115° C for 10 min. Cool to about 50° C and add to the double-strength nutrient agar (p. 98) melted and cooled to 50–55° C. Mix and distribute in Petri dishes or tubes.

Note. As the acid produced by lactose fermentation had an inhibitory effect on the hydrolysis of casein, Eddy (1960) recommended dialysis of milk before adding to the basal medium.

Citrate, Christensen's (Christensen, 1949)

Sodium citrate	3 g
Glucose	0·2 g
Yeast extract	0·5 g
Cysteine hydrochloride	0·1 g
Ferric ammonium citrate	0·4 g
KH_2PO_4	1 g
NaCl	5 g
$Na_2S_2O_3$	0·08 g
Agar	20 g
Distilled water	1000 ml
Phenol red, 0·2 % soln.	6 ml

Dissolve the solids in the water by heating, filter; adjust to pH 6·8–6·9, add the indicator, and sterilize at 115° C for 20 min.

Note. This medium is also suitable for demonstrating H_2S production; if it is not to be used for this purpose the cysteine, $Na_2S_2O_3$, and ferric ammonium citrate can be omitted.

Commercial: BBL, Difco.

Citrate, Koser's (modified from Koser, 1923; Report, 1956c)

NaCl	5 g
$MgSO_4.7H_2O$	0·2 g
$NH_4H_2PO_4$	1 g
K_2HPO_4	1 g
Distilled water	1000 ml

Dissolve the salts in the water.

Citric acid	2 g

Add to the salts solution and adjust to pH 6·8 with N-NaOH. Filter through a sintered-glass funnel. The medium should be colourless. Sterilize at 115° C for 20 min.

All glassware must be chemically clean and alkali-free (see p. 92).

Note. In his original paper, Koser (1923) used 2 g sodium citrate or 2·77 g of the hydrated salt in place of the citric acid in the formula given above; it is not known which of the three sodium salts of citric acid was used although Koser stated that it had $5\frac{1}{2}$ molecules of water of crystallization.

Citrate, Simmons' (modified from Simmons, 1926)

This is the modified Koser's citrate (above) incorporating 0·008 % bromthymol blue (i.e. 40 ml 0·2 % soln. per litre), and gelled by the addition of 2 % agar.

Commercial: BBL, Difco, Fisher.

Organic acids as carbon sources (Gordon & Mihm, 1957)

NaCl	1 g
$MgSO_4.7H_2O$	0·2 g
$(NH_4)_2HPO_4$	1 g
KH_2PO_4	0·5 g
Organic acid (sodium salt)	2 g
Agar	20 g
Distilled water	1000 ml
Phenol red, 0·2 % soln.	4 ml

Dissolve the agar by steaming in about 800 ml of the water. Dissolve the salts in the remainder of the water and add to the agar sol. Adjust to pH 6·8 and add the indicator solution. Sterilize at 115° C for 20 min.

Notes. Organic acids used as their sodium salts include: acetate, benzoate, citrate, lactate, oxalate, propionate, pyruvate, succinate, tartrate; malate is used as its calcium salt, and mucate as the free acid.

This medium resembles the modified Simmons' citrate (above) but contains less NaCl and a different indicator.

Decarboxylase medium (Møller, 1955)

Peptone	5 g
Beef extract	5 g
Pyridoxal	5 mg
Glucose	0·5 g
Distilled water	1000 ml
Bromocresol purple, 0·2 % soln.	5 ml
Cresol red, 0·2 % soln.	2·5 ml

Dissolve the solids in the water by heating. Adjust to pH 6·0. Add the indicators, mix, and distribute into four equal volumes. Sterilize at 115° C for 20 min.

For use make the following additions:

1. L-arginine hydrochloride   1 %   3. L-ornithine hydrochloride   1 %
2. L-lysine hydrochloride   1 %   4. no addition

re-adjust to pH 6·0 if necessary.

Distribute the 4 media in 1–1·5 ml volumes into small tubes (67 × 10 mm or 3 × ⅜ inch rimless) containing liquid paraffin to a height of about 5 mm and previously sterilized. After distribution sterilize at 115° C for 10 min.

Notes. Møller specifies Orthana Special peptone but we use Evans' and find it satisfactory.

When DL-amino acids are used, the concentration should be 2 %. If glutamic acid decarboxylase activity is also to be investigated, the basal medium should be divided into five portions, to the fifth of which 1 % L-glutamic acid is added.

Commercial (base): Difco.

Decarboxylase medium (modified from Falkow, 1958)

Peptone	5 g
Yeast extract	3 g
Glucose	1 g
Distilled water	1000 ml
Bromcresol purple, 0·2 % soln.	10 ml

Dissolve the solids in the water, adjust to pH 6·7, and add the indicator soln. Sterilize at 115° C for 20 min. Divide the base into four equal volumes and make the following additions:

1. L-arginine hydrochloride   0·5 %
2. L-lysine hydrochloride   0·5 %
3. L-ornithine hydrochloride   0·5 %
4. no addition

re-adjust to pH 6·7 if necessary. Tube in 2 ml volumes in small tubes and sterilize at 115° C for 10 min.

Commercial (base): Difco, Fisher.

Ferrous chloride gelatin (Report, 1958)

Beef extract	7·5 g
Peptone	25 g
NaCl	5 g
Gelatin	120 g
Distilled water	1000 ml
$FeCl_2$, 10 % aq. soln.	5 ml

Prepare the base as for nutrient gelatin (p. 116). After sterilization and before the medium gels, add the freshly prepared $FeCl_3$ soln. Tube into narrow tubes, cool immediately, and seal the tubes with corks which have been soaked in hot paraffin wax.

Gelatin agar

Gelatin	4 g
Distilled water	50 ml
Nutrient agar	1000 ml

Soak the gelatin in the water and, when thoroughly softened, add to the melted nutrient agar. Mix, and sterilize at 115° C for 10 min. Distribute into plates.

Gelatin, nutrient

Beef extract	3 g
Peptone	5 g
Gelatin	120 g
Water.	1000 ml

Add the gelatin to the water and allow to stand for 15–30 min. Heat to dissolve the gelatin; add and dissolve the other constituents. Adjust to pH 7·0, and sterilize by heating at 115° C for 20 min.

Note. This medium must not be overheated.

Commercial: BBL, Difco, Fisher, Oxoid.

Gluconate broth (Shaw & Clarke, 1955)

Peptone	1·5 g
Yeast extract	1 g
K_2HPO_4	1 g
Potassium gluconate	40 g
Distilled water	1000 ml

Dissolve in the water by heating. Adjust to pH 7·0. Filter, and sterilize at 115° C for 20 min.

Note. The potassium gluconate may be replaced by 37·25 g of sodium gluconate.

Glucose phenolphthalein broth (Clarke, 1953*b*)

Glycine buffer

Glycine	0·6 g
NaCl	0·35 g
Distilled water, freshly boiled	60 ml
0·1 N-NaOH	40 ml

Dissolve the glycine and NaCl in the water and add the alkali.

1 % Glucose broth (p. 104)	900 ml
Glycine buffer	100 ml
Phenolphthalein, 0·2 % soln.	5 ml

116

Mix and keep overnight in a refrigerator in a stoppered flask. Sterilize by filtration and aseptically distribute into sterile 5 ml screw-capped bottles leaving as little air space as possible. Incubate overnight to check sterility and discard any bottles not showing a definite pink colour.

Note. This medium should be used as soon as possible after preparation.

Hippurate agar (modified from Hajna & Damon, 1934; Thirst, 1957*a*)

NaCl	5 g
$MgSO_4.7H_2O$	0·2 g
$NH_4H_2PO_4$	1 g
K_2HPO_4	1 g
Sodium hippurate	3 g
Agar	20 g
Distilled water	1000 ml
Phenol red, 0·2 % soln.	5 ml

Dissolve the solids in the water by heating, check that the pH is 6·8–7·0, and add the indicator. Sterilize at 115° C for 20 min.

Hippurate broth (Hare & Colebrook, 1934)

Sodium hippurate	10 g
Infusion broth	1000 ml

Dissolve the hippurate in the broth and sterilize at 115° C for 20 min.

KCN broth (modified from Møller, 1954*b*; Rogers & Taylor, 1961)

Peptone	3 g
NaCl	5 g
KH_2PO_4	0·225 g
$Na_2HPO_4.2H_2O$	5·64 g
Distilled water	1000 ml

Dissolve the solids in the water, filter through a sintered-glass funnel and distribute in 100 ml volumes in screw-capped containers. Sterilize at 115° C for 20 min.

For use, add 1·5 ml of a freshly prepared 0·5 % KCN solution in sterile water to 100 ml of base. Mix and aseptically distribute 1 ml amounts into sterile 5 ml screw-capped bottles (bijou).

Note. Store at 4° C and use within 4 weeks of preparation.

Commercial (base): BBL, Difco.

Loeffler serum slopes

Glucose	5 g
Nutrient broth	250 ml
Serum, sterile	750 ml

Dissolve the glucose in the nutrient broth and steam for 10 min. Cool and add aseptically to the filtered serum. Distribute 2·5 ml volumes into sterile tubes and heat at 75° C for 2 h on each of 3 successive days, keeping the tubes in such a position that a slope is made.

Notes. It is essential that during the first period of heating the temperature is raised slowly, otherwise the surface serum will be coagulated before the dissolved air has been driven off and the finished medium will have an uneven surface.

For an alternative sterilization procedure see p. 102.

Commercial: Difco, Fisher, Oxoid.

Lowenstein-Jensen medium (modified from Jensen, 1932)

Mineral salt-starch solution

KH_2PO_4	1·2 g
$MgSO_4.7H_2O$	0·12 g
Magnesium citrate	0·3 g
Asparagine	1·8 g
Glycerol	6 g
Distilled water	300 ml

Dissolve the ingredients in the water with the aid of gentle heat.

Potato starch	15 g

Mix thoroughly with the mineral salt solution, heat in a water bath at 56–60° C for 15 min and leave in the water bath for 1 h.

Malachite green	0·2 g
Distilled water	10 ml

Mix and incubate at 37° C for 2 h or place in the water bath at 56–60° C to dissolve.

Mix the malachite green soln. with the mineral salts soln. and sterilize by autoclaving at 115° C for 10 min.

Egg mixture

Thoroughly wash 11–12 hen eggs in 70 % ethanol. Place on a sterile surface and, using a spatula, break the eggs into a 1000 ml wide-mouth stoppered flask. Mix the whites and yolks by shaking vigorously, then strain the mixture through gauze into a 1000 ml measure.

Aseptically add 500 ml of egg mixture to the mineral salt-starch and malachite green soln. Mix thoroughly and distribute in 5–7·5 ml amounts in sterile 30 ml screw-capped bottles. Screw down the caps and lay the bottles almost horizontally in an inspissator (or steamer). Slowly raise the temperature to 75° C and maintain this temperature for

1 h. Leave the bottles overnight in the inspissator and again heat at 75° C for 1 h on the following day.

Notes. The spatula, flask, strainer, and measure must be sterile. Too rapid heating on the first day may cause corrugation of the surface of the medium.

Commercial: BBL, Difco, Fisher, Oxoid.

Lowenstein-Jensen + TSC

1 % TSC in dimethylformamide	1 ml
Lowenstein-Jensen medium	1000 ml

TSC (thiosemicarbazone, thiacetazone or *p*-acetamidobenzaldehyde thiosemicarbazone) is dissolved in the solvent; the solution is added to the liquid L–J medium before inspissation. After mixing the medium is distributed and inspissated as above.

Final TSC concentration = approx. 10 μg per ml.

LV agar (Lecithovitellin agar) (Macfarlane, Oakley & Anderson, 1941)

Lecithovitellin solution (egg-yolk saline)

Hen eggs	4
NaCl, 0·85 % soln.	1000 ml

Separate the yolks from the whites and beat the yolks in the saline to form a homogeneous mixture. Add 25 g kieselguhr (diatomite), mix and clarify by filtration through paper. Sterilize the clarified material by filtration through a bacteria-proof filter.

Notes. If not to be used immediately, distribute the solution aseptically into sterile containers and keep in a refrigerator; it may decrease in sensitivity slightly over a period of 2 weeks or so, but most batches remain unaltered in sensitivity for months; if a precipitate appears, the batch should be discarded.

Yolks vary in size and in order to overcome the variations in egg-yolk saline due to this, McGaughey & Chu (1948) used 5 % w/v egg-yolk.

Billing & Luckhurst (1957) claim that filtration is easier when distilled water is used in place of saline.

Commercial: Oxoid.

Lecithovitellin agar

Lecithovitellin solution	100 ml
Nutrient agar	900 ml

Melt the nutrient agar and cool to about 55° C. Add the lecithovitellin solution aseptically, mix and pour plates.

9

Malonate-Phenylalanine medium (Shaw & Clarke, 1955)

$(NH_4)_2SO_4$	2 g
K_2HPO_4	0·6 g
KH_2PO_4	0·4 g
NaCl	2 g
Sodium malonate	3 g
DL-phenylalanine	2 g
Yeast extract	1 g
Distilled water	1000 ml
Bromthymol blue, 0·2 % soln.	12·5 ml

Dissolve the solids in the water by heating. Filter, add the indicator solution, and sterilize at 115° C for 20 min.

Notes. When L-phenylalanine is used, only 1 g is needed. Another medium, phenyl-alanine agar, for detecting phenylalanine deaminase is described on p. 122.

Commercial: Difco.

Milk, litmus

Stand fresh whole milk in a refrigerator overnight and remove the skim-milk by siphoning, taking care to avoid the cream layer. Steam for 1 h and cool in a refrigerator. Filter and measure the filtrate. Add sufficient litmus solution (p. 93) to give a bluish-purple colour. Sterilize at 115° C for 10 min *or* steam for 30 min on each of 3 successive days. After heating, this medium is colourless but the colour returns on cooling.

Notes. Overheating must be avoided to prevent caramelization.

Homogenized milk is unsuitable.

Commercial: BBL, Difco, Fisher, Oxoid.

Milk, purple: as above but replace litmus soln. with 10 ml 0·2 % bromcresol purple soln. per 1000 ml skim-milk.

Commercial: BBL, Fisher, Oxoid.

Milk, Ulrich's (Ulrich, 1944): as litmus milk but use chlorphenol red (0·0015 %) as the pH indicator, and methylene blue (0·0005%) as a redox potential indicator. To 1000 ml skim-milk, add 7·5 ml 0·2 % chlorphenol red soln. and 2·5 ml 0·2 % methylene blue soln.

Commercial: BBL, Difco, Fisher.

Motility medium (Edwards & Bruner, 1942)

Gelatin	80 g
Distilled water	1000 ml
Peptone	10 g
Beef extract	3 g
NaCl	5 g
Agar	4 g

Soak the gelatin in the water for 30 min, add the other ingredients, heat to dissolve, and sterilize at 115° C for 20 min.

Note. Hajna (1950) modified this formula to permit the simultaneous detection of H_2S production by the addition of 0·2 g cystine and 0·2 g ferrous ammonium sulphate; 2 g sodium citrate was added to clarify the medium and provide an extra nutrient for citrate-utilizing bacteria.

Commercial: BBL, Difco.

MRS lactobacillus broth (Man, Rogosa & Sharpe, 1960)

Peptone	10 g
Beef extract	10 g
Yeast extract	5 g
Glucose	20 g
Polyoxyethylene sorbitan mono-oleate (Tween 80)	1 ml
K_2HPO_4	2 g
$CH_3COONa.3H_2O$	5 g
Triammonium citrate	2 g
$MgSO_4.7H_2O$	0·2 g
$MnSO_4.4H_2O$	0·05 g
Distilled water	1000 ml

Dissolve the ingredients in the water, and sterilize at 115° C for 20 min or at 121° C for 15 min.

Notes. This medium may be gelled by the addition of 2 % agar.

As a basal medium for carbohydrate studies this formula may be modified by the omission of glucose and meat extract (see p. 110).

Nitrate-blood agar (Cook, 1950)

KNO_3, sterile 20 % aq. soln.	5 ml
Horse blood	60 ml
Nutrient agar or digest agar	1000 ml

Melt the nutrient agar, cool to 50–55° C, add the sterile KNO_3 soln. and horse blood aseptically, mix, and distribute into Petri dishes.

Nitrate broth

KNO_3	1 g
Nutrient broth	1000 ml

Dissolve the KNO_3 in the broth, distribute into tubes containing inverted Durham's tubes, and sterilize at 115° C for 20 min.

Note. Nitrite must not be present in this medium (for test see Appendix B, p. 132).

Commercial: Difco.

Nitrite broth

$NaNO_2$	0·01 g
Nutrient broth	1000 ml

Dissolve the $NaNO_2$ in the broth, distribute into tubes, and sterilize at 115° C for 20 min.

ONPG broth (Lowe, 1962)

ONPG	6 g
0·01 M-Na_2HPO_4	1000 ml

Dissolve at room temperature the ONPG (*o*-nitrophenyl-β-D-galactopyranoside) in the phosphate soln. at pH 7·5; sterilize by filtration.

Note. This solution should be stored in a refrigerator and protected from light.

ONPG solution	250 ml
Peptone water	750 ml

Aseptically add the ONPG soln. to the peptone water (p. 98) and distribute in 2·5 ml volumes in sterile tubes.

Note. The medium is stable for a month when stored at 4° C.

Phenolphthalein phosphate agar

Phenolphthalein diphosphate, Na salt 1 % aq. soln.

Sterilize by filtration and store at 4° C.

Phenolphthalein phosphate soln.	10 ml
Nutrient agar	1000 ml

Melt the nutrient agar and cool to 45–50° C. Add the phenolphthalein phosphate soln. aseptically, mix, and distribute into Petri dishes.

Phenylalanine agar (Ewing, Davis & Reavis, 1957)

DL-phenylalanine	2 g
Yeast extract	3 g
Na_2HPO_4	1 g
NaCl	5 g
Agar	20 g
Distilled water	1000 ml

Dissolve the ingredients by heating in the water, filter, tube, and sterilize at 115° C for 20 min. Solidify in a slanting position to give a long slope.

Notes. When L-phenylalanine is used, only 1 g is required.

A combined medium (with malonate) is described on p. 120.

Commercial: Difco.

Salt broth

Nutrient broth (p. 98) with the NaCl content increased to 65 g per 1000 ml.

Soil-extract agar (Gordon & Smith, 1953)

Soil extract

Garden soil, air-dried	1000 g
Water	2400 ml

Sift the air-dried soil through a no. 9 mesh sieve and add to the water. Mix well and heat the suspension in an autoclave at 121° C for 1 h or at 126° C for 20–30 min. Stir and filter through paper.

Notes. If the soil is rich in organic matter, 500 g will suffice.

If the soil is insufficiently dry the filtrate will be turbid, but may be clarified by the addition of talc, and then refiltered.

Soil-extract agar

Peptone	5 g
Beef extract	3 g
Agar	20 g
Soil extract	1000 ml

Heat to dissolve, adjust to pH 7·0, and sterilize at 115° C for 20 min.

Medium for preparation of *Streptomyces* extract (modified from Maxted, 1948)

NaCl	5 g
K_2HPO_4	2 g
$MgSO_4 . 7H_2O$	1 g
$CaCl_2$	0·04 g
$FeSO_4 . 7H_2O$	0·02 g
$ZnSO_4 . 7H_2O$	0·01 g
Yeast extract	5 g
Agar	20 g
Distilled water	1000 ml

Dissolve the agar by steaming in 750 ml of the water. Dissolve the salts and yeast extract in the remaining water and add to the agar sol. Mix and sterilize at 115° C for 20 min.

Glucose, 20 % aq. soln.	25 ml

For use, melt and cool to about 60° C, aseptically add sterile glucose solution, and distribute into sterile Roux bottles.

Todd-Hewitt broth (modified from Todd & Hewitt, 1932)

Meat, minced	450 g
Water	1000 ml

Infuse the meat in the water overnight at 4° C; skim the fat from the infused mixture, heat to 85° C, and maintain at this temperature for 30 min; filter and adjust the volume if necessary to 1000 ml.

Peptone	20 g
10 N-NaOH	2·7 ml
$NaHCO_3$	2 g
NaCl	2 g
$Na_2HPO_4 . 12H_2O$	1 g
Glucose	2 g

Add the peptone; mix well and add the alkali, followed by the other ingredients; slowly raise to boiling-point and boil for 30 min; adjust to pH 7·8, filter and sterilize at 115° C for 20 min.

Note. When this medium is to be used for streptococcal type identification, it is essential that the peptone used does not encourage production of the proteinase that destroys the M antigen (Elliott, 1945). Suitable peptones for this medium include Difco Neopeptone and Evans' peptone.

Commercial: Difco, Fisher, Oxoid.

Triple sugar iron agar (TSI) (Report, 1958)

Beef extract	3 g
Yeast extract	3 g
Peptone	20 g
Glucose	1 g
Lactose	10 g
Sucrose	10 g
$FeSO_4 . 7H_2O$	0·2 g
NaCl	5 g
$Na_2S_2O_3 . 5H_2O$	0·3 g
Agar	20 g
Distilled water	1000 ml
Phenol red, 0·2 % soln.	12 ml

Heat to dissolve the solids in the water, add the indicator soln., mix and tube. Sterilize at 115° C for 20 min and cool to form slopes with deep butts.

Commercial: Difco.

Tyrosine agar (Gordon & Smith, 1955)

Peptone	5 g
Beef extract	3 g
Agar	20 g
Distilled water	1000 ml
L-Tyrosine	5 g

Prepare the base as for nutrient agar (p. 98); add the tyrosine, mix well, and sterilize at 115° C for 20 min. Distribute as plates; ensure a uniform suspension of the insoluble tyrosine.

Urea medium, Christensen's (Christensen, 1946)

Peptone	1 g
NaCl	5 g
KH_2PO_4	2 g
Agar	20 g
Distilled water	1000 ml

Dissolve the ingredients by heating, adjust to pH 6·8, filter, and sterilize at 115° C for 20 min.

Glucose	1 g
Phenol red, 0·2 % soln.	6 ml

Add to the molten base, steam for 1 h, and cool to 50–55° C

Urea, 20 % aq. soln.	100 ml

Sterilize by filtration and add aseptically to the base. Distribute aseptically into sterile containers and allow to cool as slopes or plates.

Commercial: BBL, Difco, Fisher.

Urea medium, SSR (Stuart, van Stratum & Rustigan, 1945)

KH_2PO_4	9·1 g
Na_2HPO_4	9·5 g
Yeast extract	0·1 g
Urea	20 g
Phenol red, 0·2 % soln.	5 ml
Distilled water	1000 ml

Dissolve the solids in the water without heating, check that pH is 6·8, add the indicator, and sterilize by filtration. Aseptically distribute into sterile chemically clean tubes.

Alternatively, the base can be prepared and sterilized by autoclaving and the urea added aseptically as a sterile solution.

Commercial: BBL, Difco, Fisher.

Xanthine agar (Gordon & Mihm, 1957)

Prepared as tyrosine agar (p. 125), but substituting xanthine (4 g/l) for tyrosine.

MEDIA CONTROL

Standardized media are as important as standardized methods and reagents. Commercially prepared media are tested to show that, within certain limits, they conform to stated formulae but, as many of the media contain peptone and other material of biological origin, the analysis may not be particularly helpful and often does not indicate the suitability of the medium for the task in hand. In many laboratories, media preparation is left to junior or unskilled personnel and the room in which media is prepared is often called a 'media kitchen'. In our laboratory media preparation has been given the status of a department and the work is far removed from cookery. Although media preparation has many features of an art it also has a scientific basis.

Media control consists of quality control and evaluation; quality control is concerned solely with testing whether the product conforms to a predetermined standard, whereas evaluation implies the determination of its efficiency under the conditions of intended usage. The results of both quality control tests and bacteriological evaluation must be correlated and discrepancies or unexpected results investigated. When a sample of glucose-phosphate medium shows a yellow colour (due to overheating) it is likely to give unsatisfactory results in the methyl red test and it must be discarded. The growth of *E. coli*, or other non-utilizer of citrate, in Koser's citrate solution which appears satisfactory on the basis of chemical tests warrants further investigation; a major cause of such phenomena is the use of dirty glassware or the presence of organic matter from cotton plugs. Most laboratories have at some time omitted the lactose or bile salts from MacConkey agar, or used a wrong ingredient in media preparation.

QUALITY CONTROL

This is a continuous process extending from the raw materials, through manufacture to the final product.

RAW MATERIALS

Chemicals, reagents, and carbohydrates should be of analytical reagent quality or conform to Pharmacopoeial standards. The bacteriological laboratory is generally not equipped to carry out the necessary examination of these materials (which may involve spectrophotometry, flame-photometry, ion-exchange, chromatography, titration in non-aqueous media, or potentiometric titration, besides the more conventional assay methods) and must rely upon the integrity of the supplier. Materials of biological origin are generally more difficult to standardize and may vary considerably in composition (Report, 1956a).

Details of chemical and microbiological assays are outside the scope of this *Manual* and reference must be made to appropriate monographs and textbooks.

Agar. The concentration necessary to produce a suitable gel varies with the geographical source of the algae from which the agar was made (Table 8, p. 98). A method for estimating the gel strength of agar was described by Jones (1956). A good indication of the source of a sample of agar may be obtained by observation of the diatoms present. These are obtained either by centrifugation of a dilute agar sol or by ashing and extracting the residue with dilute hydrochloric acid; silica skeletons of diatoms, sand particles, and sponge spicules are in the acid-insoluble ash. Examination of granular or powdered agar is less rewarding as undamaged diatoms are seldom found. Forsdike (1950) examined agars from different sources and his paper illustrates many of the types of diatoms. The presence of nitrogenous material may be detected by heating with soda lime, when ammonia is evolved; adulteration with gelatin will be detectable in this way or, alternatively, by the formation of a turbidity or precipitate when a 1 % agar sol is mixed with an equal volume of 1 % aqueous picric acid.

Peptone. Although some studies on the constituents of different peptones have been published (Report, 1956a; Habeeb, 1960a,b) much work remains to be done and until more information is available it is not possible to define standards. All peptones should dissolve completely in water to give clear solutions having a pH value between 5 and 7.

Indole production requires a peptone with a high tryptophan content; a gelatin hydrolyzate is deficient in tryptophan as is an acid hydrolyzate of casein, although an enzymic casein hydrolyzate is suitable. Rosenheim's test is of value in detecting tryptophan: to 2 ml 5 % peptone soln. add 0·05 ml 1 % formaldehyde soln. and 0·05 ml 2 % $FeCl_3$ soln. Cautiously pour conc. H_2SO_4 down the side of the tube. A purple colour develops at the junction of the liquids when tryptophan is present. Peptones for use in media for carbohydrate studies must be tested for fermentable carbohydrate. Soya peptone generally contains carbohydrate and should be avoided in 'sugar' media. The influence of peptone on the methyl red and other carbohydrate reactions will be discussed under Evaluation (p. 135). It is unlikely that modern peptones will be inhibitory because of a high copper content (O'Meara & Macsween, 1936, 1937) but this possibility should be borne in mind.

Meat extract. In the absence of standards for the product the only simple tests which can be performed are the enumeration of viable organisms (which should be few) and the detection of fermentable carbohydrate (which should be absent).

Yeast extract, unlike meat extract, has a high carbohydrate content. The moisture content may be high (about 30 %) and considerable quantities of NaCl may be present; samples containing more than about 15 % NaCl should be rejected.

Bile salts. The complex nature of bile salts makes attempts at standardization difficult. Of the components present, deoxycholic acid (as its sodium salt) is widely used (Leifson, 1935). In the absence of suitable chemical standardization, biological evaluation is necessary and we recommend the method described by Burman (1955), in which a batch of bile salt is standardized against a batch known to be satisfactory; the inhibitory effect of bile salts can be influenced by other constituents of the medium such as NaCl (Leifson, 1935) and phosphates (Allen, Pasley & Pierce, 1952). The evaluation of sodium deoxycholate for use in inhibitory media is discussed by Taylor *et al.* (1964).

Gelatin comes from many animal sources and undergoes different processes, consequently it is available in several grades. For bacteriology, edible gelatin is generally used, the technical grades being unsatisfactory as they often contain preservatives and may have a high SO_2 and heavy-metal content. Leffmann & La Wall (1911) considered that a standard should be established for SO_2 in gelatin intended for bacteriological use. Some tests for physical properties and extraneous matter of gelatin are detailed in a British Standard (757:1959) to which reference may be made. This standard gives methods for determining moisture content, gel strength, viscosity, melting point, water absorption, solubility, keeping quality, pH, grease, ash, sulphur dioxide, chlorides, arsenic, and heavy metals.

Carbohydrates and related products. In our laboratory testing is restricted to solubility, clarity and reaction of solution, and simple tests such as absence of reducing sugar in non-reducing sugars, absence of aglycones in glycosides, and absence of monosaccharides in higher saccharides. Some samples of sucrose may contain invert sugar, detectable by measuring the optical rotation of a solution or more simply by testing with Fehling's or Benedict's solution (p. 146) for the presence of reducing substances. Soluble starch should be free from reducing sugars and when treated with iodine soln. should give a deep blue colour; a reddish or purple colour would indicate dextrin. Some tests for other carbohydrates are mentioned on p. 132.

Cole & Onslow's or other pancreatic extracts act by their tryptic content which must be estimated as follows:

(i) Qualitative. A 1/100 dilution should digest the gelatin from a used photographic plate or film within 30 min at 37° C.

(ii) Quantitative (modified from Douglas, 1922). To 50 ml fresh milk, from which the cream has been removed by centrifugation, add 50 ml 0.2 M-$CaCl_2$; mix thoroughly and measure 5 ml volumes of the milk into 150×16 mm ($6 \times \frac{5}{8}$ in) tubes. Place the tubes in a water bath at 38–40° C. Make dilutions of the enzyme from 1/10 to 1/100 and begin the testing using the 1/100 dilution.

Add 1 ml of the diluted enzyme preparation to a tube of calcified milk, shake thoroughly, return to the water bath and note the time. Examine the tube at intervals and note the time at which a precipitate or clotting occurs. Continue to test dilutions of the enzyme until the clotting time is between 1 and 2 minutes.

Calculation. Suppose 1 ml of a 1/60 dilution of the enzyme clots in 80 sec, then 1 ml of the original solution contains:

$$\frac{60 \times 100}{80} = 75 \text{ units}$$

A satisfactory batch of Cole & Onslow's extract should have a tryptic content of at least 50 units per ml.

Thioglycollic acid for inclusion in media should be assayed periodically and rejected when its activity falls below 75 % (Report, 1953); the acid should be kept in a tightly stoppered bottle at 4° C. The stability of thioglycollate solutions has been studied by Cook & Steel (1959*a*,*b*) and the assay method of Steel (1958) is recommended.

INTERMEDIATE CONTROL

During the preparation of digest media (p. 99) it is important to follow the course of digestion. Samples are taken at the start and at 30–45 minute intervals; the disappearance of undigested protein is most easily shown by the biuret test: heat a 5 ml sample to boiling to stop digestion, cool and add 0·5 ml 10 N-NaOH. Filter and add 0·1 ml 1 % $CuSO_4.5H_2O$ soln. to the filtrate. Proteins give a violet colour, proteoses a reddish-pink, and amino acids produce none.

FINAL PRODUCT

The final product should be examined physically and chemically, as well as by bacteriological tests which are considered under Evaluation (p. 133); some of the causes of faulty media are considered later (p. 135). Among the physical properties determined are colour, clarity, pH, viscosity, and gel strength of solid media. Determination of specific gravity does not appear to be valuable. For the pH determination of solid media a spear-shaped electrode is useful and avoids the need to melt the medium and compensate for the increased temperature.

Chemical properties tested may include the presence of the correct ingredients (testing for human error), nitrogen estimations, detection of breakdown products of components (especially those of carbohydrates), and freedom from the end-product(s) which will be looked for after the organism has grown.

Total nitrogen is usually estimated by the Kjeldahl method or some modification of it. In this, organic nitrogen is converted to ammonium sulphate by sulphuric acid in the presence of sodium sulphate with copper and selenium as catalysts. The digested reaction mixture is steam-distilled with sodium hydroxide to liberate ammonia. The ammonia is absorbed and estimated colorimetrically with Nessler's reagent or by titration. In all cases a blank determination on the reagents must be made. For details of the technique see an appropriate textbook of analytical chemistry or original papers, for example, Middleton & Stuckey (1951).

Proteose nitrogen is estimated similarly but proteoses are separated by precipitation with saturated zinc sulphate solution, and their nitrogen content determined.

Amino nitrogen: one of two methods may be used but the results given by the two methods may not be identical as they do not estimate exactly the same compounds; formol titration is the simpler method but in dark-coloured solutions the end-point may be difficult to see.

(i) Sørenson's formol titration: in this method, formaldehyde reacts with the NH_2-groups of amino acids to form acidic complexes which are titratable with alkali.

Neutralize 40 % formaldehyde soln. (formalin) with 0·1 N-NaOH, until just pink to phenolphthalein. To a 5 ml sample of medium add 0·05 ml phenolphthalein soln. and 0·1 N-NaOH until just pink. Add 5 ml neutralized formalin and titrate with 0·1 N-NaOH until the pink colour re-appears.

$$1 \text{ ml } 0·1 \text{ N-NaOH} \equiv 1·4 \text{ mg amino nitrogen}$$

(ii) Pope & Stevens' (1939) method: in this, copper phosphate reacts with amino acids to form soluble copper complexes; the amount of copper in solution is estimated iodometrically.

Copper phosphate suspension:

0·16 M-$CuCl_2$	20 ml
0·18 M-Na_3PO_4	40 ml
0·075 M-borate buffer (pH 8·5)	40 ml

Mix the three solutions. The suspension should be freshly prepared and discarded after three days.

Place a 5 ml sample of medium in a 50 ml volumetric flask and make just alkaline (blue) to thymolphthalein with N-NaOH. Add one drop of *n*-octanol to prevent foaming and 30 ml copper phosphate suspension. Make up to 50 ml with distilled water, mix well and filter. Acidify 10 ml filtrate with 0·5 ml glacial acetic acid, add 2 ml 50 % KI soln. and 10 ml 10 % KCNS soln. Titrate with 0·01 N-$Na_2S_2O_3$ using starch mucilage as indicator. The $Na_2S_2O_3$ is standardized by the same method against 0·01 N-$CuSO_4$.

$$1 \text{ ml } 0·01 \text{ N-}Na_2S_2O_3 \equiv 0·28 \text{ mg amino nitrogen}$$

A satisfactory digest medium should contain about a quarter of its total nitrogen in the form of amino nitrogen. Typical results from our laboratory for the amino acid content of digest broth (p. 99) and infusion broth (p. 100) are in the range 72–91 and 68–84 mg amino nitrogen per 100 ml respectively. To achieve some degree of standardization it is usual to adjust the amino nitrogen content of both these media to 70 mg per 100 ml by blending weak and strong batches. The amino nitrogen content of Todd-Hewitt broth (p. 124) is found to be of the order of 117–145 mg per 100 ml.

Other tests. The methods adopted to detect the presence or absence of particular components in culture media are mainly the straightforward techniques of classical chemical analysis, such as chloride estimation by Mohr titration, but the *Extra Pharmacopoeia* (1955) is useful for particular tests. Some of the test methods used have been borrowed from clinical biochemistry, and a brief selection is given below to illustrate their diversity.

Detection of bile salts in MacConkey broth (Hay's test for bile salts in urine): sprinkle powdered sulphur on the surface of the medium in a wide tube or beaker—bile salts lower the surface tension and the particles sink.

Presence of nitrate and absence of nitrite in nitrate broth: to 5 ml medium add 1 ml nitrite reagent A and 1 ml nitrite reagent B (p. 148)—a red colour indicates nitrite and the batch should be discarded; in the absence of a colour change add 20 mg powdered zinc—the development of a red colour indicates the presence of nitrate.

Molisch's test for carbohydrates: to 5 ml medium add 0·1 ml 5 % ethanolic α-naphthol, mix and cautiously pour conc. H_2SO_4 down the side of the tube—a purple colour at the junction of the liquids indicates the presence of carbohydrate.

Individual carbohydrates may be detected by standard biochemical tests; the distinction of galactose, glucose, lactose and maltose ultimately depends upon the formation of crystalline osazones and their identification by microscopical examination. Several multitests have been proposed by which different carbohydrates can be detected by the same reagent (Barakat & Abd El-Wahab, 1951; Love, 1953); the results of such tests should be confirmed by other methods.

Detection of starch in starch agar; pour an iodine soln. (e.g. Lugol's p. 139) over the medium—a blue colour indicates the presence of starch.

Pentoses may be detected by the orcinol reaction: mix equal volumes of test solution and reagent (orcinol, 0·2 g; conc. HCl, 100 ml; 10 % $FeCl_3$, 0·2 ml) and gently heat to boiling—a green or blue-green colour or precipitate indicates the presence of pentoses.

Detection of citrate in Koser's citrate: boil a 5 ml sample with 1 ml mercuric sulphate soln. (5 % HgO in 20 % v/v H_2SO_4), filter, boil, and add 5 drops 1 % $KMnO_4$ soln.—decolorization of the reagent and formation of a white precipitate indicates the presence of citrate.

Detection of hippurate in hippurate broth: add 5 % $FeCl_3$ soln.—a brownish-pink precipitate soluble in excess reagent indicates hippurate.

Hydrolysis of salicin in 'sugar media' sterilized by heat treatment is shown by the presence of reducing sugar when the medium is boiled with Benedict's reagent, and by a violet colour when $FeCl_3$ soln. is added.

Hydrolysis of starch in starch serum water is indicated by a coloured precipitate when a sample of the medium is boiled with Benedict's reagent. Such hydrolysis of starch by the action of amylase may occur when the serum has not been inactivated by heat (Goldsworthy *et al.* 1938).

Many of the tests used are not specific but give a good indication of whether the medium has been correctly prepared. In contrast to the bacteriological control methods described below, chemical tests have the advantage of speed.

EVALUATION

It is by the behaviour of media in routine use that the reputation of a media department stands or falls. Sterility is obviously of paramount importance and sterility testing will be discussed below. Bacteriological control will depend upon the nature of the individual medium. Its purposes are to test (i) the ability of nutrient media to support growth from small inocula; (ii) biochemical test media for their ability to show the desired reactions; (iii) differential media to ensure that organisms growing on them are characteristic; (iv) selective and enrichment media for growth of the desired organism and inhibition of other bacteria.

STERILITY TESTING

A sterility test is a limit test and the conventional sterility testing technique will detect only gross contamination. The sterility of a product cannot be proved unless the whole of the product (or batch) is tested. Bryce (1956) has calculated that there is a 50:50 chance of failing to detect contamination when 10 samples are tested from a batch of 500 items, 6·7 % of which are contaminated. In testing bacteriological media for sterility we have the advantage that a contaminant is more likely to develop in a nutrient medium than in a simple aqueous solution, and in many cases it suffices to incubate the medium to check its sterility. Culture media are not necessarily suitable for the growth of all micro-organisms; the pH value of a medium intended for bacteria may not be suitable for the growth of fungi. The incubation of an inhibitory medium may fail to show contamination; such a contaminated medium could be the start of a mixed culture which would reveal itself only on subculture to a non-inhibitory medium. Inhibitory media should be well diluted with sterile nutrient broth before incubation.

Media likely to be incubated for long periods, such as Dorset egg and Lowenstein-Jensen, must be free from slow-growing contaminants and it is advisable to prepare sufficient stocks to last for several months. Many contaminants grow at room

133

temperature but we should bear in mind the possible development of psychrophils in media stored at low temperatures. In medical bacteriology, the presence of thermophils is unlikely to be a serious problem in media. Theoretically our sterility tests should detect the presence of all living micro-organisms but we test only for bacteria and fungi. It is recommended that all samples of media sterilized by filtration or by heat treatment other than adequate autoclaving, be subjected to the following tests:

incubation temperature	incubation time
55–60° C	7 days in air
37° C	7 days in air
37° C	7 days anaerobically
ambient room (15–20° C)	14 days in air
4° C	14 days in air

GROWTH-SUPPORTING ABILITY

The nature of the medium determines the choice of test organisms, for example with 'chocolate' agar strains of *Haemophilus* spp. and of *Neisseria* spp. should be used, whereas with the nutrient agar less exacting organisms, such as staphylococci and coliforms, are tested. Our method is to grow the organisms in a suitable medium overnight and prepare nine 10-fold serial dilutions in sterile water. 0·02 ml of each dilution is placed on the surface of medium contained in a Petri dish (as in the Miles & Misra (1938) surface-viable counting technique) or added to 5 ml volumes of liquid media. After incubation, the highest dilution giving growth is noted. The ability of media to support the growth of anaerobic bacteria is determined in a similar manner. Messer (1947) found an inhibitory agent in a batch of nutrient agar and traced it to formaldehyde used to increase the wet strength of filter paper used during the preparation of the medium.

For MacConkey agar, the test organisms used are *Escherichia coli*, *Salmonella typhimurium*, *Shigella dysenteriae*, and *Shigella sonnei*. In addition to controlling its growth-promoting ability this test serves to show whether the medium satisfactorily differentiates these enteric bacteria. MacConkey broth should be tested for its ability to show acid and gas formation at 44° C when inoculated with a strain of *E. coli*.

BIOCHEMICAL PERFORMANCE

Samples must be tested with organisms known to produce positive and negative reactions. Examples of such control organisms are given under the individual test methods in Appendix D. Because of strain variation within species it is essential that the particular strain used for control purposes possesses the desired characters and in Table 9 (p. 175) we list suitable strains, maintained in our Collection, of the organisms required.

The need for biological control was shown by Orr Ewing & Taylor (1945) who found that certain batches of peptone were unsuitable for making carbohydrate media, for only in some of them did the Newcastle and Manchester biotypes of *Shigella flexneri* 6 produce both acid and gas. Peptone may also affect the results of a finely balanced test such as the MR (methyl red) and each batch of peptone should be tried out in the test, with known MR-positive and -negative strains (Jennens, 1954).

DIFFERENTIATION

Differential media must be tested to make sure that organisms growing on them exhibit the typical characters by which they are differentiated from other organisms. The testing of MacConkey agar for its ability to distinguish lactose- and non-lactose-fermenting bacteria has been noted above. Tellurite media should be inoculated with each of the three varieties of *Corynebacterium diphtheriae* and after incubation these should be examined for their characteristic colonial appearances.

SELECTIVITY

A selective or an enrichment medium should be able to support the growth of a particular organism or group of organisms, and at the same time inhibit others. A convenient method of testing this is to mix broth cultures of the organism to be selected with another organism to be inhibited, in varying proportions (e.g. $1:2 \ldots 2^n$). A loopful of each mixture is plated on solid media or inoculated into liquid media. After incubation an estimate of the selectivity of a solid medium may be made by inspection of the growth. The efficiency of a liquid enrichment medium cannot be judged until a subculture to a non-inhibitory solid medium has been made.

CAUSES OF FAULTY MEDIA

Major sources of trouble are errors in weighing and measuring, inadvertent use of the wrong ingredients (e.g. hydrated instead of anhydrous salts), and incorrect pH adjustment. Some faults and their possible causes are listed below:

Loss of growth-promoting capacity
> Over-sterilization; repeated re-melting of solid media; burning or charring; contamination with metallic salts; molarity incorrect due to careless pH adjustment.

Decreased gel strength
> Over-sterilization; hydrolysis of agar in media of low pH; incomplete solution of agar; repeated re-melting.

Darkening
> Over-sterilization; caramelization of sugars; local superheating due to inadequate mixing.

10   135

pH change

Over-sterilization; incomplete mixing; use of alkaline containers; hydrolysis of ingredients; repeated re-melting.

Precipitation

Chemical incompatibility; failure to remove phosphates; over-sterilization; prolonged holding of melted agar media at high temperature.

STAINING: REAGENTS AND METHODS

REAGENTS

Except Loeffler's methylene blue, staining reagents should be kept in well-closed glass-stoppered bottles and protected from direct sunlight. They should not be stored in close proximity to concentrated acids or ammonia. Distilled water for reagents should be freshly prepared and neutral in reaction.

Formulae of staining reagents are listed in alphabetical order.

Acetone-iodine decolorizer

Strong iodine solution

Iodine	10 g
Potassium iodide	6 g
Distilled water	10 ml
Ethanol (90 %)	to 100 ml

Dissolve the iodine and potassium iodide in the water and adjust to volume with the ethanol.

Acetone-iodine mixture

Strong iodine soln.	3.5 ml
Acetone	96.5 ml

Mix.

Acid-alcohol

Conc. HCl	3 ml
Ethanol (95 %)	97 ml

Mix.

Albert's stain

Malachite green	0.2 g
Toluidine blue	0.15 g
Ethanol (95 %)	2 ml
Glacial acetic acid	1 ml
Distilled water	100 ml

Dissolve the dyes in the ethanol. Mix the acid with the water and add to the dye soln. Allow to stand for 24 h and then filter.

Ammoniacal silver nitrate solution

AgNO$_3$	5 g
Distilled water	100 ml

Dissolve; to 90 ml of this soln. add strong ammonia soln. (sp. gr. 0·880) drop by drop until the precipitate which forms just dissolves; add sufficient AgNO$_3$ soln. drop by drop until the reagent remains faintly turbid even after shaking. When protected from light, this reagent is stable for several weeks.

Ammonium oxalate-crystal violet

Solution A

Crystal violet	10 g
Ethanol (95 %)	100 ml

Mix and dissolve.
Solution B

Ammonium oxalate	1 % aq. soln.

For use mix 20 ml of solution A and 80 ml of solution B.

Aqueous solutions

Simple aqueous solutions of the following are used in staining.

Bismarck brown	0·2 %
Chrysoidin	0·4 %
Malachite green	0·5 %
Malachite green	5 %
Safranin	0·5 %

Carbol-fuchsin, strong

Solution A

Basic fuchsin	10 g
Ethanol (95 %)	100 ml

Mix and dissolve in a stoppered bottle and keep at 37° C overnight.
Solution B

Phenol	5 g
Distilled water	100 ml

Mix and dissolve.
For use, pour 10 ml of solution A into 100 ml of solution B.

Carbol-fuchsin, weak

Dilute one volume of strong carbol-fuchsin with 10–20 volumes of distilled water.

India ink

A dense, homogeneous India ink free from large particles or clumps of particles is necessary. Duguid's (1951) practice is to mix the ink with a quarter of its volume of grade-12 Ballotini glass beads (0·2 mm) and shake for 1 h in a Mickle tissue disintegrator. Thin ink may be improved by evaporation to concentrate it.

Kirkpatrick's fixative

Absolute ethanol	60 ml
Chloroform	30 ml
Formaldehyde (40 %) soln.	10 ml

Mix.

Loeffler's methylene blue

Methylene blue	1 g
Ethanol (95 %)	100 ml

Prepare a saturated solution.

KOH 1 % aq. soln.	1 ml
Distilled water	99 ml
Ethanolic methylene blue	30 ml

Mix in order; this reagent must be ripened by oxidation, a process taking several months to complete, but ripening can be hastened by aeration. Bottles should be not more than half-full, the stopper replaced by a light cotton plug and the bottle shaken frequently. The stain improves with keeping and we prepare batches sufficiently large to last 5–10 years.

Note. The ripened stain is sometimes called polychrome methylene blue.

Lugol's iodine

Iodine	5 g
Potassium iodide	10 g
Distilled water	to 100 ml

Dissolve the KI and iodine in 10 ml of the water, and adjust to volume with distilled water.

Note. This reagent is Aqueous Iodine Solution of the British Pharmacopoeia (1963). For use dilute 1/5 with distilled water.

Muir's mordant

$HgCl_2$, saturated aq. soln. (about 7 %)	20 ml
Potash alum, saturated aq. soln. (about 12 %)	50 ml
Tannic acid, 20 % aq. soln.	20 ml

Mix.

Neisser's stain

Solution A

Methylene blue	0·1 g
Ethanol (95 %)	5 ml
Glacial acetic acid	5 ml
Distilled water	100 ml

Dissolve the dye in the water and add the acid and ethanol.

Solution B

Crystal violet	0·33 g
Ethanol (95 %)	3·3 ml
Distilled water	100 ml

Dissolve the dye in the ethanol-water mixture.

For use, mix 20 ml of solution A and 10 ml of solution B.

Plimmer's mordant

Tannic acid	20 g
$AlCl_3 . 6H_2O$	36 g
$ZnCl_2$	20 g
Basic fuchsin	3 g
Ethanol (60 %)	80 ml

Grind the solids together in a mortar and add the ethanol; triturate until dissolved. Before use, add 1 volume of mordant to 3 volumes of distilled water and mix well.

Rhodes' mordant

Tannic acid, 10 % aq. soln.	60 ml
Potash alum, saturated aq. soln. (about 12 %)	30 ml
Aniline, saturated aq. soln. (about 3·5 %)	6 ml
$FeCl_3$, 5 % aq. soln.	6 ml

Add the alum soln. to the tannic acid soln., followed by the aniline soln. Re-dissolve the curd which forms by shaking. Add the $FeCl_3$ soln. and allow the black soln. to stand for 10 min before use.

METHODS

In this section we describe a small selection of methods which we have used and found satisfactory; for more information refer to specialist monographs such as those by Conn, Darrow & Emmel (1960), E. Gurr, (1956) and G. T. Gurr (1963).

After examination, used slides should be sterilized by autoclaving. It must never be assumed that bacteria will have been killed by the application of the staining reagents. We have seen stained anthrax spores germinate in the immersion oil left on a slide, and Soltys (1948) reported cutaneous anthrax in a veterinary student infected from a stained film. Do not re-use slides.

SIMPLE STAINS

Loeffler's methylene blue is perhaps the most valuable reagent we have for staining bacteria. It is excellent for bacteria of the genus *Corynebacterium* where beading, barring, and granules may be demonstrated, especially when the organism has been grown on Loeffler serum (p. 117). In sporing bacilli stained with this reagent the spores appear as unstained bodies within blue cells.

1. Stain for 1 min.
2. Rinse with water.
3. Drain or blot to dry.

DIFFERENTIAL STAINS

Gram's method

In the U.S.A. the method given is often referred to as Hucker's modification (Hucker & Conn, 1923), and in this country as Lillie's (1928) modification.

1. Apply ammonium oxalate-crystal violet for $\frac{1}{2}$ min.
2. Wash in water.
3. Apply Lugol's iodine soln. for $\frac{1}{2}$ min.
4. Tip off iodine but do not wash.
5. Decolorize with a few drops of acetone.
   (*Note*: acetone decolorizes very quickly and should not be left on the film for more than 2–3 sec.)
6. Wash thoroughly in water.
7. Counterstain with 0·5 % safranin for $\frac{1}{2}$ min. (A few Gram-negative organisms are not well stained by safranin, examples are *H. influenzae* and *P. pestis*. Films of such organisms should be counterstained with weak carbol-fuchsin for $\frac{1}{2}$ min.)
8. Wash and stand on end to drain, or blot dry.

Preston & Morrell (1962) modified Lillie's method by retarding decolorization with an acetone-iodine mixture.

1. Ammonium oxalate-crystal violet for $\frac{1}{2}$ min.
2. Wash off thoroughly with Lugol's iodine soln.
3. Apply Lugol's iodine for $\frac{1}{2}$ min.
4. Wash off thoroughly with acetone-iodine.
5. Apply acetone-iodine for $\frac{1}{2}$ min.

6. Wash thoroughly with water.
7. Counterstain with weak carbol-fuchsin for $\frac{1}{2}$ min.
8. Wash and drain or blot to dry.

The whole slide must be flooded with each reagent and the previous reagent must be completely removed at each stage. Insufficient reagent may result in uneven staining or decolorization.

Gram-positive organisms are blue or purple, Gram-negative organisms are red.

Some workers prefer to counterstain with Bismarck brown which they claim gives a better contrast.

Ziehl-Neelsen's method (acid-fast stain)

1. Flood the slide with strong carbol-fuchsin and heat until steam rises (but do not boil).
2. After 3–4 min apply more heat until steam rises again; do not let the stain dry on the slide.
3. About 5–7 min after the first application of heat wash the slide thoroughly under running water.
4. Decolorize in acid-alcohol until all traces of red have disappeared from the film. Decolorization should not be attempted in one stage; there should be intermittent washings in water and re-application of acid-alcohol.
5. Wash well in water when decolorization is complete.
6. Counterstain with Loeffler's methylene blue or 0·5 % malachite green for 1 min.
7. Wash and stand on end to drain; do not blot dry.

Acid-fast organisms are red, other organisms are blue or green.

Dilute sulphuric acid or other reagents may be used for decolorization. Some authors have distinguished between acid-fast and acid-alcohol-fast; in our opinion such distinction is fallacious; it is perpetuated by plagiarism and it cannot be confirmed by practice.

Various cold-staining methods have been advocated (for example, Aubert, 1950; Hok, 1962) but they have little if any advantage over the conventional Ziehl-Neelsen method when applied to pure cultures.

SPECIAL STAINS

Spore stains

Method modified from Moeller (1891).

This is similar to Ziehl-Neelsen's method but ethanol is used for decolorization.

1. Flood the slide with strong carbol-fuchsin and steam.
2. After 5 min wash well in water.

3. Decolorize with ethanol until all traces of red have been removed. Decolorization of the vegetative bacilli can best be controlled by examining the wet film under low power (after the bottom of the slide has been wiped dry).
4. Wash thoroughly in water.
5. Counterstain with Loeffler's methylene blue for 1–2 min.
6. Wash and drain or blot to dry.

Bacterial bodies stain blue, spores red.

Schaeffer & Fulton's (1933) method

1. Flood the slide with 5 % aq. malachite green and steam for 1 min.
2. Wash under running water.
3. Counterstain with 0·5 % aq. safranin for 15 sec.
4. Rinse with water and drain or blot to dry.

Bacterial bodies stain red, spores green.

This method can be used as a cold stain by allowing the malachite green to act for 10 min.

Capsule stains

Muir's method

1. Flood with strong carbol-fuchsin and heat gently for 1 min.
2. Rinse rapidly with ethanol, then wash well in water.
3. Flood with Muir's mordant for 30 sec.
4. Wash off with water, and wash with ethanol for 30 sec or until the film is pink.
5. Wash well with water.
6. Counterstain with Loeffler's methylene blue for 30 sec.
7. Wash and drain or blot to dry.

Bacteria stain red, capsules blue.

India ink wet-film method (Duguid, 1951)

This is a 'negative' stain, which is not a stain in the true sense of the word but a means of colouring the background so that the cells are shown in relief as clear objects.

1. Place a large loopful of undiluted India ink on a slide.
2. Mix into this a small portion of the bacterial colony or a small loopful of the deposit from a centrifuged liquid culture.
3. Place a coverslip on top and press down under a pad of blotting-paper. Ideally, the film should be of the same thickness as the capsulate organisms. If the coverslip is not pressed down sufficiently, the organisms will tend to drift in the ink and may be obscured by overlying ink; if pressed down too much, the capsules may be distorted.

The capsule appears as a clear light zone between the refractile cell outline and the dark background.

To show slime production by enteric organisms, Duguid grows them on excess sugar agar, a medium containing maltose, phosphate, mineral salts, and a low concentration of peptone.

Stains for metachromatic (volutin) granules

For metachromatic granules make a smear from a culture on Loeffler serum.

Albert's stain, modified (Albert, 1921; Laybourn, 1924)

1. Stain with Albert's stain for 3–5 min.
2. Wash with water and blot to dry.
3. Stain with Lugol's iodine soln. for 1 min.
4. Wash with water and drain or blot to dry.

Cytoplasm appears light green, granules blue-black.

Neisser's stain

1. Stain with Neisser's stain for 10 sec.
2. Rinse rapidly with water.
3. Stain with 0·2 % Bismarck brown or 0·4 % chrysoidin for 30 sec.
4. Wash rapidly in water, drain or blot dry.

Cytoplasm appears light brown, granules blue-black.

Flagella stains

The arrangement of flagella on the bacterial cell has long been used as a taxonomic criterion. Unfortunately it is one which is not easily or unequivocally determined. The most satisfactory method of determining the mode of bacterial flagellation is by electron microscopy but, since a two-dimension picture of a three-dimensional object is obtained, the electron micrographs must be interpreted with caution.

Flagella staining should not be undertaken lightly, but reasonably satisfactory results can be obtained when care is taken in the preparation of the culture, the film, and the reagents. The interpretation of flagella stains has been discussed briefly by Hodgkiss (1960). For workers who wish to undertake flagella staining two methods are given below. In the U.S.A. Leifson's (1951) method is widely used, but as we have only had limited experience of it, we have omitted it from this section.

It is essential to use known peritrichous and polar flagellate organisms as controls.

Bacterial suspension. Inoculate the organism on the surface of nutrient agar slopes (or other suitable media) and incubate at 22°–30° C for 18–24 h. After incubation, carefully pipette 2–3 ml of sterile distilled water into the tubes and allow the bacteria to diffuse off the agar surface into the water. When the suspension is turbid, transfer by pipette into a clean tube containing 2 ml of 1 % formalin (0·4 % formaldehyde). On holding up to the light, the suspension should appear faintly opalescent. If it is turbid, more formalin must be added. The suspension may be washed by light centrifugation and the deposit resuspended in 1 % formalin solution.

Leifson (1961) has noted that the addition of formaldehyde to suspensions before flagella staining may cause a change in the shape of the flagella, and this must be borne in mind when examining stained films or comparing them with published illustrations (see for example Leifson, 1960).

Preparation of films. Clean slides with hot acid-dichromate (p. 92), thoroughly wash to remove all traces of acid and allow to drain; store in a closed container. Place a loopful of the bacterial suspension near one end of the dry slide which is immediately tipped to a vertical position so that the drop runs down, leaving a thin film with parallel sides. The drop reaches the bottom in a few seconds if the slide is really clean, and is then dried in the air at room temperature. Keep the slide in the vertical position to prevent dust settling on the film. If the liquid does not run down the slide smoothly, a good result is unlikely and it is advisable to make a fresh film.

Cesares-Gill's method, modified (Plimmer & Paine, 1921).

1. Treat with Kirkpatrick's fixative for 5 min.
2. Wash off the fixative thoroughly.
3. Filter the diluted Plimmer's mordant onto the slide and allow to act for 5 min.
4. Wash off with water.
5. Stain for 2 min with weak carbol-fuchsin.
6. Wash and allow to dry in air.

Rhodes' (1958) method.
This is a modification of Fontana's method of staining spirochaetes.

1. Apply iron tannate mordant for 3–5 min.
2. Thoroughly wash with water.
3. Heat the ammoniacal silver nitrate soln. nearly to boiling and apply to the film.
4. Leave to act for 3–5 min.
5. Wash well with water.
6. Drain or blot to dry.

Unless a permanent preparation is made, the stained film disintegrates after about a week on exposure to air.

APPENDIX D

CHARACTERIZATION TESTS: REAGENTS AND METHODS

Formulae of, and notes on, the reagents are listed below in alphabetical order. Standard acids and alkalis, and simple aqueous solutions are not listed.

Acid ferric chloride

$FeCl_3.6H_2O$		12 g
Conc. HCl		2·5 ml
Distilled water	to	100 ml

Dilute the acid with 75 ml of the water, dissolve the ferric chloride by warming gently, and adjust to volume with water.

Acid mercuric chloride (Frazier, 1926)

Mercuric chloride	12 g
Distilled water	80 ml
Conc. HCl	16 ml

Mix the $HgCl_2$ with the water, add the acid, and shake well until solution is complete.

Benedict's qualitative solution

Sodium citrate		17·3 g
Na_2CO_3, anhyd.		10 g
$CuSO_4.5H_2O$		1·73 g
Distilled water	to	100 ml

Dissolve the sodium citrate and carbonate in 60 ml of the water. Dissolve the copper sulphate in 20 ml of the water and add, with constant stirring, to the first solution. Adjust to volume with water.

Note. The solution is liable to crystallize in cold weather and should be stored in a warm place.

Creatine solution

1 % creatine in 0·1 N-HCl

This solution avoids the rather vague 'knife-point of creatine' and is relatively stable; a solution of creatine in alkali is often recommended, but is unstable (Levine, Epstein & Vaughn, 1934).

EHC disks (synonym: Optochin disks)

Impregnate filter paper disks of about 0·5 cm dia. with 0·02 ml of a 1/5000 solution of ethylhydrocuprein hydrochloride. Dry at 37° C or freeze-dry. Store in a closed container.

Commercial: BBL, Difco, Oxoid.

Ehrlich's reagent

p-dimethylaminobenzaldehyde	1 g
Absolute ethanol	95 ml
Conc. HCl	20 ml

Dissolve the aldehyde in the ethanol and add the acid. Protect from light.

Hydrogen peroxide

$$H_2O_2, 3\% \text{ aq. soln. ('10 volume')}$$

Protect from light and store in a cool place. Keep in a bottle closed with a glass stopper, paraffined cork or plastic screw-cap.

Kovács' (1928) reagent

p-dimethylaminobenzaldehyde	5 g
Amyl alcohol	75 ml
Conc. HCl	25 ml

Dissolve the aldehyde in the alcohol by gently warming in a water bath (about 50–55° C). Cool and add the acid. Protect from light and store at 4° C.

Note. The reagent should be light yellow to light brown in colour; some samples of amyl alcohol are unsatisfactory, and give a dark colour with the aldehyde.

For micromethods (p. 171) this reagent is prepared with *iso*-amyl alcohol (methods i and iii) or *n*-butanol (method ii).

Lugol's iodine solution see page 139.

Lytic enzyme for streptococcal grouping (Maxted, 1948)

Streptomyces sp , NCTC 7807 (incorrectly stated by Maxted, 1948, to be *Streptomyces albus*) is grown on a suitable medium (p. 123) in Roux bottles for 4–5 days at 37° C. After growth, the agar gel is destroyed by freezing in solid CO_2. The fluid which exudes on thawing contains the lytic principle and can be sterilized by filtration but this is not essential; the pH is not adjusted, nor is a preservative added. Store in a refrigerator.

Methyl red solution

Methyl red	0·04 g
Absolute ethanol	40 ml
Distilled water	to 100 ml

Dissolve the methyl red in the ethanol and dilute to volume with the water.

α-naphthol solution

5 % α-naphthol in absolute ethanol
(not 95 % ethanol)

The soln. should not be darker than straw colour; if necessary the α-naphthol should be redistilled (Fulton, Halkias & Yarashus, 1960).

Nessler's reagent

Dissolve 5 g potassium iodide in 5 ml freshly distilled water. Add cold saturated mercuric chloride solution until a slight precipitate permanently remains after thorough shaking. Add 40 ml 9 N-NaOH. Dilute to 100 ml with distilled water. Allow to stand for 24 h.

Alternative formula: dissolve 8 g potassium iodide and 11·5 g mercuric iodide in 20 ml water and adjust to 50 ml. Add 50 ml 6 N-NaOH. Mix and allow to stand for 24 h.

Notes. The water used in its preparation must be ammonia-free. Allow the reagent to settle before use. Protect from light.

Niacin test reagents

(i) 4 % aniline in 95 % ethanol
or 1·5 % o-tolidine in 95 % ethanol
(ii) 10 % aq. cyanogen bromide

Store at 4° C for up to 2 weeks. Cyanogen bromide soln. is toxic and must be treated with an equal volume of ammonia soln. (sp. gr. 0·880) or 10 N-NaOH before disposal.

Nitrite test reagents

Solution A

0·8 % sulphanilic acid in 5 N-acetic acid

Dissolve by gentle heating.

Solution B

0·6 % dimethyl-α-naphthylamine in 5 N-acetic acid
or
0·5 % α-naphthylamine in 5 N-acetic acid

Dissolve by gentle heating.

Zinc dust *or* 10% zinc dust suspended in 1% methylcellulose soln. (Steel & Fisher, 1961).

Oxidase reagent

1 % tetramethyl-p-phenylenediamine aq. soln.

The reagent should be colourless and be stored in a glass-stoppered bottle, protected from light, in a refrigerator.

Note. It should not be used if it has become deep blue. The autoxidation of the reagent may be retarded by the addition of 0·1 % ascorbic acid (Steel, 1962b).

Test papers

Cut filter paper into strips 5–10 mm wide and 50–60 mm long, impregnate with the appropriate solution, and dry at 50–60° C.

For H$_2$S detection: (Clarke, 1953a)

> hot saturated aq. lead acetate soln.

Store in a tightly-closed container.

Note. For the micromethod (p. 171), the papers should be 4–5 mm wide.

For indole detection: (Holman & Gonzales, 1923)

> hot saturated aq. oxalic acid soln.

Gillies' (1956) solution

p-dimethylaminobenzaldehyde	10 g
o-phosphoric acid	20 ml
methanol	100 ml

Dissolve the aldehyde in the methanol, and add the phosphoric acid.

Preparation of X- and V-factors (Marshall & Kelsey, 1960)

X-factor. Centrifuge the red cells from 40 ml blood and add to them with shaking 100 ml acetone containing 1·2 ml conc. HCl; filter and add 100–120 ml water to the filtrate to precipitate the haemin. Collect by filtration and wash with water. Dissolve the crude haemin in 25 ml 0·1 M-Na$_2$HPO$_4$ and sterilize at 115° C for 10 min.

V-factor. Suspend 50 g yeast in 100 ml 0·2 M-KH$_2$PO$_4$ and heat at 80° C for 20 min. Clarify by centrifugation and sterilize the supernatant by filtration. Store in a refrigerator or deep-freeze.

X-, V- and X + V-factor disks. Cut filter paper (such as Whatman no. 3 or other suitable absorbent paper) into disks of about 1 cm dia. Soak the disks with *X-, V-* or a mixture of *X-* and *V*-factor soln. Drain and dry at 37° C or freeze-dry. Store in a refrigerator in a closed container.

Commercial: Oxoid.

CHARACTERIZATION TESTS

Unless otherwise indicated, cultures are incubated at 37° C or their optimum temperature.

Recommended strains of control organisms are listed in Table 9 (p. 175).

PRIMARY TESTS

Motility

Method 1. Examine young broth cultures of the organism, incubated at and below the optimum temperature (e.g. 37° C and 22° C), microscopically in a 'hanging drop' preparation.

Method 2. Inoculate tubes of motility medium (p. 120) by stabbing into the top of the medium to a depth of about 5 mm. Incubate at optimum temperature and below.

The O–F medium (p. 107) may be used to detect motility, but it cannot be relied upon to the exclusion of one of the methods described above.

For the enhancement of motility inoculate Craigie tubes (Craigie, 1931) or U-tubes containing semi-solid nutrient agar (p. 98); serial passages may be necessary.

Catalase activity

Method 1. Grow the organism on a slope of nutrient agar or other suitable medium. Run 1 ml 3 % H_2O_2 down the slope and examine immediately and after 5 min for bubbles of gas.

Note. Blood agar and other blood-containing media are unsuitable for this test.

Method 2. Grow the organism in nutrient broth. Add 1 ml 3 % H_2O_2 and examine immediately and after 5 min for gas production.

Note. The rate of decomposition of H_2O_2 increases with increased temperature and false positive reactions may occur due to dissolved oxygen; this can be avoided by shaking a small volume of the reagent, or by agitating it with a Pasteur pipette, before use.

Controls: Positive — *Staphylococcus epidermidis*

　　　　　Negative — *Streptococcus faecalis*

Oxidase activity (Kovács, 1956)

On a piece of filter paper (7 cm dia.) in a Petri dish place 2–3 drops of the oxidase reagent (p. 148). Smear the culture under test across the impregnated paper with a platinum (not nichrome) loop. A positive reaction is indicated by the appearance of a dark purple colour on the paper within 10 sec.

Controls: Positive — *Pseudomonas aeruginosa*

　　　　　Negative — *Escherichia coli*

Acid from carbohydrates

Method 1. Peptone water and nutrient broth sugars (p. 108).

Inoculate and examine daily for 7 days for acid or acid and gas production. Reversion to alkalinity should also be noted. Negative tests should be examined at regular intervals up to 30 days.

With some organisms the ability to produce visible gas depends on the temperature of

, incubation, and if equivocal or suspect results are obtained the tests should be repeated at a lower temperature. As some anaerobes can produce gas from proteins, gas production is not reliable as an indicator of fermentation.

When incubated anaerobically, some indicators may be 'bleached' (reduced to a colourless state); in such cases, test for acid production by the addition of fresh indicator soln.

Method 2. Serum water sugars (p. 109).

Inoculate and examine for acid production or acid and clot.

Method 3. Media for neisserias (p. 109) and lactobacilli (p. 110).

Inoculate and examine for growth and acid production.

Method 4. Ammonium salt sugars (p. 109) and 10 % lactose agar (p. 110).

Inoculate the surface of the slopes and examine for growth and acid production.

Oxidation or fermentation of glucose (Hugh & Leifson, 1953)

Some workers steam the O–F medium (p. 107), to remove dissolved air, and quickly cool immediately before use.

Inoculate duplicate tubes by stabbing with a straight wire. To one of the tubes add a layer of melted soft paraffin (petrolatum) to a depth of about 1 cm. Incubate and examine daily for up to 14 days.

Results:	*open tube*	*sealed tube*
Oxidation	yellow	green
Fermentation	yellow	yellow
No action on carbohydrate	blue or green	green

Note. This medium can also be used for detecting gas production and motility.

Controls: Oxidation—*Acinetobacter anitratus*

Fermentation—*Escherichia coli*

No action—*Alcaligenes faecalis*

SECONDARY TESTS

Acetylmethylcarbinol production: see MR and V–P tests (p. 160).

Aesculin hydrolysis

Inoculate aesculin broth (p. 112) and examine daily up to 7 days for blackening, this indicates hydrolysis of the aesculin. Alternatively, inoculate aesculin agar and look for blackening in and around the bacterial growth.

Controls: Positive—*Streptococcus faecalis*

Negative—*S. agalactiae*

Arginine hydrolysis

Inoculate 5 ml arginine broth (p. 112) and after incubation for 24 h add 0·25 ml Nessler's reagent (p. 148). Arginine hydrolysis is indicated by the development of a brown colour.

Controls: Positive—*Streptococcus faecalis*
           Negative—*S. hominis*

Bile solubility

Method 1. To 5 ml of an 18-hour culture of the test organism in serum, digest, or infusion broth (pp. 99–104) add 0·5 ml 10 % sodium deoxycholate soln. and incubate at 37° C. Pneumococci are lysed within 15 min of adding the bile salt.

Note. A glucose-containing medium is unsatisfactory for this test as the reaction should be not more acid than pH 6·8.

Method 2. Grow the organism in serum broth or Todd-Hewitt broth (p. 124) for 24 h. Centrifuge and discard the supernatant. Resuspend the organisms in 0·5 ml isotonic saline adjusted to pH 7·0 or in buffer solution at pH 7·0. Add 0·5 ml 10 % sodium deoxycholate soln. and incubate at 37° C for 15–30 min. Under these conditions, a rapid clearing of the suspension occurs with pneumococci; when clearing has not taken place in 30 min the organisms are not pneumococci.

Controls: Positive—*Streptococcus pneumoniae*
           Negative—*S. faecalis*

Bile tolerance

Inoculate onto 10 % and 40 % bile agar plates (p. 105) and incubate at 37° C for 24–48 h. Growth indicates resistance to bile. Alternatively, 'ditch' plates comprising blood agar on one side and bile agar on the other may be used; strains should not be regarded as bile tolerant unless they grow right across the bile agar half.

Controls: Positive (10 % and 40 %)—*Streptococcus faecalis*
           Positive (10 % only)—*S. hominis*
           Negative—*S. dysgalactiae*

Citrate utilization

Make a light suspension of the organisms in sterile water or saline; inoculate citrate media with a straight wire. Incubate at 30° C (enterobacteria) or optimum temperature (other organisms).

Method 1. Inoculate Koser's citrate (p. 113) and examine daily up to 7 days for turbidity. Confirm positives by subculture to Koser's citrate.

turbidity   = citrate utilized
no turbidity = citrate not utilized

Method 2. Inoculate by making a single streak over the surface of a slope of Simmons' citrate (p. 114). Examine daily up to 7 days for growth and colour change. Confirm positives by subculture to Koser's citrate.

> blue colour and streak of growth = citrate utilized
> original green colour   = citrate not utilized

Controls: Positive—*Klebsiella aerogenes*
              Negative—*Escherichia coli*

Method 3. Inoculate Christensen's citrate (p. 113) by stabbing the butt and then drawing the wire over the surface of the slope. Examine for up to 7 days for colour change.

> magenta colour = citrate utilized
> yellow colour   = citrate not utilized

Note. An organism positive in Koser's or Simmons' test will be positive in Christensen's, but an organism positive in Christensen's test may or may not be positive in Koser's or Simmons'.

Controls: Positive—*K. aerogenes*
              Negative—*Shigella sonnei*

Utilization, by mycobacteria, of other organic acids as carbon sources

Inoculate the appropriate media (p. 114) and examine at intervals up to 1 month; use of the carbon compound is indicated by alkali production, shown by the colour change of the indicator from yellow to red.

Controls:	Positive	Negative
benzoate		
mucate	*M. smegmatis*	*M. phlei*
oxalate		

Coagulase test

Tube tests: In both methods, a positive result is indicated by definite clot formation; granular or ropy growth is regarded as doubtful and the organism should be re-tested.

Method 1 (Cowan, 1938*b*). Mix 0·5 ml undiluted plasma with an equal volume of an 18–24-hour broth culture and incubate at 37° C for 4 h. Examine after 1 and 4 h for a coagulum. Negative tubes should be left at room temperature overnight and then re-examined.

Method 2 (Gillespie, 1943). To 0·5 ml of 1/10 dilution of plasma in saline add 0·1 ml of an 18–24-hour broth culture of the organism. Incubate at 37° C and examine after 1, 3, and 6 h for a coagulum. Negative tubes should be left at room temperature overnight and then re-examined.

Slide test (Cadness-Graves *et al.* 1943; Williams & Harper, 1946)

Emulsify a colony in a drop of water on a microscope slide to produce a thick suspension with the minimum of spreading. Stir the bacterial suspension with a straight wire which has been dipped into plasma. A positive result is indicated by macroscopical clumping within 5 sec. Delayed clumping does not constitute a positive reaction.

Notes. If the plasma has been stored in a refrigerator it may be sufficiently cold to delay coagulation; it is advisable to allow the plasma to attain room temperature before use.

The slide test is a valuable presumptive test but negative results must be confirmed by a tube test.

Known coagulase-positive and negative strains must always be tested in parallel and, with the tube tests, an uninoculated control must also be set up.

Controls: Positive—*Staphylococcus aureus*

Negative—*S. epidermidis*

Decarboxylase reactions

Method 1 (Møller, 1955). From a plate culture lightly inoculate, with a straight wire, tubes of the four media (arginine, lysine, ornithine, and control, p. 114) through the paraffin layer. Incubate and examine daily for up to 4 days. The media first become yellow due to acid production from the glucose; later if decarboxylation occurs, the medium becomes violet. The control should remain yellow.

Note. In the diagnostic tables, plus signs indicate only the production of a violet colour in the medium. When a positive reaction is obtained with arginine, the medium may be tested with Nessler's reagent (p. 148) for the presence of NH_3; in the absence of urease, the formation of NH_3 indicates that the arginine dihydrolase system has been involved in the reaction (Møller, 1955).

Method 2 (Falkow, 1958). Inoculate tubes of the four media (p. 115) with a straight wire. Incubate and examine daily for up to 4 days. Decarboxylation is indicated by a purple colour, whereas the control and negative tubes are yellow. Falkow's method is not satisfactory with the genera *Enterobacter* and *Klebsiella*.

Controls: Arginine Lysine Ornithine

Arginine	Lysine	Ornithine	
−	−	−	*Proteus vulgaris*
+	−	−	*Aeromonas liquefaciens*
−	+	−	*Klebsiella aerogenes*
−	−	+	*Proteus morganii*
+	+	−	*Salmonella typhi*
+	−	+	*Enterobacter cloacae*
−	+	+	*Enterobacter aerogenes*
+	+	+	*Salmonella typhimurium*

Decomposition of tyrosine or xanthine

Inoculate plates of the appropriate media (pp. 125–6) and examine at intervals up to a month for dissolution of the crystals under and around the bacterial growth.

Controls:	Positive	Negative
tyrosine	*Nocardia brasiliensis*	*Mycobacterium phlei*
xanthine	*N. caviae*	*M. phlei*

Dextran and levan production

Inoculate sucrose broth (p. 112) and incubate. Much dextran formation is shown by an increased viscosity of the culture and the dextran may be flocculated by the addition of ethanol. The dextran is best recognized by a precipitin test in which the broth culture is set up against an antiserum to *Streptococcus pneumoniae* type 2.

Inoculate a plate of sucrose agar (p. 112) and incubate. Levan-producing organisms grow as large mucoid colonies; dextran-producing organisms (e.g. *Streptococcus sanguis*) may form small glassy colonies on this medium.

Controls: dextran produced—*Streptococcus sanguis*

levan produced—*S. hominis*

dextran and levan negative—*S. faecalis*

Digestion of casein

Inoculate plates of casein agar (p. 112) and examine at intervals up to 14 days for clearing of the medium around the bacterial growth.

Note. In a few instances clearing may be due to solution of the milk proteins by acid or alkaline metabolic products (see Hastings, 1904); this may be distinguished from true proteolysis by the addition of acid mercuric chloride (p. 146), when a decrease in the cleared area shows that the casein has not been digested.

Controls: Positive—*Bacillus subtilis*

Negative—*Mycobacterium phlei*

Digestion of egg

Inoculate a slope of Dorset egg (p. 102) and examine at intervals up to 14 days for liquefaction.

Digestion of meat

Inoculate cooked meat medium (p. 99) and on the container mark the level of the meat. Incubate and examine at intervals up to 14 days for diminution in the volume of the meat, disintegration, or softening of the meat particles. Blackening or reddening of the meat and/or production of small white feathery crystals of tyrosine may also occur.

Digestion of serum

Inoculate a slope of Loeffler serum (p. 117) and examine at intervals up to 14 days for liquefaction of the medium. With anaerobes, inoculate and examine for digestion of the serum after incubation in a jar.

Eijkman test, modified (44° C fermentation test of Report, 1956c)

Inoculate MacConkey broth (p. 110), warmed to 37 °C, and incubate at $44 \pm 0.1°$ C for 48 h. A positive result is indicated by the production of both acid and gas.

Note. Many workers concerned with the bacteriology of water have suggested other media to replace MacConkey broth in this test.

Controls: Positive —*Escherichia coli*

Negative—*Enterobacter cloacae*

Ethylhydrocuprein (EHC) sensitivity

Place a disk impregnated with ethylhydrocuprein (p. 147) on the surface of a blood agar plate inoculated with the organism. Incubate and examine after 18–24 h. Sensitivity to the compound is shown by inhibition of bacterial growth around the disk for a distance of at least 5 mm; resistant organisms will grow up to the disk or may show a small inhibition zone of not more than 1–2 mm.

Controls: Sensitive—*Streptococcus pneumoniae*

Insensitive—*S. faecalis*

Gelatin liquefaction

Method 1. Inoculate nutrient gelatin (p. 116) with a straight wire and incubate at 22° C; observe daily up to 30 days for growth and presence of liquefaction.

Method 2. Inoculate nutrient gelatin and incubate at 37° C for up to 14 days; every 2–3 days, cool in a refrigerator for 2 h and then examine for liquefaction. Set up a control tube of uninoculated medium in parallel.

Method 3 (Frazier, 1926). Inoculate a slope or plate of gelatin agar (p. 116) and incubate for 3 days. Flood the surface with 5–10 ml acid mercuric chloride soln. (p. 146); clear zones indicate areas of gelatin hydrolysis.

When glass Petri dishes are used, metal tops should be avoided; plastic disposable dishes prevent contamination of glassware with mercuric ions.

Method 4. Ferrous chloride gelatin may be used for the determination of both gelatin liquefaction and H_2S production (see method 2, p. 158).

Controls: Positive—*Aeromonas liquefaciens*

Negative—*Escherichia coli*

Gluconate oxidation

Inoculate gluconate broth (p. 116) and incubate for 2 days.

Method 1. Add 1 ml Benedict's qualitative soln. (p. 146), mix, and boil for 10 min. The formation of a brown, orange, or tan precipitate constitutes a positive reaction.

Method 2 (Carpenter, 1961). Add one Clinitest tablet (Ames & Co.) in place of the Benedict's reagent and observe for the formation of a coloured precipitate as above.

Controls: Positive—*Klebsiella aerogenes*
Negative—*Escherichia coli*

Growth in or on special media

This character occurs in several of the tables. The media concerned are:

Bile agar (10 and 40 %)	—Table I*b*
Bordet-Gengou agar	—Table II*g*
Fildes' digest agar	—Table II*g*
Glucose broth (anaerobically)	—Table I*e*
MacConkey agar	—Tables I*gb*, II*c*, II*d*, II*e* and II*f*
Nutrient agar	—Tables II*a* and II*f*
Tomato juice agar	—Table I*d*

Media are inoculated and incubated for a suitable period in accordance with the growth rate of the bacteria. Growth is looked for and, with MacConkey agar, any colour change of the indicator is recorded; colour change of the indicator is one of the characters used to delineate *Mycobacterium* species and in this case incubation should be continued for a month.

Growth at pH 9·6

Inoculate a bottle of glucose phenolphthalein broth (p. 116) and incubate at 37° C for 24 h. Tolerance of pH 9·6 is indicated by heavy growth and decolorization of the indicator.

Controls: Positive—*Streptococcus faecalis*
Negative—*S. dysgalactiae*

Growth in 6·5 % NaCl

Inoculate salt broth (p. 123) and incubate at 37° C for 24–48 h. Growth indicates tolerance of 6·5% NaCl.

Controls: Positive—*Streptococcus faecalis*
Negative—*S. agalactiae*

Hippurate hydrolysis

Method 1 (Hare & Colebrook, 1934). Grow the organism in hippurate broth (p. 117) for 4 days. Set up a control tube of uninoculated medium in parallel. Hydrolysis of hippurate to benzoate is detected by the addition of acid ferric chloride soln. (p. 146).

To 1 ml volumes of the control medium, add varying amounts of acid ferric chloride soln. (0·2, 0·3, 0·4, 0·5 ml) rapidly, and shake immediately. With the smaller amounts a precipitate usually appears, soluble in excess; with the larger a clear solution is obtained; the smallest amount of acid ferric chloride soln. giving such a clear solution is then added to 1 ml volumes of clear supernatant fluids from the broth cultures. A heavy precipitate is taken as evidence of hydrolysis of sodium hippurate by the growing organisms.

Controls: Positive—*Streptococcus agalactiae*
          Negative—*S. hominis*

Method 2 (Thirst, 1957*a*). Lightly inoculate slopes of hippurate agar (p. 117) and examine daily for up to 7 days. Hydrolysis of hippurate is indicated by growth and a pink colour due to alkali production.
Controls: Positive—*Klebsiella aerogenes* (not all strains)
          Negative —*Enterobacter cloacae*

Hydrogen sulphide production

Method 1. Inoculate a tube of triple sugar iron agar (p. 124) by stabbing the butt and steaking the slope; observe daily for up to 7 days for blackening due to H_2S production.

Method 2. Inoculate as a stab a tube of ferrous chloride gelatin (p. 115) and incubate at 22° C. Read daily for 7 days for blackening due to H_2S. Gelatin liquefaction may also be observed in this medium; for this incubation is continued up to 30 days.

Method 3. Grow the organism in nutrient broth or peptone water, and insert a lead acetate paper (p. 149) between the cap or plug and the tube. Examine for blackening of the paper daily for 7 days.

Method 4, for *Brucella* spp. Inoculate a serum glucose agar slope (p. 104) and insert a lead acetate paper strip as in method 3. Examine and change the paper daily for 7 days.

Controls: Positive —*Proteus vulgaris*
          Negative—*Shigella sonnei*

Indole production

Method 1. Inoculate peptone water or nutrient broth, place an oxalic acid paper (p. 149) between the plug or cap and the tube. Incubate and examine daily for up to 7 days. Indole production is shown by the development of a pink colour on the paper.

Method 2. Inoculate peptone water or nutrient broth and incubate for 48 h. Add 0·5 ml Kovács' reagent (p. 147), shake well and examine after 1 min. A red colour in the reagent layer indicates the presence of indole.

Method 3. To a 48-hour culture in peptone water or nutrient broth, add about 1 ml ether or xylol; shake; run 0·5 ml Ehrlich's reagent (p. 147) down the side of the tube. A pink or red colour in the solvent indicates the presence of indole.

Controls: Positive—*Escherichia coli*
　　　　　Negative—*Enterobacter cloacae*

KCN test

Inoculate KCN broth (p. 117) with one loopful of an overnight or 24-hour broth culture. Tightly screw down the cap of the bottle and incubate for up to 48 h. Examine after 24 and 48 h for turbidity indicating growth, which constitutes a positive reaction.

After use, care should be exercised in the disposal of cyanide-containing media; add a crystal of $FeSO_4$ and 0·1 ml 40 % KOH before sterilization.

Controls: Positive—*Klebsiella aerogenes*
　　　　　Negative—*Escherichia coli*

LV reaction

Inoculate LV agar (p. 119) and after incubation examine for (i) growth, (ii) opalescence within the medium, (iii) 'pearly layer' formation over and around the colonies; and (iv) constitute positive reactions.

Flood the plate with saturated aq. $CuSO_4$ soln., remove excess reagent and allow the plate to dry in an incubator for 20 min. An insoluble bright greenish-blue copper soap is formed in those areas containing free fatty acid.

Controls: Opalescence—*Clostridium welchii*
　　　　　Pearly layer—*C. sporogenes*
　　　　　No reaction—*Bacillus subtilis*

Malonate utilization

Inoculate malonate-phenylalanine medium (p. 120) and incubate for 24 h. Examine for colour change and keep the culture for the phenylalanine test (p. 162). A positive malonate reaction is indicated by a deep blue colour; a negative reaction by the unchanged greenish colour of the medium (with some negative strains a yellow colour appears).

Controls: Positive—*Klebsiella aerogenes*
　　　　　Negative—*Proteus vulgaris*

Milk media

Inoculate the appropriate medium (p. 120) and examine daily for 14 days for colour change and clotting. The following reactions may be seen:

Litmus milk: acid production indicated by pink colour,
　　　　　　alkali production indicated by blue colour,
　　　　　　reduction of the indicator shown by colourless (white) medium,

159

acid clot shown by a firm pink clot which does not retract and which is soluble in alkali,

rennet clot shown by a soft clot which retracts and expresses a clear greyish fluid (whey), the clot is insoluble in alkali; peptonization or digestion of the clot may follow,

'stormy fermentation' in which the acid clot is broken up by gas production.

Purple milk: as above, but acid production is shown by a yellow colour.

Reduction of the indicator is not seen.

Ulrich milk: the colour changes may be interpreted as follows:

bluish grey — unchanged,

pale yellow green to yellowish orange — acid,

pale bluish purple to reddish purple — alkaline,

bluish green — oxidation,

white — reduction,

acidity or alkalinity are best observed in the lower (reduced) portion of the medium.

Controls: Acid — *Escherichia coli*

Alkaline — *Alcaligenes faecalis*

Stormy fermentation — *Clostridium welchii*

No change — *Proteus vulgaris*

MR (methyl red) and V–P (Voges-Proskauer) reactions

Methyl red

Inoculate MR and V–P medium (p. 111) and incubate at 30° C for 5 days; some workers prefer 37° C for 2 days. Add 2 drops methyl red soln. (p. 147), shake and examine; keep for the Voges-Proskauer test.

Red colour = +, orange colour = ±, yellow colour = −.

Controls: Positive — *Escherichia coli*

Negative — *Enterobacter cloacae*

Voges-Proskauer

Barritt's (1936) method. After completion of the methyl red test, add 0·6 ml α-naphthol soln. (p. 148) and 0·2 ml 40% KOH aq. soln.; shake, slope the tube, and examine after 15 min and 1 h. A positive reaction is indicated by a strong red colour.

O'Meara's (1931) method. After completion of the methyl red test add 2 drops (about 0·05 ml) of creatine soln. (p. 146) and 1 ml 40% KOH aq. soln.; shake, slope, and examine after 1 and 4 h. A positive reaction is indicated by an eosin-pink colour.

Controls: Positive — *Enterobacter cloacae*

Negative — *Escherichia coli*

Niacin test

Method 1 (Marks & Trollope, 1960). Heavily inoculate the surface of Dorset egg medium (p. 102) contained in a bijou bottle; add 0·4 ml sterile water and incubate with the cap loose for 2 weeks at 37° C; a moist atmosphere must be maintained. Transfer the aqueous extract to a test tube and add 0·6 ml 4 % ethanolic aniline followed by 0·6 ml 10 % aq. cyanogen bromide (p. 148). The presence of niacin is indicated by a yellow colour.

Method 2 (Gutiérrez-Vázquez, 1960; modified by Collins & Massey, 1963). Add 0·3 ml sterile water to a 30-day culture on Lowenstein-Jensen medium; autoclave at 115° C for 15 min. When cool, remove 2 drops of liquor and place on a white tile. Add 2 drops 1·5 % ethanolic *o*-tolidine and 2 drops 10 % aq. cyanogen bromide. A positive result is shown by a pink to orange colour; negatives remain blue-grey.

Note. Cyanogen bromide is toxic; the test must be carried out in a fume cupboard and, after completion, alkali should be added to decompose the reagent before sterilization.

Nitrate reduction

Inoculate nitrate broth (p. 121) and incubate for up to 5 days. Note any gas formation in the Durham's tube. Add 1 ml nitrite reagent A followed by 1 ml reagent B (p. 148). Red colour indicates presence of nitrite.

To tubes not showing a red colour add powdered zinc (up to 5 mg/ml of culture) and allow to stand. Red colour = nitrate present in the medium (i.e. not reduced by the organism). Absence of red colour = nitrate absent in the medium (i.e. reduced by the organism to nitrite, which in turn was reduced).

Note. Incubation for 5 days is unnecessary with many organisms and Daubner (1962) reported that with the exception of two *Erwinia* spp., all members of the Enterobacteriaceae reduced nitrate to nitrite in 8 h; it is convenient to test a sample of the inoculated medium daily and re-incubate if nitrate has not been reduced.

Controls: Reduced — *Escherichia coli*
　　　　　Not reduced — *Acinetobacter anitratus*

Nitrite reduction

Inoculate nitrite broth (p. 122) and incubate for 7–14 days. Add nitrite reagents (p. 148) as for the nitrate reduction test.

Red colour = nitrite present. Absence of red colour = nitrite absent, i.e. reduced by the organism.

Controls: Reduced — *Escherichia coli*
　　　　　Not reduced — *Acinetobacter anitratus*

ONPG test (Lowe, 1962)

Inoculate a tube of ONPG broth (p. 122) and incubate for 24 h. β-galactosidase activity is indicated by the appearance of a yellow colour due to *o*-nitrophenol.

Controls: Positive—*Escherichia coli*

Negative—*Proteus morganii*

Phenylalanine deamination

Method 1 (Shaw & Clarke, 1955). After recording the result of the malonate test (p. 159), acidify with 0·1–0·2 ml 0·1 N-HCl and add 0·2 ml 10 % FeCl$_3$ aq. soln.; shake and observe any colour change. Observe immediately; a positive reaction is denoted by a green colour which quickly fades.

Method 2 (Report, 1958). Inoculate heavily a phenylalanine agar slope (p. 122). Incubate overnight and run 0·2 ml 10 % FeCl$_3$ aq. soln. over the growth. A positive result is indicated by the appearance of a green colour on the slope and in the free liquid at the base.

Controls: Positive—*Proteus vulgaris*

Negative—*Klebsiella aerogenes*

Phosphatase test

Lightly inoculate phenolphthalein phosphate agar (p. 122) to obtain discrete colonies, and incubate for 18 h. Place 0·1 ml ammonia soln. (sp. gr. 0·880) in the lid of the Petri dish and invert the medium above it. Alternatively the medium may be exposed to ammonia vapour by holding above an open bottle. Free phenolphthalein liberated by phosphatase reacts with the ammonia and phosphatase-positive colonies become bright pink.

Note. Baird-Parker (1963) recommends incubation of cultures at 30° C for 3–5 days before applying the test, and thereby obtains more positives than in cultures incubated at 37° C for 18 h.

Controls: Positive—*Staphylococcus aureus*

Negative—*S. epidermidis*

Pigment production

For *Chromobacterium* spp. use mannitol yeast-extract agar (p. 107). Incubate at 22° or 30° C.

In *Mycobacterium* spp. the production of pigment and the influence of light are important characters in the classification of so-called atypical or anonymous mycobacteria. For incubation in continuous light, Marks & Richards (1962) recommend that a 37° C incubator be fitted with a 25 watt lamp; cultures on Lowenstein-Jensen slopes (p. 118) should be placed at a distance of 30–60 cm from the lamp.

For *Pseudomonas* spp. use King, Ward & Raney media (p. 107). Incubate medium A at 37° C for 24–96 h and medium B at 37° C for 24 h followed by 22° C (or room temperature) for 72 h.

For *Serratia marcescens* use nutrient agar, mannitol yeast-extract agar or King, Ward & Raney medium A at 22° or 30° C.

Note. Non-pigmented strains are not uncommon and a suitable medium for inducing pigment production by such organisms has not yet been evolved.

Staphylococci and micrococci produce pigment best in diffuse daylight.

Starch hydrolysis

Inoculate starch agar (p. 111) and incubate plates at 30° C for 5 days.

Method 1. Flood the plate with Lugol's iodine solution (p. 139); the medium turns blue where starch has not been hydrolyzed, while hydrolysis is indicated by clear colourless zones.

Method 2 (Kellerman & McBeth, 1912). Flood the plate with 95 % ethanol; milkywhite areas indicate unhydrolyzed starch, whereas hydrolysis is indicated by clear zones. This reaction is not instantaneous and is best observed 30 min after addition of the ethanol.

Note. Some strains of *Bacillus* spp. produce only restricted zones of hydrolysis that may not be obvious until the bacterial growth has been scraped away.

Controls: Positive — *Bacillus subtilis*

Negative — *Escherichia coli*

Streptococcal grouping

Preparation of the extract

1. Acid extraction (modified from Lancefield, 1933). Mix the growth from a quarter of a blood agar plate or the centrifuged deposit from 10 ml of a culture in Todd-Hewitt broth (p. 124) with 0·4 ml 0·2 N-HCl and place in a boiling water bath for 10 min. Cool and neutralize the supernatant with 0·2 N-NaOH, using phenol red as the indicator. Centrifuge and use the supernatant.

2. Formamide extraction (Fuller, 1938). Mix the growth from a quarter of a blood agar plate or the centrifuged deposit from 5 ml of a culture in Todd-Hewitt broth with 0·1 ml formamide and heat in an oil bath at 160° C for 15 min or until the growth is almost completely dissolved. Add 0·25 ml 95 % ethanol containing 0·5 % HCl, shake and centrifuge. Discard the precipitate and add 0·5 ml acetone to the supernatant. Shake, centrifuge, and discard the supernatant. Dissolve the precipitate in 0·4 ml saline, and neutralize with 0·2 N-NaOH using phenol red as the indicator.

3. Enzymic extraction (Maxted, 1948). Suspend a loopful of growth from a blood

agar plate in 0·25 ml enzyme solution (p. 147) and heat in a water bath at 50° C until clear (about 1½ h).

The test method

Prepare 'grouping pipettes' from 5 mm dia. glass tubing by drawing out one end into a capillary. Cut to a total length of about 3 cm and stand vertically by placing the capillary end in a block of Plasticine (modelling clay). Place a drop of antiserum in the pipette and layer the extract on top. The formation of a precipitate at the interface of the two layers within 2–3 min indicates a positive reaction.

Notes. Streptococcal groups A–H and K–S have been recognized and the grouping test should be made against all available group antisera. In Lancefield's acid extraction, some strains are better extracted with 0·07 N-HCl, and others, particularly group B strains, produce better extracts at 50° C for 2 h (Williams, 1958).

Cross-reaction may occur when the extract prepared by the formamide method is too alkaline. This method tends to destroy the group O antigens.

Maxted's enzyme method is suitable for streptococci of groups A, C and G but strains of other groups (especially D) are less easily lysed by the enzyme.

Group D strains do not always give good reactions and, when suspected, should be grown in broth containing 0·5 % glucose.

Tellurite tolerance

Inoculate blood tellurite agar plates (p. 105) and incubate at 37° C for 24 h. Tellurite-resistant organisms show a heavy growth of jet-black colonies; tellurite-sensitive organisms fail to grow or show a very light growth, the colonies being visible only with a hand lens.

Controls: Positive—*Streptococcus faecalis*
Negative—*S. agalactiae*

Temperature range for growth

The general principle of this type of test is that a suitable medium is lightly inoculated with the organism under test and incubated at different temperatures. For temperatures above 37° C, a thermostatically controlled (±0·5° C) water bath is preferable to an incubator.

With aerobic spore-forming bacilli, mycobacteria, and actinomycetes a solid medium (as a slope) is preferable; with other organisms liquid media are used.

For streptococci, Abd-el-Malek & Gibson (1948a) recommend litmus milk; for organisms showing little activity in plain milk they add 0·25 % each of glucose and yeast extract.

At 22° C and above examine cultures for growth daily for up to 7 days; at lower temperatures after 7 and 14 days. The exact length of incubation will obviously depend upon the normal growth rate of the organism. The ability of an organism to grow at a particular temperature should be confirmed by growth at that temperature after subculture.

Temperature tolerance

60° C for 30 min (streptococci and similar organisms). Place 1 ml of a 24-hour broth or serum broth culture in a small test tube, and place in a water bath at 60° C for 30 min. Cool under a cold tap and incubate at 37° C for 24 h. Subculture to a serum agar slope and incubate for 24 h. Examine for growth which indicates the ability of the organism to survive the conditions.

60° C for 4 h and 50° C for 8 h (mycobacteria and nocardias). Inoculate duplicate tubes of suitable solid media. Place one of the pair in a water bath at the required temperature and after the requisite time cool quickly. Incubate both tubes at 30° C for up to 1 month and examine periodically for growth.

Urease activity

Method 1. Inoculate heavily a slope of Christensen's urea medium (p. 125); examine after 4 h and daily for 5 days.

Method 2. Inoculate fairly heavily a tube of SSR urea medium (p. 125); examine daily for 7 days.

Red colour = urea hydrolyzed.

Controls: Positive — *Proteus vulgaris*
              Negative — *Escherichia coli*

Voges-Proskauer (V–P) reaction: see under MR and V–P reactions (p. 160).

'X' and 'V' requirements

Method 1. Inoculate a blood agar plate and a nutrient agar plate with the organism and spot inoculate a strain of *Staphylococcus aureus* on each plate. Observe each plate for growth and for 'satellitism'.

Growth on blood agar plate only	—requires X factor
Growth shows 'satellitism' on blood agar	—requires X and V factors
Shows 'satellitism' on both media	—requires V factor
Growth on both media but not showing 'satellitism'	—neither X nor V required.

Method 2. Inoculate a nutrient agar plate and lay an X-factor and a V-factor disk (p. 149) on the surface at a distance of about 2 cm from each other. Examine for growth in the vicinity of one or both disks.

APPENDIX E

MICROMETHODS

Micromethods suitable for characterization tests are given; for a more complete list see Table 2 (p. 38). Reagents used in the tests are in general those described in Appendix D.

BUFFER SOLUTIONS

McIlvaine's buffer

Solution A: 0·1 M-citric acid ($C_6H_8O_7.H_2O$, mol. wt. = 210·15)

Solution B: 0·2 M-disodium phosphate (Na_2HPO_4, mol. wt. = 141·97)

	soln. A	+	soln. B
pH 4·0	61·45 ml		38·55 ml
pH 6·0	36·85 ml		63·15 ml

Phthalate buffer, 0·0125 M, pH 5·0

Solution A: 0·05 M-potassium hydrogen phthalate

$$(C_6H_4(COOH)COOK, \text{ mol. wt.} = 204·23)$$

Solution B: 0·05 N-NaOH (carbonate-free)

	soln. A	+	soln. B
pH 5·0	50 ml		23·85 ml

dilute to 200 ml with distilled water.

In the micromethod for decarboxylases, 5 ml 1 % ethanolic bromcresol purple is added to 200 ml buffer.

Phosphate buffer, 0·025 M

Solution A: 0·025 M-Na_2HPO_4

$(Na_2HPO_4$, mol. wt. = 141·97; $Na_2HPO_4.12H_2O$, mol. wt = 358·16)

Solution B: 0·025 M-KH_2PO_4 (mol. wt. = 136·09)

	soln. A	+	soln. B
pH 6·0	12 ml		88 ml
pH 6·8	50 ml		50 ml

For the malonate and urease micromethods, 5 ml 0·1 % ethanolic phenol red is added to 100 ml buffer.

166

Sørensen's citrate buffer, 0·01 M, pH 5·6

Solution A: 0·1 M-citric acid ($C_6H_8O_7.H_2O$, mol. wt. = 210·15)

Solution B: 0·1 M-*tri*-sodium citrate ($Na_3C_6H_5O_7.2H_2O$, mol. wt. = 294·11)

	soln. A	+	soln. B
pH 5·6	13·7 ml		36·3 ml

dilute to 500 ml with distilled water.

All buffer solutions should be stored in well-closed bottles made of alkali-free glass; they should not be used later than 3 months after preparation.

TESTS

Acetylmethylcarbinol production

(i) Fabrizio & Weaver (1951).

Medium: glucose, 0·7 %; Trypticase, 1·0 %; NaCl, 0·5 % in filtered horsemeat infusion; pH 6·8 before sterilization. Dispense medium in 0·5 ml volumes in 75×10 mm tubes, and heat at 37° C before inoculation. Large inoculum from 10–12 h culture on infusion agar. Incubate tubes in 30° C water bath for 90 min.

Test: add 0·15 ml 5 % ethanolic α-naphthol (p. 148); shake 5 sec, then add 0·05 ml 40 % KOH containing 0·3 % creatine; shake again for 5 sec. The duration of shaking is said to be important as longer shaking may give false positives. Return to the water bath and read 30 min later.

(ii) NCTC method (Clarke & Cowan, 1952)

Suspension: grow culture overnight on 1 % glucose agar; wash off with water or saline; spin and resuspend deposit in water or saline so that density corresponds approximately to 10^9 *E. coli*/ml.

Test: using capillary pipettes that deliver 50 drops per ml, pipette into small tubes (we use 65×10 mm).

10 % glucose	1 drop	0·02 ml
0 2 % creatine	1 drop	0·02 ml
0·025 M-phosphate buffer, pH 6·8	2 drops	0·04 ml
Suspension from glucose agar	2 drops	0·04 ml

Incubate in water bath at 37° C. Test after 2 h. Add 3 drops (0·06 ml) 5 % α-naphthol in ethanol (p. 148); shake well to mix; then add 2 drops (0·04 ml) 40 % KOH, shake, leave on bench and after 10 min read result. Red colour = positive.

Carbohydrate breakdown

(i) Hannan & Weaver (1948).

Klebsiella aerogenes is grown in 7·5 % Difco beef heart infusion to remove fermentable sugar; after 40 h growth the medium is filtered and to it are added: proteose peptone no. 3, 1 %; KH_2PO_4, 0·1 %; NaCl, 0·5 %. The pH is adjusted to 7·0, indicator added and the basal medium sterilized by autoclaving. 20 % solutions of carbohydrate are added to give 5 % final concentration.

The volume of medium in each tube is small (0·15 ml) and plugs are not used. A large inoculum in the form of growth in the logarithmic phase from a solid medium is added. After mixing, a layer of 1 % agar (+indicator) is added to cap the culture and any gas produced will collect beneath it. Tubes are incubated in a water bath at 37° C. Controls of medium (less carbohydrate)+inoculum are needed to avoid false positives from transfer of acid with the large inoculum. With a heavy inoculum acid is produced in 10–230 min (depending on the sugar) and gas in 35–240 min.

(ii) McDade & Weaver (1959b) modify the Hannan & Weaver test by doubling the strength of the medium (and using an equal volume of suspension as inoculum), reducing the KH_2PO_4 content to 0·08 %, and adding phenol red 0·0072 %. The pH value of the medium is made 7·5–7·6 instead of 7·0 as in the original formula. This medium is recommended for the Enterobacteriaceae, but a richer medium is advised for streptococci and one without buffer and of lower pH value (7·3) for neisserias. Adequate controls are necessary.

(iii) Kaufman & Weaver's (1960) method for anaerobes.

Grow organisms anaerobically in brain heart broth for 15–18 h, spin and resuspend deposit from 10 ml in 3 ml supernatant; one drop sterile 0·04 % aq. phenol red is added and enough N-NaOH to neutralize. 0·2 ml of this suspension is added to 1 ml cystine trypticase agar (BBL)+0·1 % Na thioglycollate, pH 7·5, +2 % filtered test sugar as a shake culture in 75 × 10 mm tubes. Incubate in a water bath at 37° C and read after 10–12 and again at 24 h.

(iv) Bergquist & Searcy (1962).

0·3 ml phenol red broth + 1 % sugar is put into 50 × 6 mm tubes. A capillary (10 × 1·4 mm), sealed at one end, is inverted in each tube which is then stoppered with plastic foam and autoclaved at 15 lb for 5 min so that the capillary will fill on cooling.

Single colonies are picked and used to inoculate each tube. Tubes are placed in wells in a constant temperature aluminium block at 37° C. Acid can be seen in 10 min and gas after about 30 min.

Citrate utilization

Hargrove & Weaver (1951) found that this test depended on induced enzymes. For quick results the inoculum is grown on: Bacto tryptose, 2 %; Na citrate, 1·5 %; beef extract, 0·5 %; NaCl, 0·5 %; agar, 2 % in distilled water; pH 6·8.

Medium for the test: Na citrate, 0·5 %; KH_2PO_4, 0·25 %; K_2HPO_4, 0·05 %; agar,

0·4 % in distilled water; pH 6·4. Distribute in 1·5 ml volumes in 75 × 10 mm tubes. Heat in 40° C water bath before inoculation.

Test: inoculate surface of test medium with a heavy inoculum from 10–12 h culture on the Tryptose-citrate medium. Replace tubes in 40° C water bath. After 90 min add 1 drop 0·05 % aq. bromthymol blue (blue colour = positive; green = negative). Negatives can be retested after a further 2 h (210 min in all).

Decarboxylases

NCTC method (Shaw & Clarke, 1955).

Suspension: grow culture overnight on nutrient agar or other suitable medium, wash off in water, spin, resuspend in a small volume of water so that the density is at least equal to 10^9 E. coli/ml.

Test: 0·03 M-amino acid (pH 5·0)	0·04 ml
0·0125 M-phthalate buffer,	
pH 5·0 + bromcresol purple	0·04 ml
Suspension	0·04 ml

Place tubes in 37° C water bath. When decarboxylation takes place a colour change is seen. Readings are taken after 2, 4, and 24 h. Each set of tests should include a suspension control without amino acid; when this control is alkaline (blue) buffer is added to all tubes until the control becomes yellow.

This method is not suitable for decarboxylation of glutamic acid.

Gelatin hydrolysis

(i) Greene & Larks (1955) adapted Kohn's (1953) gelatin disks to a micromethod, with a consequent increase in speed. Formalized gelatin disks are washed in water, sterilized by steaming for 30 min and are stored in a refrigerator. Disks are added to 1 ml volumes of 1 % peptone water, placed in a 37° C water bath and heavily inoculated with culture from an agar slope. With positive cultures the disks disintegrate in 2–6 h.

(ii) Kaufman & Weaver (1960) recommend a method for anaerobes in which the test for indole is combined with that for hydrolysis of gelatin.

Medium: gelatin, 1 %; agar, 1 %; Na thioglycollate, 0·1 % in distilled water; 1 ml volumes put into 75 × 10 mm tubes.

Inoculum: spin 10 ml 18-hour brain heart broth cultures grown anaerobically; resuspend in 3 ml supernatant. Add 0·2 ml inoculum to solidified medium and cap it with 0·5 ml agar (pH 7·4) containing tryptophan, 0·06 %; Na thioglycollate, 0·1 % in distilled water. Incubate at 37° C (water bath) and test after 24 h.

Test reagent: Kovács' indole reagent (p. 147) made up in butanol, 1 part + Frazier's reagent (p. 146), 3 parts. Mix just before use. Test reagent is taken up in a Pasteur pipette which is plunged through the top layer and sufficient reagent forced into the space between the layers to raise the cap about 5 mm. If, 5 min after the test reagent is added, the upper part of the gelatin-agar column is clear, hydrolysis has occurred; when it is opaque, the test is negative.

(iii) NCTC method (Clarke & Cowan, 1952).

Columns are made by half filling Durham's tubes with melted gelatin agar (gelatin, 0·4 %; agar, 1·0 % in distilled water; add sufficient methylene blue to give a pale blue colour). When the agar has set add 2 drops of suspension (see Decarboxylases, above) to each of two columns. Incubate (air incubator) at 37° C. After 4 h test one tube (the second is tested after 24 h) by adding a few drops of acid mercuric chloride (p. 146). After 30 min on the bench compare with a blank gelatin-agar tube treated in the same way. A positive reaction is shown by a clear zone below the meniscus; a negative shows an opaque zone.

Gluconate

NCTC method (Cowan, 1955b)

Suspensions are made from growth on glucose agar (see Acetylmethylcarbinol (ii), p. 167). The gluconate microtest is a series of tests which exploit the combinations of pH value and duration of incubation found most useful. The test is run in duplicate at pH 4 and pH 6, and the tests for reducing substances are carried out after incubation for 4 and 24 h.

Two gluconate solutions are needed; 1 % gluconic acid is adjusted with N-NaOH or N-KOH to pH 4 and pH 6. The test mixtures consist of gluconate solution, McIlvaine's buffer solution of the same pH value, and suspension. Control tubes of water and suspension are included because of the possibility that the suspension(s) may consist of organisms which will reduce Benedict's reagent.

	Test	Controls
1 % gluconate, pH 4	0·06 ml	—
Water	—	0·06 ml
McIlvaine's buffer, pH 4	0·06 ml	0·06 ml
Suspension	0·04 ml	0·04 ml
1 % gluconate, pH 6	0·06 ml	—
Water	—	0·06 ml
McIlvaine's buffer, pH 6	0·06 ml	0·06 ml
Suspension	0·04 ml	0·04 ml

The mixtures are incubated at 37° C and after 4 h two sets of tubes (one test and one control at pH 4 and another pair at pH 6) are tested by adding 0·1 ml Benedict's reagent (p. 146) to each tube. All four tubes are placed in a water bath at 100° C for 5 min. Reduction of the Benedict's reagent indicates a positive gluconate test.

The other sets of tubes are tested after incubation at 37° C for 24 h by adding the Benedict's reagent. Generally the reaction is stronger at 24 h, but occasionally an organism gives a positive test only at 4 h, hence the need to carry out the test after the different periods of incubation.

Hydrogen sulphide production

(i) Morse & Weaver (1950).

Medium: 2 % Thiopeptone in distilled water, pH 6·8; dispense in 0·8 ml volumes in 75 × 10 mm tubes; heat to 37° C before heavy inoculation by means of a swab from a 6-hour culture on a solid medium. A 5 mm wide strip of lead acetate paper (p. 149) is folded 1 cm from the end and inserted into the mouth of the tube. Incubation at 37° C is continued in a water bath and readings are made after 15, 30, 45 and 60 min. Morse & Weaver say that the method is more sensitive than macrotests and that the 45 min reading gives the best correlation.

(ii) NCTC method (Clarke, 1953*a*).

Suspensions are made from growth on nutrient agar (see Decarboxylases, p. 169).

0·1 % cysteine hydrochloride, pH 7·4	0·04 ml
0·025 M-phosphate buffer, pH 6·8	0·04 ml
Suspension	0·04 ml

Place a small lead acetate paper (p. 149) in mouth of tube and keep it in position by a loose cotton plug. Do not allow paper to touch suspension-reagent mixture. Incubate at 37° C; read at intervals of 15 min for 1 h.

Indole production

(i) Arnold & Weaver (1948).

Medium 1: Tryptone, 1%; beef extract, 0·3%, in distilled water. Medium 2: tryptophan, 0·03 %; peptone 0·1 %; K_2HPO_4, 0·5% in distilled water. Media adjusted to pH 7·4.

Inoculate medium heavily from a culture in the logarithmic phase; incubate in a 37° C water bath. Test by adding 4 drops of Kovács' reagent (p. 147, use *iso*-amyl alcohol as solvent). Medium 2 gives positive results more quickly than medium 1, (but with both media the tests should be complete within 2 h).

(ii) Kaufman & Weaver (1960) combined their method for anaerobes with a test for gelatin hydrolysis (q.v. above). Indole production is shown by the development of a pink colour in the globules of butanol; a pink colour in the aqueous phase does not indicate indole.

(iii) NCTC method (Clarke & Cowan, 1952).

Suspensions are made from growth on nutrient agar (see Decarboxylases, p. 169).

0·1 % tryptophan	0·06 ml
0·025 M-phosphate buffer, pH 6·8	0·04 ml
Suspension	0·04 ml

Incubate in water bath at 37° C and test at 1 h by adding 0·06 ml Kovács' reagent (p. 147, prepared with *iso*-amyl alcohol); shake. Read immediately; red colour indicates indole.

Malonate

NCTC method (Shaw & Clarke, 1955).

Suspensions are made from growth on nutrient agar (see Decarboxylases, p. 169).

1 % Na malonate	0·04 ml
0·025 M-phosphate buffer, pH 6·0	
(phenol red)	0·04 ml
Suspension	0·04 ml

Incubate in water bath at 37° C; read at intervals up to 24 h. Red colour indicates a positive test.

Nitrate reduction

(i) Brough (1950) used small volumes (1 ml in 75 × 10 mm tubes) of medium (0·1 % KNO_3 in nutrient broth) heated at 37° C before inoculation with a heavy suspension and a rapid return to a 37° C water bath. Test after 15 min with 3 drops each of sulphanilic acid and α-naphthylamine reagents (p. 148).

(ii) Bachmann & Weaver (1951).

Medium: peptone, 1 %; beef extract, 0·3 %; KNO_3, 0·1 % in distilled water; sterilize and store in flasks. Dispense in 1·0 ml volumes into clean, non-sterile 75 × 10 mm tubes. Heat tubes in 37° C water bath and then inoculate with two 3 mm loopsful of 6-hour culture (inoculum should not be broken up but allowed to settle). After 15 min add 1 drop each of sulphanilic acid and dimethyl-α-naphthylamine reagents (p. 148). When nitrite is present a pink colour develops in 5 min.

(iii) NCTC method (Clarke & Cowan, 1952).

Suspensions are made from growth on nutrient agar (see Decarboxylases, p. 169).

0·05 % $NaNO_3$	0·04 ml
0·025 M-phosphate buffer, pH 6·8	0·04 ml
Suspension	0·04 ml

Incubate in water bath at 37° C and test after 1 h. Add 0·06 ml nitrite test solution A and 0·06 ml test solution B (dimethyl-α-naphthylamine) (p. 148). Shake and read after

1–2 min. A pink colour is indicative of nitrite. In each series of tests a blank without suspension should be made to exclude the presence of nitrite in the substrate.

Phenylalanine deamination

(i) Henriksen (1950).

Make a heavy suspension of the organism by suspending the growth from one agar slope in 0·5 ml saline. Add 0·2 ml suspension to 0·2 ml 0·2 % DL-phenylalanine in saline. Shake and place the tube in an almost horizontal position in an incubator. After 4 h acidify the mixture by adding 10 % H_2SO_4 using phenol red as indicator. Next add 4–5 drops half-saturated $FeSO_4.(NH_4)_2SO_4.6H_2O$, shake the tube and watch for a green colour (=positive) within a minute; the colour quickly fades.

(ii) NCTC method (Shaw & Clarke, 1955).

Suspensions are made from growth on nutrient agar (see Decarboxylases, p. 169).

0·03 M-phenylalanine	0·04 ml
0·025 M-phosphate buffer, pH 6·8	0·04 ml
Suspension	0·04 ml

Incubate at 37° C in a water bath. Test after 2 h by adding 0·04 ml 2 % ferric chloride; shake. Read a minute later; a green colour indicates the presence of phenylpyruvic acid.

Phosphatase

White & Pickett (1953).

Substrate: dissolve 30 mg phenol-free phenyl disodium phosphate in 100 ml 0·01 M-Sørensen's citrate-NaOH buffer at pH 5·6; (keeps for 3 months at 4° C in a stoppered bottle).

Indicator: dissolve 50 mg 2:6-dibromo-N-chloro-p-quinone imine in 10 ml methanol; (stable for 2 months at 4° C in a dark, stoppered bottle).

Test: pipette 0·5 ml substrate into 100 × 13 mm tube. In this make a heavy suspension (10^{10}/ml) of the organism under test; incubate the tube at 37° C for 4 h. Add 4 drops indicator solution; shake and stand the tube at room temperature for 15 min. Add 0·3 ml n-butanol; shake, stand for 5 min. A purple or blue colour in the butanol layer indicates a positive result.

Urease

(i) Stuart, van Stratum & Rustigian (1945).

Medium for rapid test: to 380 ml distilled water add KH_2PO_4, 364 mg; Na_2HPO_4, 380 mg; urea, 8 g; yeast extract, 40 mg; 0·02 % phenol red, 20 ml. The pH is 6·8. Filter to sterilize.

Test: pipette 1·5 ml volumes into small tubes and inoculate heavily with 3 loopsful of culture from a solid medium. Incubate at 37° C in a water bath. *Proteus* spp. produce red colour in 5–60 min.

(ii) Hormaeche & Munilla (1957).

Test solution: To 100 ml 2 % urea solution add 2 ml 0·04 % cresol red. Distribute in 1 ml volumes into small tubes; sterilization is not necessary when the test is to be made on the same day. Inoculate tubes with 2 loopsful of growth from 24-hour agar culture (old cultures are too alkaline). Place tubes in water bath at 45–50° C for 2 h. Urease-positive cultures produce a violet red colour.

(iii) NCTC method (unpublished).

Suspensions are made from growth on either nutrient or glucose agar; the latter usually give stronger reactions.

2 % urea soln.	0·06 ml
0·025 M-phosphate buffer, pH 6·0	
(phenol red)	0·06 ml
Suspension	0·04 ml

Place in 37° C water bath and observe at intervals of 15 min for the first hour; leave negatives for a final reading at 4 h. Positive tests show a red colour.

This is better than the test given in Clarke & Cowan (1952).

TEST ORGANISMS

Many of the biochemical tests described in this *Manual* are controlled by the use of test organisms that are known to give either positive or negative reactions under the appropriate test conditions. As far as possible we chose species readily available and we have given in Table 9 the catalogue numbers of suitable strains in our own Collection*, and in many cases, in the American Type Culture Collection† (ATCC).

Table 9. *Recommended strains of test organisms*

	NCTC	ATCC
Acinetobacter anitratus	7844	15308
Aeromonas liquefaciens	7810	9071
Alcaligenes faecalis	655	
Bacillus subtilis	3610	6051
Clostridium sporogenes	533	10000
Clostridium welchii	6719	9856
Enterobacter aerogenes	10006	13048
Enterobacter cloacae	10005	13047
Escherichia coli	9001	11775
Klebsiella aerogenes	418	15380
Mycobacterium phlei	8151	
Mycobacterium smegmatis	8159	
Nocardia brasiliensis	10300	
Nocardia caviae	1934	
Proteus morganii	10041	
Proteus vulgaris	4175	13315
Pseudomonas aeruginosa	7244	7700
Salmonella typhi	786	
Salmonella typhimurium	74	13311
Shigella dysenteriae I	4837	13313
Shigella sonnei	8220	
Staphylococcus aureus	8532	12600
Staphylococcus epidermidis	4276	
Streptococcus agalactiae	8181	13813
Streptococcus dysgalactiae	4669	
Streptococcus faecalis	8213	
Streptococcus hominis	8618	7073
Streptococcus pneumoniae	7465	10015
Streptococcus sanguis	7863	10556

Freeze-dried (lyophilized) cultures retain their characters indefinitely and are preferred to ordinary 'stock cultures' on growth media. For laboratories which do not have

* National Collection of Type Cultures, Central Public Health Laboratory, Colindale Avenue, London, N.W. 9.
† American Type Culture Collection, 12301 Parklawn Drive, Rockville, Maryland 20852, U.S.A.

facilities for freeze-drying we recommend the method of drying described by Rhodes (1950), which requires a vacuum pump and phosphorus pentoxide. Some workers still prefer to maintain their cultures in nutrient media and we give a list (Table 10) of suitable media in which the test organisms can be kept, and indicate the frequency of subculture needed to assure survival.

Table 10. *Conditions for maintenance of test organisms*

Genus	Medium	Incubation temp. (°C)	time (h)	Storage °C	Interval between subculture (months)
Acinetobacter	Nutrient agar	37	18	5–25	3
Aeromonas	Nutrient agar	37	18	5–25	3
Alcaligenes	Nutrient agar	37	18	5–25	3
Bacillus	Nutrient agar	30	48	5–25	12
Clostridium	Cooked meat	37	48	5–25	12
Enterobacter	Nutrient agar	37	18	5–25	6
Escherichia	Nutrient agar	37	18	5–25	6
Klebsiella	Nutrient agar	37	18	5–25	3
Mycobacterium	Dorset egg	37	48–72	15–25	6
Nocardia	Dorset egg	37	48–72	15–25	3
Proteus	Nutrient agar	37	18	5–25	3
Pseudomonas	Peptone water agar	30	18	5–25	3
Salmonella	Dorset egg	37	18	5–25	12
Shigella	Nutrient agar	37	18	5–25	6
Staphylococcus	Nutrient agar	37	18	5–25	3
Streptococcus	Cooked meat or	37	18	5–25	3
	Blood broth	37	8	5	1

Cooked meat is an excellent maintenance medium for most organisms including anaerobes. Poorly nutrient are often preferable to richer media, for example shigellas tend to go rough on rich media. Media containing fermentable carbohydrate should be avoided for maintaining cultures, and selective media must never be used for this purpose. Cultures must not be allowed to dry out and tightly-closed screw-capped containers are preferable to waxed or corked tubes.

REFERENCES

AARONSON, S. (1956). A biochemical-taxonomic study of a marine micrococcus, *Gaffkya homari*, and a terrestrial counterpart. *J. gen. Microbiol.* **15**, 478.

ABD-EL-MALEK, Y. & GIBSON, T. (1948*a*). Studies in the bacteriology of milk. I. The streptococci of milk. *J. Dairy Res.* **15**, 233.

ABD-EL-MALEK, Y. & GIBSON, T. (1948*b*). Studies in the bacteriology of milk. II. The staphylococci and micrococci of milk. *J. Dairy Res.* **15**, 249.

ABD-EL-MALEK, Y. & GIBSON, T. (1952). Studies in the bacteriology of milk. III. The corynebacteria of milk. *J. Dairy Res.* **19**, 153.

ALBERT, H. (1921). Modification of stain for diphtheria bacilli. *J. Amer. med. Ass.* **76**, 240.

ALLEN, L. A., PASLEY, S. M. & PIERCE, M. S. F. (1952). Conditions affecting the growth of *Bacterium coli* on bile salts media. Enumeration of this organism in polluted waters. *J. gen. Microbiol.* **7**, 257.

AMIES, C. R. & GARABEDIAN, M. (1963). The bacteriology of human vaginitis. *Canad. J. publ. Hlth*, **54**, 50.

ANDERSON, J. S., HAPPOLD, F. C., McLEOD, J. W. & THOMSON, J. G. (1931). On the existence of two forms of diphtheria bacillus—*B. diphtheriae gravis* and *B. diphtheriae mitis*—and a new medium for their differentiation and for the bacteriological diagnosis of diphtheria. *J. Path. Bact.* **34**, 667.

ANDRADE, E. (1906). Influence of glycerin in differentiating certain bacteria. *J. med. Res.* **14**, 551.

ANDREWES, F. W. (1918). Dysentery bacilli: the differentiation of the true dysentery bacilli from allied species. *Lancet*, i, 560.

ANDREWES, F. W. & INMAN, A. C. (1919). A study of the serological races of the Flexner group of dysentery bacilli. *Spec. Rep. Ser. med. Res. Coun., Lond.* no. 42.

ARNOLD, W. M. JR. & WEAVER, R. H. (1948). Quick microtechniques for the identification of cultures. I. Indole production. *J. Lab. clin. Med.* **33**, 1334.

ASHLEY, D. J. B. & KWANTES, W. (1961). Four cases of human infection with *Achromobacter anitratus*. *J. clin. Path.* **14**, 670.

AUBERT, E. (1950). 'Cold' stain for acid-fast bacteria. *Canad. J. publ. Hlth*, **41**, 31.

AYERS, S. H. & RUPP, P. (1922). Differentiation of hemolytic streptococci from human and bovine sources by the hydrolysis of sodium hippurate. *J. infect. Dis.* **30**, 388.

BABUDIERI, B. (1961). Laboratory diagnosis of leptospirosis. *Bull. World Hlth Org.* **24**, 45.

BACHMANN, B. & WEAVER, R. H. (1951). Rapid microtechnics for identification of cultures. V. Reduction of nitrates to nitrites. *Amer. J. clin. Path.* **21**, 195.

BAILEY, J. H. (1933). A medium for the isolation of *Bacillus pertussis*. *J. infect. Dis.* **52**, 94.

BAIRD-PARKER, A. C. (1962). The occurrence and enumeration, according to a new classification, of micrococci and staphylococci in bacon and on human and pig skin. *J. appl. Bact.* **25**, 352.

BAIRD-PARKER, A. C. (1963). A classification of micrococci and staphylococci based on physiological and biochemical tests. *J. gen. Microbiol.* **30**, 409.

BARAKAT, M. Z. & ABD EL-WAHAB, M. E. (1951). The differentiation of monosaccharides from disaccharides and polysaccharides and identification of fructose. *J. Pharm. Pharmacol.* **3**, 511.

BARBER, M. & KUPER, S. W. A. (1951). Identification of *Staphylococcus pyogenes* by the phosphatase reaction. *J. Path. Bact.* **63**, 65.

BARKSDALE, W. L., LI, K., CUMMINS, C. S. & HARRIS, H. (1957). The mutation of *Corynebacterium pyogenes* to *Corynebacterium haemolyticum*. *J. gen. Microbiol.* **16**, 749.

BARNES, E. M. (1956). Tetrazolium reduction as a means of differentiating *Streptococcus faecalis* from *Streptococcus faecium*. *J. gen. Microbiol.* **14**, 57.

BARRITT, M. M. (1936). The intensification of the Voges-Proskauer reaction by the addition of α-naphthol. *J. Path. Bact.* **42**, 441.

BATTY-SMITH, C. G. (1941). The detection of acetyl-methyl-carbinol in bacterial cultures. A comparative study of the methods of O'Meara and of Barritt. *J. Hyg., Camb.* **41**, 521.

BEERENS, H. (1953–4). Amélioration des techniques d'étude et d'identification des bactéries anaérobies. *Ann. Inst. Pasteur, Lille*, **6**, 36.

BEIJERINCK, M. W. (1900). Schwefelwasserstoffbildung in den Stadtgräben und Aufstellung der Gattung Aërobacter. *Zbl. Bakt., II Abt.* **6**, 193.

BEN HAMIDA, F. & LE MINOR, L. (1956). Une méthode rapide de recherche de la transformation de la L-phényl-alanine en acide phényl-pyruvique. *Ann. Inst. Pasteur*, **90**, 671.

BERGER, U. (1960a). *Neisseria haemolysans* (Thjötta und Böe, 1938): Untersuchungen zur Stellung im System. *Z. Hyg. InfektKr.* **146**, 253.

BERGER, U. (1960b). *Neisseria animalis* nov. spec. *Z. Hyg. InfektKr.* **147**, 158.

BERGER, U. (1961). A proposed new genus of Gram-negative cocci: *Gemella*. *Int. Bull. bact. Nom. Tax.* **11**, 17.

BERGER, U. (1963). Die anspruchslosen Neisserien. *Ergebn. Mikrobiol.* **36**, 97.

Bergey's Manual of Determinative Bacteriology (1923–57). Seven editions: 1, 1923; 2, 1925; 3, 1930; 4, 1934; 5, 1939; 6, 1948; 7, 1957. Baltimore: The Williams and Wilkins Company.

BERGQUIST, L. M. & SEARCY, R. L. (1962). A new micro fermentation technique for rapid detection of acid and gas. *Amer. J. med. Tech.* **28**, 337.

BEVERIDGE, W. I. B. (1934). A study of twelve strains of *Bacillus necrophorus*, with observations on the oxygen intolerance of the organism. *J. Path. Bact.* **38**, 467.

BIBERSTEIN, E. L. & CAMERON, H. S. (1961). The family Brucellaceae in veterinary research. *Annu. Rev. Microbiol.* **15**, 93.

BIBERSTEIN, E. L., GILLS, M. & KNIGHT, H. (1960). Serological types of *Pasteurella haemolytica*. *Cornell Vet.* **50**, 283.

BILLING, E. (1955). Studies on a soap tolerant organism: a new variety of *Bacterium anitratum*. *J. gen. Microbiol.* **13**, 252.

BILLING, E. & LUCKHURST, E. R. (1957). A simplified method for the preparation of egg yolk media. *J. appl. Bact.* **20**, 90.

BORDET, J. & GENGOU, O. (1906). Le microbe de la coqueluche. *Ann. Inst. Pasteur*, **20**, 731.

BORMAN, E. K., STUART, C. A. & WHEELER, K. M. (1944). Taxonomy of the family Enterobacteriaceae. *J. Bact.* **48**, 351.

BÖVRE, K. & TÖNJUM, A. M. (1963). Non-pigmented *Serratia marcescens* var. *kielensis* [sic] as a probable cause of bronchopneumonia. *Acta. path. microbiol. scand.* **58**, 251.

BOWEN, M. K., THIELE, L. C., STEARMAN, B. D. & SCHAUB, I. G. (1957). The optochin sensitivity test: a reliable method for identification of pneumococci. *J. Lab. clin. Med.* **49**, 641.

BOWERS, E. F. & JEFFRIES, L. R. (1955). Optochin in the identification of *Str. pneumoniae*. *J. clin. Path.* **8**, 58.

BOYD, J. S. K. (1938). The antigenic structure of the mannitol-fermenting dysentery bacilli. *J. Hyg., Camb.* **38**, 477.

BRADLEY, S. G. & ANDERSON, D. L. (1958). Comparative study of *Nocardia* and *Streptomyces*. *Bact. Proc.* p. 49.

BRANHAM, S. E. (1930). A new meningococcus-like organism (*Neisseria flavescens*, n. sp.) from epidemic meningitis. *Publ. Hlth Rep., Wash.* **45**, 845.

BRAY, P. T. & CRUICKSHANK, J. C. (1943). Meningitis due to *Diplococcus mucosus*. *Brit. med. J.* i, 601.

BREED, R. S. & BREED, M. E. (1924). The type species of the genus *Serratia*, commonly known as *Bacillus prodigiosus*. *J. Bact.* **9**, 545.

BREWER, J. H. (1940). Clear liquid mediums for the 'aerobic' cultivation of anaerobes. *J. Amer. med. Ass.* **115**, 598.

BRIGGS, M. (1953*a*). An improved medium for lactobacilli. *J. Dairy Res.* **20**, 36.

BRIGGS, M. (1953*b*). The classification of lactobacilli by means of physiological tests. *J. gen. Microbiol.* **9**, 234.

BRINDLE, C. S. & COWAN, S. T. (1951). Flagellation and taxonomy of Whitmore's bacillus. *J. Path. Bact.* **63**, 571.

BRISOU, J. (1953). Essai sur la systématique du genre *Achromobacter*. *Ann. Inst. Pasteur*, **84**, 812.

BRISOU, J. & MORICHAU-BEAUCHANT, R. (1952). Identité biochimique entre certaines souches de *B. anitratum* et *Moraxella lwoffi*. *Ann. Inst. Pasteur*, **82**, 640.

BRISOU, J. & PRÉVOT, A. R. (1954). Étude de systématique bactérienne. X. Révision des espèces réunies dans le genre *Achromobacter*. *Ann. Inst. Pasteur*, **86**, 722.

BRISOU, J., TYSSET, C., RAUTLIN DE LA ROY, Y. DE & JARRIAULT, J. (1962). Intérêt taxinomique des oxydases et cytochromeoxydases microbiennes. *C.R. Soc. Biol., Paris*, **156**, 1904.

British Pharmacopoeia (1963). London: The Pharmaceutical Press.

BRITISH STANDARD (1934). B.S. 541:1934. Determining the Rideal-Walker coefficients of disinfectants. London: British Standards Institution.

BRITISH STANDARD (1952). B.S. 611:1952. Petri dishes. London: British Standards Institution.

BRITISH STANDARD (1954). B.S. 1991: Part 1:1954. Letter symbols, signs and abbreviations. Part 1, General. London: British Standards Institution.

BRITISH STANDARD (1959). B.S. 757:1959. Methods of sampling and testing gelatines. London: British Standards Institution.

BRONFENBRENNER, J. & SCHLESINGER, M. J. (1918). A rapid method for the identification of bacteria fermenting carbohydrates. *Amer. J. publ. Hlth*, **8**, 922.

BROOKS, M. E. & EPPS, H. B. G. (1959). Taxonomic studies of the genus *Clostridium: Clostridium bifermentans* and *C. sordellii*. *J. gen. Microbiol.* **21**, 144.

BROOKS, M. E., STERNE, M. & WARRACK, G. H. (1957). A re-assessment of the criteria used for type differentiation of *Clostridium perfringens*. *J. Path. Bact.* **74**, 185.

BROUGH, F. K. (1950). A rapid microtechnique for the determination of nitrate reduction by microorganisms. *J. Bact.* **60**, 365.

BROWN, A. E. (1961). A simple and efficient method of filtering agar. *J. med. Lab. Tech.* **18**, 109.

BROWN, J. A. (1959). Preparing egg base media for tubercle bacilli in the autoclave. *Amer. J. med. Tech.* **25**, 53.

BROWN, J. H. (1919). The use of blood agar for the study of streptococci. *Monogr. Rockefeller Inst. med. Res.* no. 9.

BROWN, R. L. & EVANS, J. B. (1963). Comparative physiology of antibiotic-resistant strains of *Staphylococcus aureus*. *J. Bact.* **85**, 1409.

BROWN, W. R. L. & RIDOUT, C. W. (1960). An investigation of some sterilization indicators. *Pharm. J.* **184**, 5.

BRYCE, D. M. (1956). The design and interpretation of sterility tests. *J. Pharm. Pharmacol.* **8**, 561.

BUCHANAN, B. B. & PINE, L. (1962). Characterization of a propionic acid producing actinomycete. *Actinomyces propionicus*, sp. nov. *J. gen. Microbiol.* **28**, 305.

BUCHANAN, R. E., COWAN, S. T., WIKÉN, T. & CLARK, W. A. (1958). *International Code of Nomenclature of Bacteria and Viruses*. Ames, Iowa: State College Press. Reprinted with corrections 1959: Iowa State University Press.

BUCHANAN, R. E., ST JOHN-BROOKS, R. & BREED, R. S. (1948). International bacteriological code of nomenclature. *J. Bact.* **55**, 287.

BURDON, K. L. & WENDE, R. D. (1960). On the differentiation of anthrax bacilli from *Bacillus cereus*. *J. infect. Dis.* **107**, 224.

BURMAN, N. P. (1955). The standardization and selection of bile salt and peptone for culture media used in the bacteriological examination of water. *Proc. Soc. Wat. Treat. Exam.* **4**, 10.

BUTTIAUX, R., OSTEUX, R., FRESNOY, R. & MORIAMEZ, J. (1954). Les propriétés biochimiques caractéristiques du genre *Proteus*. Inclusion souhaitable des *Providencia* dans celui-ci. *Ann. Inst. Pasteur*, **87**, 375.

CABRERA, H. A. & DAVIS, G. H. (1961). Epidemic meningitis of the newborn caused by flavobacteria. I. Epidemiology and bacteriology. *Amer. J. Dis. Child.* **101**, 289.

CADNESS-GRAVES, B., WILLIAMS, R., HARPER, G. J. & MILES, A. A. (1943). Slide-test for coagulase-positive staphylococci. *Lancet*, i, 736.

CARPENTER, K. P. (1961). The relationship of the enterobacterium A.12 (Sachs) to *Shigella boydii* 14. *J. gen. Microbiol.* **26**, 535.

CARPENTER, K. P. & LACHOWICZ, K. (1959). The catalase activity of *Shigella flexneri*. *J. Path. Bact.* **77**, 645.

CASTAÑEDA, M. R. (1961). Laboratory diagnosis of brucellosis in man. *Bull. World Hlth Org.* **24**, 73.

CASTELLANI, A. & CHALMERS, A. J. (1919). *Manual of tropical medicine*. ed. 3. London: Baillière, Tindall & Cox.

CHAPMAN, G. H. (1946). A single culture medium for selective isolation of plasma-coagulating staphylococci and for improved testing of chromogenesis, plasma coagulation, mannite fermentation, and the Stone reaction. *J. Bact.* **51**, 409.

CHAPMAN, G. H. (1952). A simple method for making multiple tests of a microorganism. *J. Bact.* **63**, 147.

CHICK, H. (1908). An investigation of the laws of disinfection. *J. Hyg., Camb.* **8**, 92.

CHILDS, E. & ALLEN, L. A. (1953). Improved methods for determining the most probable number of *Bacterium coli* and of *Streptococcus faecalis*. *J. Hyg., Camb.* **51**, 468.

CHILTON, M. L. & FULTON, M. (1946). A presumptive medium for differentiating paracolon from Salmonella organisms. *J. Lab. clin. Med.* **31**, 824.

CHRISTENSEN, W. B. (1946). Urea decomposition as a means of differentiating Proteus and paracolon cultures from each other and from Salmonella and Shigella. *J. Bact.* **52**, 461.

CHRISTENSEN, W. B. (1949). Hydrogen sulfide production and citrate utilization in the differentiation of the enteric pathogens and the coliform bacteria. *Res. Bull., Weld County Hlth Dept.* **1**, 3.

CHRISTIE, R. & KEOGH, E. V. (1940). Physiological and serological characteristics of staphylococci. *J. Path. Bact.* **51**, 189.

CLARK, F. E. (1952). The generic classification of the soil corynebacteria. *Int. Bull. bact. Nom. Tax.* **2**, 45.

CLARK, W. M. & LUBS, H. A. (1915). The differentiation of bacteria of the colon-aerogenes family by the use of indicators. *J. infect. Dis.* **17**, 160.

CLARKE, P. H. (1953a). Hydrogen sulphide production by bacteria. *J. gen. Microbiol.* **8**, 397.

CLARKE, P. H. (1953b). Growth of streptococci in a glucose phenolphthalein broth. *J. gen. Microbiol.* **9**, 350.

CLARKE, P. H. & COWAN, S. T. (1952). Biochemical methods for bacteriology. *J. gen. Microbiol.* **6**, 187.

COBB, R. W. (1963). Cultural characteristics of some corynebacteria of animal origin, with special reference to *C. bovis* and *C. pyogenes*. *J. med. Lab. Tech.* **20**, 199.

COLBECK, J. C. & PROOM, H. (1944). Use of dried rabbit plasma for the staphylococcus coagulase test. *Brit. med. J.* ii, 471.

COLE, S. W. & ONSLOW, H. (1916). On a substitute for peptone and a standard nutrient medium for bacteriological purposes. *Lancet*, ii, 9.

COLLINS, C. H. (1962). The classification of 'anonymous' acid fast bacilli from human sources. *Tubercle, Lond.* **43**, 292.

COLLINS, C. H. & MASSEY, M. L. (1963). The laboratory diagnosis of mycobacterial infections. In *Progress in medical laboratory technique*—2. edited by F. J. Baker. London: Butterworth & Co.

CONN, H. J. (1936). On the detection of nitrate reduction. *J. Bact.* **31**, 225.

CONN, H. J. (1942). Validity of the genus *Alcaligenes*. *J. Bact.* **44**, 353.

CONN, H. J. (1947). A protest against the misuse of the generic name *Corynebacterium*. *J. Bact.* **54**, 10.

CONN, H. J., DARROW, M. A. & EMMEL, V. M. (1960). *Staining procedures used by the Biological Stain Commission*, ed. 2. Baltimore: The Williams & Wilkins Co.

CONN, H. J. & DIMMICK, I. (1947). Soil bacteria similar in morphology to *Mycobacterium* and *Corynebacterium*. *J. Bact.* **54**, 291.

COOK, A. M. & STEEL, K. J. (1959a). The stability of thioglycollate solutions. Part I. Effects of method of preparation of solutions, pH and temperature upon the oxidation of thioglycollate. *J. Pharm. Pharmacol.* **11**, 216.

COOK, A. M. & STEEL, K. J. (1959b). The stability of thioglycollate solutions. Part II. Miscellaneous factors associated with the oxidation and stability. *J. Pharm. Pharmacol.* **11**, 434.

COOK, G. T. (1948). Urease and other biochemical reactions of the Proteus group. *J. Path. Bact.* **60**, 171.

COOK, G. T. (1950). A plate test for nitrate reduction. *J. clin. Path.* **3**, 359.

COOK, G. T. & JEBB, W. H. H. (1952). Starch-fermenting, gelatin-liquefying corynebacteria and their differentiation from *C. diphtheriae gravis*. *J. clin. Path.* **5**, 161.

COOK, G. T. & KNOX, R. (1949). Bacteriological examination of faeces. *J. Path. Bact.* **61**, 353.

COWAN, S. T. (1938a). Unusual infections following cerebral operations. With a description of *Diplococcus mucosus* (von Lingelsheim). *Lancet*, ii, 1052.

COWAN, S. T. (1938b). The classification of staphylococci by precipitation and biological reactions. *J. Path. Bact.* **46**, 31.

COWAN, S. T. (1939) Classification of staphylococci by slide agglutination. *J. Path. Bact.* **48**, 169.

COWAN, S. T. (1953a). Fermentations: biochemical micromethods for bacteriology. *J. gen. Microbiol.* **8**, 391.

COWAN, S. T. (1953b). Micromethod for the methyl red test. *J. gen. Microbiol.* **9**, 101.

COWAN, S. T. (1955a). Biochemical tests for bacterial characterization. 1. Hippurate test. *Int. Bull. bact. Nom. Tax.* **5**, 97.

COWAN, S. T. (1955b). Biochemical tests for bacterial characterization. 2. Gluconate test. *Int. Bull. bact. Nom. Tax.* **5**, 141.

COWAN, S. T. (1956). 'Ordnung in das Chaos' Migula. *Canad. J. Microbiol.* **2**, 212.

COWAN, S. T. (1962). The microbial species—a macromyth? *Symp. Soc. gen. Microbiol.* **12**, 433.

COWAN, S. T. & STEEL, K. J. (1960). A device for the identification of microorganisms. *Lancet*, i, 1172.

COWAN, S. T. & STEEL, K. J. (1961). Diagnostic tables for the common medical bacteria. *J. Hyg., Camb.* **59**, 357.

COWAN, S. T. & STEEL, K. J. (1964). Comparison of differentiating criteria for staphylococci and micrococci. *J. Bact.* **88**, 804.

COWAN, S. T., STEEL, K. J., SHAW, C. & DUGUID, J. P. (1960). A classification of the Klebsiella group. *J. gen. Microbiol.* **23**, 601.

CRAIGIE, J. (1931). Studies on the serological reactions of the flagella of *B. typhosus*. *J. immunol.* **21**, 417.

CRUICKSHANK, J. C. (1935). A study of the so-called *Bacterium typhi flavum*. *J. Hyg., Camb.* **35**, 354.

CUMMINS, C. S. (1962). Chemical composition and antigenic structure of cell walls of *Corynebacterium, Mycobacterium, Nocardia, Actinomyces* and *Arthrobacter*. *J. gen. Microbiol.* **28**, 35.

CUMMINS, C. S. & HARRIS, H. (1956). The chemical composition of the cell wall in some Gram-positive bacteria and its possible value as a taxonomic character. *J. gen. Microbiol.* **14**, 583.

CUMMINS, C. S. & HARRIS, H. (1958). Studies on the cell-wall composition and taxonomy of Actinomycetales and related groups. *J. gen. Microbiol.* **18**, 173.

DACK, G. M. (1940). Non-sporeforming anaerobic bacteria of medical importance. *Bact. Rev.* **4**, 227.

DACRE, J. C. & SHARPE, M. E. (1956). Catalase production by lactobacilli. *Nature, Lond.* **178**, 700.

DARMADY, E. M., HUGHES, K. E. A. & JONES, J. D. (1958). Thermal death-time of spores in dry heat in relation to sterilization of instruments and syringes. *Lancet*, ii, 766.

DAUBNER, I. (1962). Die Reduktion der Nitrate durch Bakterien der Familie Enterobacteriaceae. *Arch. Hyg., Berl.* **146**, 147.

DAVIS, G. H. G. (1955). The classification of lactobacilli from the human mouth. *J. gen. Microbiol.* **13**, 481.

DAVIS, G. H. G. (1960). Lactobacilli of the human mouth. *J. appl. Bact.* **22**, 350.

DAVIS, G. H. G. & PARK, R. W. A. (1962). A taxonomic study of certain bacteria currently classified as *Vibrio* species. *J. gen. Microbiol.* **27**, 101.

DAVIS, J. G. (1960). The lactobacilli—I. *Prog. industr. Microbiol.* **2**, 1.

DAVIS, J. G. & ROGERS, H. J. (1939). The effect of sterilization upon sugars. *Zbl. Bakt., II Abt.* **101**, 102.

DAWSON, B., FARNWORTH, E. H., MCLEOD, J. W. & NICHOLSON, D. E. (1951). Observations on the value of Bordet-Gengou medium for the cultivation of *Haemophilus pertussis*. *J. gen. Microbiol.* **5**, 408.

DE, S. N., BHATTACHARYYA, K. & ROYCHANDHURY, P. K. (1954). The haemolytic activities of *Vibrio cholerae* and related vibrios. *J. Path. Bact.* **67**, 117.

DEACON, W. E. (1945). A note on the tribe Mimeae (de Bord). *J. Bact.* **49**, 511.

DE BORD, G. G. (1939). Organisms invalidating the diagnosis of gonorrhea by the smear method. *J. Bact.* **38**, 119.

DE BORD, G. G. (1942). Descriptions of Mimeae Trib. nov. with three genera and three species and two new species of Neisseria from conjunctivitis and vaginitis. *Iowa St. Coll. J. Sci.* **16**, 471.

DE BORD, G. G. (1943). Species of the tribes Mimeae, Neisserieae, and Streptococceae which confuse the diagnosis of gonorrhea by smears. *J. Lab. clin. Med.* **28**, 710.

DEIBEL, R. H., LAKE, D. E. & NIVEN, C. F. JR. (1963). Physiology of the enterococci as related to their taxonomy. *J. Bact.* **86**, 1275.

DEIBEL, R. H. & NIVEN, C. F. JR. (1960). Comparative study of *Gaffkya homari*, *Aerococcus viridans*, tetrad-forming cocci from meat curing brines, and the genus *Pediococcus*. *J. Bact.* **79**, 175.

Difco Manual of dehydrated culture media and reagents for microbiological and clinical laboratory procedures. (1953). ed. 9. Anonymous. Detroit, Michigan: Difco Laboratories Inc.

DOETSCH, R. N. & PELCZAR, M. J. JR. (1948). The Microbacteria. I. Morphological and physiological characteristics. *J. Bact.* **56**, 37.

DONALD, R. (1913). An apparatus for liquid measurement by drops and applications in counting bacteria and other cells and in serology, etc. *Proc. roy. Soc. B*, **86**, 198.

DOUGLAS, H. C. & GUNTER, S. E. (1946). The taxonomic position of *Corynebacterium acnes*. *J. Bact.* **52**, 15.

DOUGLAS, S. R. (1922). A new medium for the isolation of *B. diphtheriae*. *Brit. J. exp. Path.* **3**, 263.

DOWNIE, A. W., STENT, L. & WHITE, S. M. (1931). The bile solubility of pneumococcus, with special reference to the chemical structure of various bile-salts. *Brit. J. exp. Path.* **12**, 1.

13

DREA, W. F. (1942). Growth of small numbers of tubercle bacilli, H 37, in Long's liquid synthetic medium and some interfering factors. *J. Bact.* **44**, 149.

DUGUID, J. P. (1951). The demonstration of bacterial capsules and slime. *J. Path. Bact.* **63**, 673.

DURHAM, H. E. (1898). A simple method for demonstrating the production of gas by bacteria. *Brit. med. J.* i, 1387.

EDDY, B. P. (1960). Cephalotrichous, fermentative Gram-negative bacteria: the genus *Aeromonas*. *J. appl. Bact.* **23**, 216.

EDDY, B. P. (1961). The Voges-Proskauer reaction and its significance: a review. *J. appl. Bact.* **24**, 27.

EDDY, B. P. (1962). Further studies on *Aeromonas*. I. Additional strains and supplementary biochemical tests. *J. appl. Bact.* **25**, 137.

EDDY, B. P. & CARPENTER, K. P. (1964). Further studies on Aeromonas. II. Taxonomy of Aeromonas and C 27 strains. *J. appl. Bact.* **27**, 96.

EDWARDS, P. R. & BRUNER, D. W. (1942). Serological identification of salmonella cultures. *Circ. Ky agric. Exp. Sta.* no. 54.

EDWARDS, P. R. & EWING, W. H (1962) *Identification of Enterobacteriaceae* ed. 2. Minneapolis: Burgess Publishing Company.

EDWARDS, P. R. & KAUFFMANN, F. (1952). A simplification of the Kauffmann-White Schema. *Amer. J. clin. Path.* **22**, 692.

ELEK, S. D. (1948). Rapid identification of Proteus. *J. Path. Bact.* **60**, 183.

ELEK, S. D. & LEVY, E. (1954). The nature of discrepancies between haemolysins in culture filtrates and plate haemolysin patterns of staphylococci. *J. Path. Bact.* **68**, 31.

ELLIOTT, S. D. (1945). A proteolytic enzyme produced by group A streptococci with special reference to its effect on the type-specific M antigen. *J. exp. Med.* **81**, 573.

ELSTON, H. R. (1961). *Kurthia bessonii* isolated from clinical material. *J. Path. Bact.* **81**, 245.

ELTINGE, E. T. (1956). Nitrate reduction in the genus *Chromobacterium*. *Antonie van Leeuwenhoek J. Microbiol. Serol.* **22**, 139.

ELTINGE, E. T. (1957). Status of the genus *Chromobacterium*. *Int. Bull. bact. Nom. Tax.* **7**, 37.

EVANS, J. B. (1948). Studies of staphylococci with special reference to the coagulase-positive types. *J. Bact.* **55**, 793.

EVANS, J. B., BRADFORD, W. L. JR. & NIVEN, C. F. JR. (1955). Comments concerning the taxonomy of the genera *Micrococcus* and *Staphylococcus*. *Int. Bull. bact. Nom. Tax.* **5**, 61.

EVANS, J. B., BUETTNER, L. G. & NIVEN, C. F. JR. (1952). Occurrence of streptococci that give a false-positive coagulase test. *J. Bact.* **64**, 433.

EWING, W. H. (1949a). The relationship of *Bacterium anitratum* and members of the tribe *Mimeae* (de Bord). *J. Bact.* **57**, 659.

EWING, W. H. (1949b). The relationship of *Shigella dispar* to certain coliform bacteria. *J. Bact.* **58**, 497.

EWING, W. H. (1962). The tribe Proteeae: its nomenclature and taxonomy. *Int. Bull. bact. Nom. Tax.* **12**, 93.

EWING, W. H. (1963). An outline of nomenclature for the family Enterobacteriaceae. *Int. Bull. bact. Nom. Tax.* **13**, 95.

EWING, W. H., DAVIS, B. R. & REAVIS, R. W. (1957). Phenylalanine and malonate media and their use in enteric bacteriology. *Publ. Hlth Lab.* **15**, 153.

EWING, W. H., DAVIS, B. R. & REAVIS, R. W. (1959). Studies on the Serratia group. U.S. Dept. Hlth, Educ. Welfare, Communicable Disease Center, Atlanta, Ga.

EWING, W. H., HUGH, R. & JOHNSON, J. G. (1961). Studies on the Aeromonas group. U.S. Dept. Hlth, Educ. Welfare, Communicable Disease Center, Atlanta, Ga.

EWING, W. H. & JOHNSON, J. G. (1960). The differentiation of *Aeromonas* and C 27 cultures from Enterobacteriaceae. *Int. Bull. bact. Nom. Tax.* **10**, 223.

Extra Pharmacopoeia (Martindale). (1955). Vol. II. ed. 23. London: The Pharmaceutical Press.

FABRIZIO, A. & WEAVER, R. H. (1951). Rapid microtechnics for identification of cultures. IV. Acetylmethylcarbinol production. *Amer. J. clin. Path.* **21**, 192.

FALKOW, S. (1958). Activity of lysine decarboxylase as an aid in the identification of Salmonellae and Shigellae. *Amer. J. clin. Path.* **29**, 598.

FEELEY, J. C. & PITTMAN, M. (1963). Studies on the haemolytic activity of El Tor vibrios. *Bull. World Hlth Org.* **28**, 347.

FELTON, E. A., EVANS, J. B. & NIVEN, C. F. JR. (1953). Production of catalase by pediococci. *J. Bact.* **65**, 481.

FERGUSON, W. W. & HENDERSON, N. D. (1947). Description of strain C 27: a motile organism with the major antigen of *Shigella sonnei* phase I. *J. Bact.* **54**, 179.

FILDES, P. (1920). A new medium for the growth of *B. influenzae*. *Brit. J. exp. Path.* **1**, 129.

FLEMING, A. (1909). On the etiology of acne vulgaris, and its treatment by vaccines. *Lancet*, i, 1035.

FLOCH, H. (1953). Étude comparative des genres *Moraxella*, *Achromobacter* et *Alcaligenes*. *Ann. Inst. Pasteur*, **85**, 675.

FLOODGATE, G. D. [printed C.D.] (1962). Some comments on the Adansonian taxonomic method. *Int. Bull. bact. Nom. Tax.* **12**, 171.

FORSDIKE, J. L. (1950). A comparative study of agars from various geographical sources. *J. Pharm. Pharmacol.* **2**, 796.

FOSTER, A. R. & COHN, C. (1945). A method for the rapid preparation of Loffler's and Petroff's media. *J. Bact.* **50**, 561.

FOSTER, W. D. & BRAGG, J. (1962). Biochemical classification of Klebsiella correlated with the severity of the associated disease. *J. clin. Path.* **15**, 478.

FRAZIER, W. C. (1926). A method for the detection of changes in gelatin due to bacteria. *J. infect. Dis.* **39**, 302.

FULLER, A. T. (1938). The formamide method for the extraction of polysaccharides from haemolytic streptococci. *Brit. J. exp. Path.* **19**, 130.

FULLER, A. T. & MAXTED, W. R. (1939). The production of haemolysins and peroxide by haemolytic streptococci in relation to the non-haemolytic variants of group A. *J. Path. Bact.* **49**, 83.

FULTON, M. (1943). The identity of *Bacterium columbensis* Castellani. *J. Bact.* **46**, 79.

FULTON, M., FORNEY, C. E. & LEIFSON, E. (1959). Identification of Serratia occurring in man and animals. *Canad. J. Microbiol.* **5**, 269.

FULTON, M., HALKIAS, D. & YARASHUS, D. A. (1960). Voges-Proskauer test using 1-naphthol purified by steam distillation. *Appl. Microbiol.* **8**, 361.

GABY, W. L. & HADLEY, C. (1957). Practical laboratory test for the identification of *Pseudomonas aeruginosa*. *J. Bact.* **74**, 356.

GAGNON, M., HUNTING, W. M. & ESSELEN, W. B. (1959). New method for catalase determination. *Analyt. Chem.* **31**, 144.

GALTON, M. M., HARDY, A. V. & MITCHELL, R. B. (1950). The public health laboratory diagnosis of enteric infections. *Amer. J. trop. Med.* **30**, 77.

GARDNER, A. D. & VENKATRAMAN, K. V. (1935). The antigens of the cholera group of vibrios. *J. Hyg., Camb.* **35**, 262.

GARVIE, E. I. (1960). The genus *Leuconostoc* and its nomenclature. *J. Dairy Res.* **27**, 283.

GERSHMAN, M. (1961). Use of a tetrazolium salt for an easily discernible KCN reaction. *Canad. J. Microbiol.* **7**, 286.

GIBSON, T. (1944). A study of *Bacillus subtilis* and related organisms. *J. Dairy Res.* **13**, 248.

GIBSON, T. & ABDEL-MALEK, Y. (1945). The formation of carbon dioxide by lactic acid bacteria and *Bacillus licheniformis* and a cultural method of detecting the process. *J. Dairy Res.* **14**, 35.

GILBERT, R. & STEWART, F. C. (1926–7). *Corynebacterium ulcerans:* a pathogenic micro-organism resembling *C. diphtheriae*. *J. Lab. clin. Med.* **12**, 756.

GILLESPIE, E. H. (1943). The routine use of the coagulase test for staphylococci. *Mon. Bull. Emerg. publ. Hlth Lab. Serv.* **2**, 19.

GILLIES, R. R. (1956). An evaluation of two composite media for preliminary identification of Shigella and Salmonella. *J. clin. Path.* **9**, 368.

GIRARD, G. (1953). Plague. *Annu. Rev. Microbiol.* **9**, 253.

GNEZDA, J. (1899). Sur des réactions nouvelles des bases indoliques et des corps albuminoides. *C.R. Acad. Sci., Paris*, **128**, 1584.

GOLDSWORTHY, N. E. & STILL, J. L. (1936). The effect of meat extract and other substances upon pigment production. *J. Path. Bact.* **43**, 555.

GOLDSWORTHY, N. E. & STILL, J. L. (1938). The effect of various meat extracts on pigment production by *B. prodigiosus*. *J. Path. Bact.* **46**, 634.

GOLDSWORTHY, N. E., STILL, J. L. & DUMARESQ, J. A. (1938). Some sources of error in the interpretation of fermentation reactions, with special reference to the effects of serum enzymes. *J. Path. Bact.* **46**, 253.

GORDON, J. & MCLEOD, J. W. (1928). The practical application of the direct oxidase reaction in bacteriology. *J. Path. Bact.* **31**, 185.

GORDON, R. E. & MIHM, J. M. (1957). A comparative study of some strains received as Nocardiae. *J. Bact.* **73**, 15.

GORDON, R. E. & MIHM, J. M. (1959). A comparison of four species of mycobacteria. *J. gen. Microbiol.* **21**, 736.

GORDON, R. E. & MIHM, J. M. (1962*a*). The type species of the genus *Nocardia*. *J. gen. Microbiol.* **27**, 1.

GORDON, R. E. & MIHM, J. M. (1962*b*). Identification of *Nocardia caviae* (Erikson) *nov. comb.* *Ann. N.Y. Acad. Sci.* **98**, 628.

GORDON, R. E. & RYNEARSON, T. K. (1963). Variation in pigmentation by a strain of *Mycobacterium smegmatis*. *Canad. J. Microbiol.* **9**, 737.

GORDON, R. E. & SMITH, M. M. (1953). Rapidly growing, acid fast bacteria. I. Species' descriptions of *Mycobacterium phlei* Lehmann and Neumann and *Mycobacterium smegmatis* (Trevisan) Lehmann and Neumann. *J. Bact.* **66**, 41.

GORDON, R. E. & SMITH, M. M. (1955). Rapidly growing, acid fast bacteria. II. Species' description of *Mycobacterium fortuitum* Cruz. *J. Bact.* **69**, 502.

GRÄSSER, R. (1962). Mikroaerophile Actinomyceten aus Gesäugeaktinomykosen des Schweines. *Zbl. Bakt., I Abt. Orig.* **184**, 478.

GRÄSSER, R. (1963). Untersuchungen über fermentative und serologische Eigenschaften mikroaerophiler Actinomyceten. *Zbl. Bakt., I Abt. Orig.* **188**, 251.

GRATIA, A. (1920). Nature et génèse de l'agent coagulant du Staphylocoque ou 'Staphylocoagulase'. *C.R. Soc. Biol., Paris*, **83**, 584.

GREENE, R. A. & LARKS, G. G. (1955). A quick method for the detection of gelatin liquefying bacteria. *J. Bact.* **69**, 224.

GRIFFITH, L. J. & OSTRANDER, W. E. (1959). A capillary tube method for the determination of the coagulase reaction. *J. Lab. clin. Med.* **53**, 804.

GÜNTHER, H. L. & WHITE, H. R. (1961). The cultural and physiological characters of the pediococci. *J. gen. Microbiol.* **26**, 185.

GURR, E. (1956), *A practical manual of medical and biological staining techniques.* ed. 2. London: Leonard Hill Ltd.

GURR, G. T. (1963). *Biological staining methods.* ed. 7. London: George T. Gurr Ltd.

GUTEKUNST, R. R., DELWICHE, E. A. & SEELEY, H. W. (1957). Catalase activity in *Pediococcus cerevisiae* as related to hydrogen ion activity. *J. Bact.* **74**, 693.

GUTIÉRREZ-VÁZQUEZ, J. M. (1960). Further studies on the spot test for the differentiation of tubercle bacilli of human origin from other mycobacteria. *Amer. Rev. resp. Dis.* **81**, 412.

HABEEB, A. F. S. A. (1960a). A study of bacteriological media. The examination of Proteose-Peptone. *J. Pharm. Pharmacol.* **12**, 119.

HABEEB, A. F. S. A. (1960b). A study of bacteriological media: the examination of peptides in Casamin E. *Canad. J. Microbiol.* **6**, 237.

HABS, H. & SCHUBERT, R. H. W. (1962). Über die biochemischen Merkmale und die taxonomische Stellung von *Pseudomonas shigelloides* (Bader). *Zbl. Bakt., I Abt. Orig.* **186**, 316.

HAJNA, A. A. (1950). A semi-solid medium suitable for both motility and hydrogen sulfide tests. *Publ. Hlth Lab.* **8**, 36.

HAJNA, A. A. & DAMON, S. R. (1934). Differentiation of *Aerobacter aerogenes* and *A. cloacae* on the basis of the hydrolysis of sodium hippurate. *Amer. J. Hyg.* **19**, 545.

HALVORSEN, J. F. (1963). Gliding motility in the organisms *Bacterium anitratum* (B5W), *Moraxella lwoffi* and *Alkaligenes haemolysans*, as compared to *Moraxella nonliquefaciens*. *Acta path. microbiol. scand.* **59**, 200.

HANNAN, J. & WEAVER, R. H. (1948). Quick microtechniques for the identification of cultures. II. Fermentations. *J. Lab. clin. Med.* **33**, 1338.

HARDEN, A. & NORRIS, D. (1912). The bacterial production of acetylmethylcarbinol and 2,3-butylene glycol from various substances. *Proc. roy. Soc. B*, **84**, 492.

HARE, R. & COLEBROOK, L. (1934). The biochemical reactions of haemolytic streptococci from the vagina of febrile and afebrile parturient women. *J. Path. Bact.* **39**, 429.

HARE, R., WILDY, P., BILLETT, F. S. & TWORT, D. N. (1952). The anaerobic cocci: gas formation, fermentation reactions, sensitivity to antibiotics and sulphonamides. Classification. *J. Hyg., Camb.* **50**, 295.

HARGROVE, R. E. & WEAVER, R. H. (1951). Rapid microtechnics for identification of cultures. VI. Citrate utilization. *Amer. J. clin. Path.* **21**, 286.

HARPER, E. M. & CONWAY, N. S. (1948). Clotting of human citrated plasma by Gram-negative organisms. *J. Path. Bact.* **60**, 247.

HARRISON, A. P. JR. & HANSEN, P. A. (1950). A motile lactobacillus from the cecal feces of turkeys. *J. Bact.* **59**, 444.

HARTLEY, P. (1922). The value of Douglas's medium for the production of diphtheria toxin. *J. Path. Bact.* **25**, 479.

HASTINGS, E. G. (1903). Milchagar als Medium zur Demonstration der Erzeugung proteolytischer Enzyme. *Zbl. Bakt., II Abt.* **10**, 384.

HASTINGS, E. G. (1904). The action of various classes of bacteria on casein as shown by milk-agar plates. *Zbl. Bakt., II Abt.* **12**, 590.

HAYNES, W. C. (1951). *Pseudomonas aeruginosa*—its characterization and identification. *J. gen. Microbiol.* **5**, 939.

HAYWARD, N. J. & MILES, A. A. (1943). Inhibition of Proteus in cultures from wounds. *Lancet*, ii, 116.

HEIBERG, B. (1936). The biochemical reactions of vibrios. *J. Hyg., Camb.* **36**, 114.

HENDRY, C. B. (1938). The effect of serum maltase on fermentation reactions with gonococci. *J. Path. Bact.* **46**, 383.

HENRIKSEN, S. D. (1950). A comparison of the phenylpyruvic acid reaction and the urease test in the differentiation of Proteus from other enteric organisms. *J. Bact.* **60**, 225.

HENRIKSEN, S. D. (1952). *Moraxella:* classification and taxonomy. *J. gen. Microbiol.* **6**, 318.

HENRIKSEN, S. D. (1960). *Moraxella.* Some problems of taxonomy and nomenclature. *Int. Bull. bact. Nom. Tax.* **10**, 23.

HENRIKSEN, S. D. (1962). Some Pasteurella strains from the human respiratory tract. A correction and supplement. *Acta path. microbiol. scand.* **55**, 355.

HENRIKSEN, S. D. (1963). Mimeae. The standing in nomenclature of the names of this tribus and of its genera and species. *Int. Bull. bact. Nom. Tax.* **13**, 51.

HENRIKSEN, S. D. & CLOSS, K. (1938). The production of phenylpyruvic acid by bacteria. *Acta path. microbiol. scand.* **15**, 101.

HENRIKSEN, S. D. & GRELLAND, R. (1952). Toxigenicity, serological reactions and relationships of the diphtheria-like corynebacteria. *J. Path. Bact.* **64**, 503.

HENRIKSEN, S. D. & JYSSUM, K. (1960). A new variety of *Pasteurella haemolytica* from the human respiratory tract. *Acta path. microbiol. scand.* **50**, 443.

HILL, L. R. (1959). The Adansonian classification of the staphylococci. *J. gen. Microbiol.* **20**, 277.

HILL, L. R., TURRI, M., GILARDI, E. & SILVESTRI, L. G. (1961). Quantitative methods in the systematics of Actinomycetales. II. *G. Microbiol.* **9**, 56.

HITCHNER, E. R. & SNIESZKO, S. F. (1947). A study of a microorganism causing a bacterial disease of lobsters. *J. Bact.* **54**, 48.

HOBBS, B. C. (1948). A study of the serological type differentiation of *Staphylococcus pyogenes*. *J. Hyg., Camb.* **46**, 222.

HODGKISS, W. (1960). The interpretation of flagella stains. *J. appl. Bact.* **23**, 398.

HOK, T. T. (1962). A simple and rapid cold-staining method for acid-fast bacteria. *Amer. Rev. resp. Dis.* **85**, 753.

HOLMAN, W. L. & GONZALES, F. L. (1923). A test for indol based on the oxalic reaction of Gnezda. *J. Bact.* **8**, 577.

HOOD, A. M. (1961). A growth medium without blood cells for *Pasteurella tularensis*. *J. gen. Microbiol.* **26**, 45.

HORMAECHE, E. & EDWARDS, P. R. (1958). Observations on the genus *Aerobacter* with a description of two species. *Int. Bull. bact. Nom. Tax.* **8**, 111.

HORMAECHE, E. & EDWARDS, P. R. (1960). A proposed genus *Enterobacter*. *Int. Bull. bact. Nom. Tax.* **10**, 71.

HORMAECHE, E. & MUNILLA, M. (1957). Biochemical tests for the differentiation of *Klebsiella* and *Cloaca*. *Int. Bull. bact. Nom. Tax.* **7**, 1.

HOWELL, A., MURPHY, W. C., PAUL, F. & STEPHAN, R. M. (1959). Oral strains of *Actinomyces*. *J. Bact.* **78**, 82.

HOYLE, L. (1941). A tellurite blood-agar medium for the rapid diagnosis of diphtheria. *Lancet*, i, 175.

HOYT, R. E. (1951). Tabletted substrates in the detection of indol and urease production by bacteria. *Amer. J. clin. Path.* **21**, 892.

HOYT, R. E. & PICKETT, M. J. (1957). Use of 'rapid substrate' tablets in the recognition of enteric bacteria. *Amer. J. clin. Path.* **27**, 343.

HUCKER, G. J. (1924a). Studies on the Coccaceae. II. A study of the general characters of the micrococci. *Tech. Bull. N.Y. St. agric. Exp. Sta.* no. 100.

HUCKER, G. J. (1924b). Studies on the Coccaceae. IV. The classification of the genus *Micrococcus* Cohn. *Tech. Bull. N.Y. St. agric. Exp. Sta.* no. 102.

HUCKER, G. J. & CONN, H. J. (1923). Methods of Gram staining. *Tech. Bull. N.Y. St. agric. Exp. Sta.* no. 93.

HUGH, R. (1959). Oxytoca group organisms isolated from the oropharyngeal region. *Canad. J. Microbiol.* **5**, 251.

HUGH, R. & LEIFSON, E. (1953). The taxonomic significance of fermentative versus oxidative metabolism of carbohydrates by various Gram negative bacteria. *J. Bact.* **66**, 24.

HUGH, R. & RYSCHENKOW, E. (1961). *Pseudomonas maltophilia*, an Alcaligenes-like species. *J. gen. Microbiol.* **26**, 123.

IKARI, P. & HUGH, R. (1963). *Pseudomonas alcaligenes* Monias (1928), a polar monotrichous dextrose non-oxidizer. *Bact. Proc.* p. 41.

JAMESON, J. E. & EMBERLEY, N. W. (1956). A substitute for bile salts in culture media. *J. gen. Microbiol.* **15**, 198.

JAWETZ, E. (1950). A pneumotropic pasteurella of laboratory animals. I. Bacteriological and serological characteristics of the organism. *J. infect. Dis.* **86**, 172.

JENNENS, M. G. (1954). The methyl red test in peptone media. *J. gen. Microbiol.* **10**, 121.

JENSEN, H. L. (1952). The coryneform bacteria. *Annu. Rev. Microbiol.* **6**, 77.

JENSEN, K. A. (1932). Reinzüchtung und Typenbestimmung von Tuberkelbazillenstämmen. Eine Vereinfachung der Methoden für die Praxis. *Zbl. Bakt., I Abt. Orig.* **125**, 222.

JONES, D., DEIBEL, R. H. & NIVEN, C. F. JR. (1963). Identity of *Staphylococcus epidermidis*. *J. Bact.* **85**, 62.

Jones, D. M. (1962). A pasteurella-like organism from the human respiratory tract. *J. Path. Bact.* **83**, 143.

Jones, L. M. & Morgan, W. J. B. (1958). A preliminary report on a selective medium for the culture of Brucella, including fastidious types. *Bull. World Hlth Org.* **19**, 200.

Jones, N. R. (1956). A tentative method for the determination of the grade strength of agars. *Analyst*, **81**, 243.

Jordan, E. O. (1890). A report on certain species of bacteria observed in sewage. *Rep. Mass. St. Bd Hlth*, Pt. II, 821.

Kauffmann, F. (1953). On the classification and nomenclature of Enterobacteriaceae. *Riv. Ist. sieroter. ital.* **28**, 485.

Kauffmann, F. (1954). *Enterobacteriaceae.* ed. 2. Copenhagen: Ejnar Munksgaard.

Kauffmann, F. (1959a). On the principles of classification and nomenclature of Enterobacteriaceae. *Int. Bull. bact. Nom. Tax.* **9**, 1.

Kauffmann, F. (1959b). Definition of genera and species of Enterobacteriaceae. Request for an Opinion. *Int. Bull. bact. Nom. Tax.* **9**, 7.

Kauffmann, F. (1963a). Zur Differentialdiagnose der Salmonella-Sub-Genera I, II und III. *Acta path. microbiol. scand.* **58**, 109.

Kauffmann, F. (1963b). On the species-definition. *Int. Bull. bact. Nom. Tax.* **13**, 181.

Kauffmann, F. & Edwards, P. R. (1952). Classification and nomenclature of Enterobacteriaceae. *Int. Bull. bact. Nom. Tax.* **2**, 2.

Kauffmann, F., Edwards, P. R. & Ewing, W. H. (1956). The principles of group differentiation within the Enterobacteriaceae by biochemical methods. *Int. Bull. bact. Nom. Tax.* **6**, 29.

Kaufman, L. & Weaver, R. H. (1960). Rapid methods for the identification of clostridia. *J. Bact.* **79**, 119.

Kellerman, K. F. & McBeth, I. G. (1912). The fermentation of cellulose. *Zbl. Bakt., II Abt.* **34**, 485.

Kelly, A. T. & Fulton, M. (1953). Use of triphenyl tetrazolium in motility test medium. *Amer. J. clin. Path.* **23**, 512.

Kelsey, J. C. (1958). The testing of sterilizers. *Lancet*, i, 306.

Kelsey, J. C. (1961). The testing of sterilizers. 2. Thermophilic spore papers. *J. clin. Path.* **14**, 313.

Khairat, O. (1940). Endocarditis due to a new species of *Haemophilus*. *J. Path. Bact.* **50**, 497.

Kharasch, M. S., Conway, E. A. & Bloom, W. (1936). Some chemical factors influencing growth and pigmentation of certain microörganisms. *J. Bact.* **32**, 533.

King, B. M., Ranck, B. A., Daugherty, F. D. & Rau, C. A. (1963). *Clostridium tertium* septicemia. *New Engl. J. Med.* **269**, 467.

King, E. O. (1959). Studies on a group of previously unclassified bacteria associated with meningitis in infants. *Amer. J. clin. Path.* **31**, 241.

King, E. O. (1962). The laboratory recognition of *Vibrio fetus* and a closely related *Vibrio* isolated from cases of human vibriosis. *Ann. N.Y. Acad. Sci.* **98**, 700.

King, E. O. & Tatum, H. W. (1962). *Actinobacillus actinomycetemcomitans* and *Hemophilus aphrophilus*. *J. infect. Dis.* **111**, 85.

KING, E. O., WARD, M. K. & RANEY, D. E. (1954). Two simple media for the demonstration of pyocyanin and fluorescin. *J. Lab. clin. Med.* **44**, 301.

KLIGLER, I. J. (1917). A simple medium for the differentiation of members of the typhoid-paratyphoid group. *Amer. J. publ. Hlth*, **7**, 1042.

KLIGLER, I. J. (1918). Modifications of culture media used in the isolation and differentiation of typhoid, dysentery, and allied bacilli. *J. exp. Med.* **28**, 319.

KLINGE, K. (1960). Differential techniques and methods of isolation of *Pseudomonas*. *J. appl. Bact.* **23**, 442.

KLUYVER, A. J. & NIEL, C. B. VAN (1936). Prospects for a natural system of classification of bacteria. *Zbl. Bakt., II Abt.* **94**, 369.

KNOX, R. (1949). A screening plate for the rapid identification of faecal organisms. *J. Path. Bact.* **61**, 343.

KOCUR, M. & MARTINEC, T. (1962). Taxonomická studie rodu *Micrococcus*. Folia Fac. Sci. nat., Brně (Biol. 1), 3, no. 3.

KOCUR, M. & MARTINEC, T. (1963). The taxonomic status of *Sporosarcina ureae* (Beijerinck) Orla-Jensen. *Int. Bull. bact. Nom. Tax.* **13**, 201.

KOHN, J. (1953). A preliminary report of a new gelatin liquefaction method. *J. clin. Path.* **6**, 249.

KOHN, J. (1954). A two-tube technique for the identification of organisms of the Enterobacteriaceae group. *J. Path. Bact.* **67**, 286.

KOONTZ, F. B. & FABER, J. E. (1963). A taxonomic study of some Gram-negative, non-fermenting bacteria. *Canad. J. Microbiol.* **9**, 499.

KOSER, S. A. (1923). Utilization of the salts of organic acids by the colon-aerogenes group. *J. Bact.* **8**, 493.

KOVÁCS, N. (1928). Eine vereinfachte Methode zum Nachweis der Indolbildung durch Bakterien. *Z. ImmunForsch.* **55**, 311.

KOVÁCS, N. (1956). Identification of *Pseudomonas pyocyanea* by the oxidase reaction. *Nature, Lond.* **178**, 703.

KOVÁCS, N. (1959). A micro method for detecting indol formation. *J. clin. Path.* **12**, 90.

KRIEBEL, R. M. (1934). A comparative bacteriological study of a group of non-lactose-fermenting bacteria isolated from stools of healthy food-handlers. *J. Bact.* **27**, 357.

KULP, W. L. & WHITE, V. (1932). A modified medium for plating *L. acidophilus*. *Science*, **76**, 17.

LANCEFIELD, R. C. (1933). A serological differentiation of human and other groups of hemolytic streptococci. *J. exp. Med.* **57**, 571.

LANGFORD, G. C. & HANSEN, P. A. (1954). The species of *Erysipelothrix*. *Antonie van Leeuwenhoek J. Microbiol. Serol.* **20**, 87.

LÁNYI, B. & ÁDÁM, M. M. (1960). Agar diffusion test and micromethods for the rapid biochemical differentiation of enteric bacteria. *Acta microbiol. Acad. Sci. hung.* **7**, 313.

LAPAGE, S. P. (1961). *Haemophilus vaginalis* and its role in vaginitis. *Acta path. microbiol. scand.* **52**, 34.

LAUTROP, H. (1956a). A modified Kohn's test for the demonstration of bacterial gelatin liquefaction. *Acta path. microbiol. scand.* **39**, 357.

LAUTROP, H. (1956b). Gelatin-liquefying Klebsiella strains (*Bacterium oxytocum* (Flügge)). *Acta path. microbiol. scand.* **39**, 375.

LAUTROP, H. (1960). Laboratory diagnosis of whooping cough or *Bordetella* infections. *Bull. World Hlth Org.* **23**, 15.

LAUTROP, H. (1961). *Bacterium anitratum* transferred to the genus *Cytophaga*. *Int. Bull. bact. Nom. Tax.* **11**, 107.

LAWRENCE, W. E. (1961). Ovine brucellosis: a review of the disease in sheep manifested by epididymitis and abortion. *Brit. vet. J.* **117**, 435.

LAYBOURN, R. L. (1924). A modification of Albert's stain for the diphtheria bacilli. *J. Amer. med. Ass.* **83**, 121.

LECLERC, H. & BEERENS, H. (1962). Une technique simple de mise en évidence de l'oxydase chez les bactéries. *Ann. Inst. Pasteur, Lille,* **13**, 187.

LEDERBERG, J. (1950). The beta-D-galactosidase of *Escherichia coli*, strain K-12. *J. Bact.* **60**, 381.

LEFFMANN, H. & LA WALL, C. H. (1911). Sulphur dioxide in commercial gelatins. *Analyst,* **36**, 271.

LEGROUX, R. & GENEVRAY, J. (1933). Étude comparative entre le bacille de Whitmore et le bacille pyocyanique. *Ann. Inst. Pasteur,* **51**, 249.

LEIFSON, E. (1933). The fermentation of sodium malonate as a means of differentiating *Aerobacter* and *Escherichia*. *J. Bact.* **26**, 329.

LEIFSON, E. (1935). New culture media based on sodium desoxycholate for the isolation of intestinal pathogens and for the enumeration of colon bacilli in milk and water. *J. Path. Bact.* **40**, 581.

LEIFSON, E. (1951). Staining, shape, and arrangement of bacterial flagella. *J. Bact.* **62**, 377.

LEIFSON, E. (1956). Morphological and physiological characteristics of the genus *Chromobacterium*. *J. Bact.* **71**, 393.

LEIFSON, E. (1960). *Atlas of Bacterial Flagellation*. New York: Academic Press.

LEIFSON, E. (1961). The effect of formaldehyde on the shape of bacterial flagella. *J. gen. Microbiol.* **25**, 131.

LEIFSON, E. (1963). Determination of carbohydrate metabolism of marine bacteria. *J. Bact.* **85**, 1183.

LEISE, J. M., CARTER, C. H., FRIEDLANDER, H. & FREED, S. W. (1959). Criteria for the identification of *Bacillus anthracis*. *J. Bact.* **77**, 655.

LE MINOR, L. & BEN HAMIDA, F. (1962). Avantages de la recherche de la β-galactosidase sur celle de la fermentation du lactose en milieu complexe dans le diagnostic bactériologique, en particulier des Enterobacteriaceae. *Ann. Inst. Pasteur,* **102**, 267.

LE MINOR, L. & PIÉCHAUD, M. (1963). Note technique. Une méthode rapide de recherche de la protéolyse de la gélatine. *Ann. Inst. Pasteur,* **105**, 792.

LEPPER, E. & MARTIN, C. J. (1929). The chemical mechanisms exploited in the use of meat media for the cultivation of anaerobes. *Brit. J. exp. Path.* **10**, 327.

LEVIN, M. (1943). Two agar-less media for the rapid isolation of *Corynebacterium* and *Neisseria*. *J. Bact.* **46**, 233.

LEVINE, M., EPSTEIN, S. S. & VAUGHN, R. H. (1934). Differential reactions in the colon group of bacteria. *Amer. J. publ. Hlth,* **24**, 505.

LEWIS, B. (1961). Phosphatase production by staphylococci—a comparison of two methods. *J. med. Lab. Tech.* **18**, 112.

LEWIS, P. A. & SHOPE, R. E. (1931). Swine influenza. II. A hemophilic bacillus from the respiratory tract of infected swine. *J. exp. Med.* **54**, 361.

LILLIE, R. D. (1928). The Gram stain. I. A quick method for staining Gram-positive organisms in the tissues. *Arch. Path.* **5**, 828.

LINELL, F. & NORDÉN, A. (1952). Hudinfektioner i simhall genom ny art av Mycobacterium. *Nordisk Med.* **47**, 888.

LINGELSHEIM, W. VON. (1906). Die bakteriologischen Arbeiten der Kgl. Hygienischen Station zu Beuthen O.-Schl. während der Genickstarreepidemie in Oberschlesien im Winter 1904/5. *Klin. Jahrb.* **15**, 373.

LINGELSHEIM, W. VON. (1908). Beiträge zur Ätiologie der epidemischen Genickstarre nach den Ergebnessen der letzten Jahre. *Z. Hyg. InfectKr.* **59**, 457.

LINTON, C. S. (1925). A note on the Voges-Proskauer reaction. *J. Amer. Wat. Wks Ass.* **13**, 547.

LOCKHART, W. R. & HARTMAN, P. A. (1963). Formation of monothetic groups in quantitative bacterial taxonomy. *J. Bact.* **85**, 68.

LOEB, L. (1903). The influence of certain bacteria on the coagulation of the blood. *J. med. Res.* **10**, 407.

VAN LOGHEM, J. J. (1944–5). The classification of the plague-bacillus. *Antonie van Leeuwenhoek J. Microbiol. Serol.* **10**, 15.

LOVE, R. M. (1953). A qualitative test for monosaccharides. *Analyst,* **78**, 732.

LOVELL, R. (1946). Studies on *Corynebacterium renale*. I. A systematic study of a number of strains. *J. comp. Path.* **56**, 196.

LOWE, G. H. (1962). The rapid detection of lactose fermentation in paracolon organisms by the demonstration of β-D-galactosidase. *J. med. Lab. Tech.* **19**, 21.

LURIA, S. E. & BURROUS, J. W. (1957). Hybridization between *Escherichia coli* and Shigella. *J. Bact.* **74**, 461.

LWOFF, A. (1939). Revision et démembrement des Hemophilae, le genre *Moraxella nov. gen. Ann. Inst. Pasteur,* **62**, 168.

LWOFF, A. (1958). L'espèce bactérienne. *Ann. Inst. Pasteur,* **94**, 137.

LYSENKO, O. (1961). *Pseudomonas*—An attempt at a general classification. *J. gen. Microbiol.* **25**, 379.

MACCALLUM, P., TOLHURST, J. C., BUCKLE, G. & SISSONS, H. A. (1948). A new mycobacterial infection in man. *J. Path. Bact.* **60**, 93.

MACCONKEY, A. T. (1908). Bile salt media and their advantages in some bacteriological examinations. *J. Hyg., Camb.* **8**, 322.

MCDADE, J. J. & WEAVER, R. H. (1959a). Rapid methods for the detection of gelatin hydrolysis. *J. Bact.* **77**, 60.

MCDADE, J. J. & WEAVER, R. H. (1959b). Rapid methods for the detection of carbohydrate fermentation. *J. Bact.* **77**, 65.

MACDONALD, R. E. & MACDONALD, S. W. (1962). The physiology and natural relationships of the motile, sporeforming sarcinae. *Canad. J. Microbiol.* **8**, 795.

MCFARLAN, A. M. (1941). *Diplococcus mucosus* von Lingelsheim: a description of a strain with comments on the systematic position of the organism. *J. Path. Bact.* **53**, 446.

MACFARLANE, R. G., OAKLEY, C. L. & ANDERSON, C. G. (1941). Haemolysis and the production of opalescence in serum and lecitho-vitellin by the α toxin of *Clostridium welchii*. *J. Path. Bact.* **52**, 99.

McGAUGHEY, C. A. & CHU, H. P. (1948). The egg-yolk reaction of aerobic sporing bacilli. *J. gen. Microbiol.* **2**, 334.

McINTOSH, J. (1920). A litmus solution suitable for bacteriological purposes. *Brit. J. exp. Path.* **1**, 70.

McINTOSH, J., JAMES, W. W. & LAZARUS-BARLOW, P. (1922). An investigation into the aetiology of dental caries. I: The nature of the destructive agent and the production of artificial caries. *Brit. J. exp. Path.* **3**, 138.

MACLEAN, P. D., LIEBOW, A. A. & ROSENBERG, A. A. (1946). A hemolytic corynebacterium resembling *Corynebacterium ovis* and *Corynebacterium pyogenes* in man. *J. Infect. Dis.* **79**, 69.

McLEOD, J. W. (1947). Smear and culture diagnosis in gonorrhoea. *Brit. J. vener. Dis.* **23**, 53.

McLEOD, J. W., COATES, J. C., HAPPOLD, F. C., PRIESTLEY, D. P. & WHEATLEY, B. (1934). Cultivation of the gonococcus as a method in the diagnosis of gonorrhoea with special reference to the oxydase reaction and to the value of air reinforced in its carbon dioxide content. *J. Path. Bact.* **39**, 221.

MADOFF, S. (1959). Isolation and identification of PPLO. *Ann. N.Y. Acad. Sci.* **79**, 383.

MAIR, W. (1917). The preparation of desoxycholic acid. *Biochem. J.* **11**, 11.

MAN, J. C. DE, ROGOSA, M. & SHARPE, M. E. (1960). A medium for the cultivation of lactobacilli. *J. appl. Bact.* **23**, 130.

MANCLARK, C. R. & PICKETT, M. J. (1961). Diagnostic bacteriological screening procedures. *Lab Wld*, **12**, 446.

MARCUS, S. & GREAVES, C. (1950). Danger of false results using screw-capped tubes in diagnostic bacteriology. *J. Lab. clin. Med.* **36**, 134.

MARKS, J. & RICHARDS, M. (1962). Classification of the anonymous mycobacteria as a guide to their significance. *Mon. Bull. Minist. Hlth Lab. Serv.* **21**, 200.

MARKS, J. & TROLLOPE, D. R. (1960). A study of the 'anonymous' mycobacteria. I. Introduction; colonial characteristics and morphology; growth rates; biochemical tests. *Tubercle, Lond.* **41**, 51.

MARMUR, J., FALKOW, S. & MANDEL, M. (1963). New approaches to bacterial taxonomy. *Annu. Rev. Microbiol.* **17**, 329.

MARSHALL, J. H. & KELSEY, J. C. (1960). A standard culture medium for general bacteriology. *J. Hyg., Camb.* **58**, 367.

MARTINEC, T. & KOCUR, M. (1961). Taxonomická studie rodu *Serratia*. *Folia Fac. Sci. nat., Brně* (Biol. 2), **2**, no. 3.

MATTHEWS, P. R. J. & PATTISON, I. H. (1961). The identification of a Haemophilus-like organism associated with pneumonia and pleurisy in the pig. *J. comp. Path.* **71**, 44.

MAXTED, W. R. (1948). Preparation of streptococcal extracts for Lancefield grouping. *Lancet*, ii, 255.

MAXTED, W. R. (1953). The use of bacitracin for identifying group A haemolytic streptococci. *J. clin. Path.* **6**, 224.

MEMORANDUM (1943). Notes on gas gangrene prevention: diagnosis: treatment. *Med. res. Coun. War. Memo.* no. 2.

MERLINO, C. P. (1924). Bartolomeo Bizio's letter to the most eminent priest, Angelo Bellani, concerning the phenomenon of the red-colored polenta. *J. Bact.* **9**, 527.

MESSER, A. I. (1947). Formalin in filter paper. *Mon. Bull. Minist. Hlth Lab. Serv.* **6**, 94.

MIDDLETON, G. & STUCKEY, R. E. (1951). The standardization of the digestion process in the Kjeldahl determination of nitrogen. *J. Pharm. Pharmacol.* **3**, 829.

MILES, A. A. & MISRA, S. S. (1938). The estimation of the bactericidal power of the blood. *J. Hyg., Camb.* **38**, 732.

MITCHELL, P. D. & BURRELL, R. G. (1964). Serology of the *Mima-Herellea* group and the genus *Moraxella*. *J. Bact.* **87**, 900.

MOELLER, H. (1891). Ueber eine neue Methode der Sporenfärbung. *Zbl. Bakt., I Abt. Orig.* **10**, 273.

MOLLARET, H. & LE MINOR, L. (1962). Recherche de la β-galactosidase chez les différentes *Pasteurella* et conséquences quant à leur taxinomie. *Ann. Inst. Pasteur*, **102**, 649.

MØLLER, V. (1954a). Activity determination of amino acid decarboxylases in Enterobacteriaceae. *Acta path. microbiol. scand.* **34**, 102.

MØLLER, V. (1954b). Diagnostic use of the Braun KCN test within the Enterobacteriaceae. *Acta path. microbiol. scand.* **34**, 115.

MØLLER, V. (1954c). Distribution of amino acid decarboxylases in Enterobacteriaceae. *Acta path. microbiol. scand.* **35**, 259.

MØLLER, V. (1955). Simplified tests for some amino acid decarboxylases and for the arginine dihydrolase system. *Acta path. microbiol. scand.* **36**, 158.

DE MOOR, C. E. (1949). Paracholera (El Tor): enteritis choleriformis El Tor van Loghem. *Bull. World Hlth Org.* **2**, 5.

MOORE, H. B. & PICKETT, M. J. (1960). Organisms resembling *Alcaligenes faecalis*. *Canad. J. Microbiol.* **6**, 43.

MOORE, H. F. (1915). The action of ethylhydrocuprein (optochin) on type strains of pneumococci in vitro and in vivo, and on some other microorganisms in vitro. *J. exp. Med.* **22**, 269.

MOORE, W. E. C. & CATO, E. P. (1963). Validity of *Propionibacterium acnes* (Gilchrist) Douglas and Gunter comb. nov. *J. Bact.* **85**, 870.

MORGAN, H. DE R. (1906). Upon the bacteriology of the summer diarrhoea of infants. *Brit. med. J.* i, 908.

MORSE, M. L. & WEAVER, R. H. (1950). Rapid microtechnics for identification of cultures. III. Hydrogen sulfide production. *Amer. J. clin. Path.* **20**, 481.

MOSSELL, D. A. A. (1962). Attempt in classification of catalase-positive staphylococci and micrococci. *J. Bact.* **84**, 1140.

MOUSSA, R. S. (1959). Antigenic formulae for *Clostridium septicum* and *Clostridium chauvoei*. *J. Path. Bact.* **77**, 341.

MUCH, H. (1908). Über eine Vorstufe des Fibrinfermentes in Kulturen von Staphylokokkus aureus. *Biochem. Z.* **14**, 143.

MUDGE, C. S. (1917). The effect of sterilization upon sugars in culture media. *J. Bact.* **2**, 403.

MURRAY, E. G. D. (1918). An attempt at classification of *Bacillus dysenteriae*, based upon an examination of the agglutinating properties of fifty-three strains. *J.R. Army med. Cps*, **31**, 257, 353.

MURRAY, E. G. D., WEBB, R. A. & SWANN, M. B. R. (1926). A disease of rabbits characterized by a large mononuclear leucocytosis, caused by a hitherto undescribed bacillus *Bacterium monocytogenes* (n. sp.). *J. Path. Bact.* **29**, 407.

NAGLER, F. P. O. (1939). Observations on a reaction between the lethal toxin of *Cl. welchii* (type A) and human serum. *Brit. J. exp. Path.* **20**, 473.

NAKAGAWA, A. & KITAHARA, K. (1959). Taxonomic studies on the genus *Pediococcus*. *J. gen. appl. Microbiol.* **5**, 95.

NEWSOM, I. E. & CROSS, F. (1932). Some bipolar organisms found in pneumonia in sheep. *J. Amer. vet. med. Ass.* **80**, 715.

NIVEN, C. F. JR., KIZIUTA, Z. & WHITE, J. C. (1946). Synthesis of a polysaccharide from sucrose by Streptococcus s.b.e. *J. Bact.* **51**, 711.

NIVEN, C. F. JR., SMILEY, K. L. & SHERMAN, J. M. (1941). The production of large amounts of a polysaccharid by *Streptococcus salivarius*. *J. Bact.* **41**, 479.

NIVEN, C. F. JR., SMILEY, K. L. & SHERMAN, J. M. (1942). The hydrolysis of arginine by streptococci. *J. Bact.* **43**, 651.

NYBERG, C. (1934–5). *Bacillus faecalis alcaligenes* Petruschky. *Zbl. Bakt., I Abt. Orig.* **133**, 443.

OAKLEY, C. L. & WARRACK, G. H. (1959). The soluble antigens of *Clostridium oedematiens* type D (*Cl. haemolyticum*). *J. Path. Bact.* **78**, 543.

OAKLEY, C. L., WARRACK, G. H. & CLARKE, P. H. (1947). The toxins of *Clostridium oedematiens* (*Cl. novyi*). *J. gen. Microbiol.* **1**, 91.

OEDING, P. (1952). Serological typing of staphylococci. *Acta path. microbiol. scand.* Suppl. 93, 356.

OEDING, P. (1960). Antigenic properties of *Staphylococcus aureus*. *Bact. Rev.* **24**, 374.

OLSUFIEV, N. G., EMELYANOVA, O. S. & DUNAYEVA, T. N. (1959). Comparative study of strains of *B. tularense* in the old and new world and their taxonomy. *J. Hyg. Epidem., Prague*, **3**, 138.

O'MEARA, R. A. Q. (1931). A simple delicate and rapid method of detecting the formation of acetylmethylcarbinol by bacteria fermenting carbohydrate. *J. Path. Bact.* **34**, 401.

O'MEARA, R. A. Q. & MACSWEEN, J. C. (1936). The failure of staphylococcus to grow from small inocula in routine laboratory media. *J. Path. Bact.* **43**, 373.

O'MEARA, R. A. Q. & MACSWEEN, J. C. (1937). The influence of copper in peptones on the growth of certain pathogens in peptone broth. *J. Path. Bact.* **44**, 225.

OPINION NO. 4 (revised). (1954). Rejection of the generic name *Bacterium*. *Int. Bull. bact. Nom. Tax.* **4**, 141.

OPINION NO. 16. (1958). Conservation of the generic name *Chromobacterium* Bergonzini 1880 and designation of the type species and the neotype culture of the type species. *Int. Bull. bact. Nom. Tax.* **8**, 151.

ORCUTT, M. L. & HOWE, P. E. (1922). Hemolytic action of a staphylococcus due to a fat-splitting enzyme. *J. exp. Med.* **35**, 409.

ORLA-JENSEN, S. (1919). *The lactic acid bacteria.* Copenhagen: Andr. Fred. Høst & Søn.

ORR EWING, J. & TAYLOR, J. (1945). Variations in the fermentative reactions of antigenically identical strains of *Bact. newcastle*. *Mon. Bull. Emerg. publ. Hlth Lab. Serv.* **4**, 130.

ORTALI, V. & SAMARANI, E. (1955). Micrometodi in microbiologia—I. Determinazione della ureasi. *R.C. Ist. sup. Sanit.* **18**, 1301.

PAINE, F. S. (1927). The destruction of acetyl-methyl-carbinol by members of the colon-aerogenes group. *J. Bact.* **13**, 269.

PARK, R. W. A., MUNRO, I. B., MELROSE, D. R. & STEWART, D. L. (1962). Observations on the ability of two biochemical types of *Vibrio fetus* to proliferate in the genital tract of cattle and their importance with respect to infertility. *Brit. vet. J.* **118**, 411.

PARTRIDGE, B. M. & JACKSON, F. L. (1962). Fluorescence of erythrasma. *Lancet*, i, 590.

PAYNE, L. C. (1963). Towards medical automation. *World med. Electron.* **2**, 6.

PEDERSON, C. S. (1949). The genus *Pediococcus*. *Bact. Rev.* **13**, 225.

PEDERSON, C. S. & BREED, R. S. (1928). The fermentation of glucose by organisms of the genus *Serratia*. *J. Bact.* **16**, 163.

PELCZAR, M. J. JR. (1953). *Neisseria caviae* nov spec. *J. Bact.* **65**, 744.

PHILLIPS, J. E. (1960). The characterization of *Actinobacillus lignieresi*. *J. Path. Bact.* **79**, 331.

PHILLIPS, J. E. (1961). The commensal role of *Actinobacillus lignieresi*. *J. Path. Bact.* **82**, 205.

PICKETT, M. J. (1955). Fermentation tests for identification of Brucellae. *Amer. J. med. Tech.* **21**, 166.

PICKETT, M. J. & NELSON, E. L. (1955). Speciation within the genus *Brucella*. IV. Fermentation of carbohydrates. *J. Bact.* **69**, 333.

PICKETT, M. J. & SCOTT, M. L. (1955). A medium for rapid VP tests. *Bact. Proc.* p. 110.

PICKETT, M. J., SCOTT, M. L. & HOYT, R. E. (1955). Tableted mediums for biochemical tests in diagnostic bacteriology. *Amer. J. med. Tech.* **21**, 170.

PICKFORD, G. E. & DORRIS, F. (1934). Micro-methods for the detection of proteases and amylases. *Science* **80**, 317.

PIÉCHAUD, D. & SZTURM-RUBINSTEN, S. (1963). Étude de quelques entérobactéries n'utilisant pas l'acide citrique. *Ann. Inst. Pasteur*, **105**, 460.

PIÉCHAUD, M. (1963). Mobilité chez les *Moraxella*. *Ann. Inst. Pasteur*, **104**, 291.

PINE, L., HOWELL, A. & WATSON, S. J. (1960). Studies of the morphological, physiological, and biochemical characters of *Actinomyces bovis*. *J. gen. Microbiol.* **23**, 403.

PITTMAN, M. & DAVIS, D. J. (1950). Identification of the Koch-Weeks bacillus (*Hemophilus aegyptius*). *J. Bact.* **59**, 413.

PLIMMER, H. G. & PAINE, S. G. (1921). A new method for the staining of bacterial flagella. *J. Path. Bact.* **24**, 286.

POHJA, M. S. & GYLLENBERG, H. G. (1962). Numerical taxonomy of micrococci of fermented meat origin. *J. appl. Bact.* **25**, 341.

POLLITZER, R. (1954). Plague. *Monogr. Ser. Wld Hlth Org.* no. 22.

POLLITZER, R. (1959). Cholera. *Monogr. Ser. Wld Hlth Org.* no. 43.

POLLITZER, R. (1960). A review of recent literature on plague. *Bull. Wld Hlth Org.* **23**, 313.

POLLOCK, M. R. (1948). Unsaturated fatty acids in cotton wool plugs. *Nature, Lond.* **161**, 853.

POLLOCK, M. R., HOWARD, G. A. & BROUGHTON, B. W. (1949). Long-chain unsaturated fatty acids as essential bacterial growth factors. Substances able to replace oleic acid for the growth of *Corynebacterium* 'Q' with a note on a possible method for their microbiological assay. *Biochem. J.* **45**, 417.

POPE, C. G. & SMITH, M. L. (1932). The routine preparation of diphtheria toxin of high value. *J. Path. Bact.* **35**, 573.

POPE, C. G. & STEVENS, M. F. (1939). The determination of amino-nitrogen using a copper method. *Biochem. J.* **33**, 1070.

POPE, H. & SMITH, D. T. (1946). Synthesis of B-complex vitamins by tubercle bacilli when grown on synthetic media. *Amer. Rev. Tuberc.* **54**, 559.

PORTERFIELD, J. S. (1950). Classification of the streptococci of subacute bacterial endocarditis. *J. gen. Microbiol.* **4**, 92.

POWNALL, M. (1935). A motile streptococcus. *Brit. J. exp. Path.* **16**, 155.

PRENTICE, A. W. (1957). *Neisseria flavescens* as a cause of meningitis. *Lancet*, i, 613.

PRESTON, N. W. & MAITLAND, H. B. (1952). The influence of temperature on the motility of *Pasteurella pseudotuberculosis*. *J. gen. Microbiol.* **7**, 117.

PRESTON, N. W. & MORRELL, A. (1962). Reproducible results with the Gram stain. *J. Path. Bact.* **84**, 241.

PRÉVOT, A.-R. (1961). *Traité de Systématique Bactérienne*, vol. 2. Paris: Dunod.

RAMMELL, C. G. (1962). Inhibition by citrate of the growth of coagulase-positive staphylococci. *J. Bact.* **84**, 1123.

RAUSS, K. & VÖRÖS, S. (1959). The biochemical and serological properties of *Proteus morganii*. *Acta microbiol. Acad. Sci. hung.* **6**, 233.

RAUSS, K. F. (1936). The systematic position of Morgan's bacillus. *J. Path. Bact.* **42**, 183.

REED, G. B. & ORR, J. H. (1941). Rapid identification of gas gangrene anaerobes. *War Med., Chicago* **1**, 493.

REED, R. W. (1942). Nitrate, nitrite and indole reactions of gas gangrene anaerobes. *J. Bact.* **44**, 425.

REIMANN, H. A. & KOUCKY, R. W. (1939). Meningitis caused by atypical Gram-negative cocci. *J. Bact.* **37**, 401.

RENTSCH, R. (1963). Zur Diagnostik nicht sporenbildender Anaerobier. *Path. et Microbiol., Basel* **26**, 635.

REPORT (1953). Diphtheria and pertussis vaccination. Report of a conference of heads of laboratories producing diphtheria and pertussis vaccines. *Tech. Rep. World Hlth Org.* no. 61.

REPORT (1956a). *Constituents of bacteriological culture media*. Special report Society for General Microbiology. London: Cambridge University Press.

REPORT (1956b). The nomenclature of coli-aerogenes bacteria. Report of the Coli-aerogenes (1956) Sub-Committee of the Society for Applied Bacteriology. *J. appl. Bact.* **19**, 108.

REPORT (1956c). The bacteriological examination of water supplies. *Rep. publ. Hlth med. Subj., Lond.* no. 71.

REPORT (1958). Report of the Enterobacteriaceae Subcommittee of the Nomenclature Committee of the International Association of Microbiological Societies. *Int. Bull. bact. Nom. Tax.* **8**, 25.

RHODES, M. (1950). Viability of dried bacterial cultures. *J. gen. Microbiol.* **4**, 450.

RHODES, M. E. (1958). The cytology of *Pseudomonas* spp. as revealed by a silver-plating staining method. *J. gen. Microbiol.* **18**, 639.

RHODES, M. E. (1959). The characterization of *Pseudomonas fluorescens*. *J. gen. Microbiol.* **21**, 221.

RIDDLE, J. W., KABLER, P. W., KENNER, B. A., BORDNER, R. H., ROCKWOOD, S. W. & STEVENSON, H. J. R. (1956). Bacterial identification by infrared spectrophotometry. *J. Bact.* **72**, 593.

RIFKIND, D. & COLE, R. M. (1962). Non-beta-hemolytic group M-reacting streptococci of human origin. *J. Bact.* **84**, 163.

ROBERTSON, M. (1916). Notes upon certain anerobes isolated from wounds. *J. Path. Bact.* **20**, 327.

ROBINSON, W. & WOOLLEY, P. B. (1957). Pseudohaemoptysis due to *Chromobacterium prodigiosum. Lancet*, i, 819.

ROCHE, A. & MARQUET, F. (1935). Recherches sur le vieillissement du sérum. *C.R. Soc. Biol., Paris* **119**, 1147.

ROGERS, K. B. & TAYLOR, J. (1961) Laboratory diagnosis of gastro-enteritis due to *Escherichia coli. Bull. World Hlth Org.* **24**, 59.

ROGOSA, M., FRANKLIN, J. G. & PERRY, K. D. (1961). Correlation of the vitamin requirements with cultural and biochemical characters of *Lactobacillus* spp. *J. gen. Microbiol.* **25**, 473.

ROGOSA, M. & SHARPE, M. E. (1959). An approach to the classification of the lactobacilli. *J. appl. Bact.* **22**, 329.

ROGOSA, M. & SHARPE, M. E. (1960). Species differentiation of human vaginal lactobacilli. *J. gen. Microbiol.* **23**, 197.

ROLFE, R. & MESELSON, M. (1959). The relative homogeneity of microbial DNA. *Proc. nat. Acad. Sci., Wash.* **45**, 1039.

ROWATT, E. (1957). The growth of *Bordetella pertussis*: a review. *J. gen. Microbiol.* **17**, 297.

RUCHHOFT, C. C., KALLAS, J. G., CHINN, B. & COULTER, E. W. (1931). Coli-aerogenes differentiation in water analysis. II. The biochemical differential tests and their interpretation. *J. Bact.* **22**, 125.

RUNYON, E. H. (1959). Anonymous mycobacteria in pulmonary disease. *Med. Clin. N. Amer.* **43**, 273.

RUSSELL, F. F. (1911). The isolation of typhoid bacilli from urine and feces with the description of a new double sugar tube medium. *J. med. Res.* **25**, 217.

RUSTIGIAN, R. & STUART, C. A. (1945). The biochemical and serological relationships of the organisms of the genus *Proteus. J. Bact.* **49**, 419.

SAKAZAKI, R. (1961). Studies on the Hafnia group of Enterobacteriaceae. *Jap. J. med. Sci.* **14**, 223.

SARKANY, I., TAPLIN, D. & BLANK, H. (1962). Organism causing erythrasma. *Lancet*, ii, 304.

SCHAEFFER, A. B. & FULTON, M. (1933). A simplified method of staining endospores. *Science* **77**, 194.

SCHAUB, I. G. & HAUBER, F. D. (1948). A biochemical and serological study of a group of identical unidentifiable Gram-negative bacilli from human sources. *J. Bact.* **56**, 379.

SEELIGER, H. (1952–3). Zur Systematik des *Bacterium anitratum* (Schaub und Hauber). *Zbl. Bakt., I Abt. Orig.* **159**, 173.

SEELIGER, H. P. R. (1961). *Listeriosis*. Basel: Karger.

SEGAL, B. (1940). The utilization of acetyl methyl carbinol by *Staphylococcus albus* and *aureus. J. Bact.* **39**, 747.

SHARPE, M. E. (1955). A serological classification of lactobacilli. *J. gen. Microbiol.* **12**, 107.

SHATTOCK, P. M. F. (1949). The streptococci of group D; the serological grouping of *Streptococcus bovis* and observations on serologically refractory group D strains. *J. gen. Microbiol.* **3**, 80.

14

SHAW, C. (1956). Distinction between Salmonella and Arizona by Leifson's sodium malonate medium. *Int. Bull. bact. Nom. Tax.* **6**, 1.

SHAW, C. & CLARKE, P. H. (1955). Biochemical classification of Proteus and Providence cultures. *J. gen. Microbiol.* **13**, 155.

SHAW, C., STITT, J. M. & COWAN, S. T. (1951). Staphylococci and their classification. *J. gen. Microbiol.* **5**, 1010.

SHERRIS, J. C., SHOESMITH, J. G., PARKER, M. T. & BRECKON, D. (1959). Tests for the rapid breakdown of arginine by bacteria: their use in the identification of pseudomonads. *J. gen. Microbiol.* **21**, 389.

SHEWAN, J. M., HOBBS, G. & HODGKISS, W. (1960). A determinative scheme for the identification of certain genera of Gram-negative bacteria, with special reference to the Pseudomonadaceae. *J. appl. Bact.* **23**, 379.

SIMMONS, J. S. (1926). A culture medium for differentiating organisms of typhoid-colon aerogenes groups and for isolation of certain fungi. *J. infect. Dis.* **39**, 209.

SINGER, J. & BAR-CHAY, J. (1954). Biochemical investigation of Providence strains and their relationship to the Proteus group. *J. Hyg., Camb.* **52**, 1.

SINGER, J. & VOLCANI, B. E. (1955). An improved ferric chloride test for differentiating Proteus-Providence group from other Enterobacteriaceae. *J. Bact.* **69**, 303.

SKADHAUGE, K. & PERCH, B. (1959). Studies on the relationship of some alpha-haemolytic streptococci of human origin to the Lancefield group M. *Acta path. microbiol. scand.* **46**, 239.

SKERMAN, V. B. D. (1959). *A guide to the identification of the genera of bacteria.* Baltimore: The Williams and Wilkins Company.

SMITH, D. G. & SHATTOCK, P. M. F. (1962). The serological grouping of *Streptococcus equinus.* *J. gen. Microbiol.* **29**, 731.

SMITH, G. R. (1961). The characters of two types of *Pasteurella haemolytica* associated with different pathological conditions in sheep. *J. Path. Bact.* **81**, 431.

SMITH, H. W. (1953). Modifications of Dubos's media for the cultivation of *Mycobacterium johnei. J. Path. Bact.* **66**, 375.

SMITH, I. W. (1963). The classification of 'Bacterium salmonicida'. *J. gen. Microbiol.* **33**, 263.

SMITH, L. DS. (1955). *Introduction to the pathogenic anaerobes.* Chicago: University Press.

SMITH, L. DS. & KING, E. (1962a). *Clostridium innocuum,* sp. n., a spore-forming anaerobe isolated from human infections. *J. Bact.* **83**, 938.

SMITH, L. DS. & KING, E. O. (1962b). Occurrence of *Clostridium difficile* in infections of man. *J. Bact.* **84**, 65.

SMITH, M. L. (1932). The effect of heat on sugar solutions used for culture media. *Biochem. J.* **26**, 1467.

SMITH, N. R., GIBSON, T., GORDON, R. E. & SNEATH, P. H. A. (1964). Type cultures and suggested neotype cultures of some species in the genus *Bacillus. J. gen. Microbiol.* **34**, 269.

SMITH, N. R., GORDON, R. E. & CLARK, F. E. (1946). Aerobic mesophilic sporeforming bacteria. *U.S. Dep. Agric. Misc. Publ.* no. 559.

SMITH, N. R., GORDON, R. E. & CLARK, F. E. (1952). Aerobic sporeforming bacteria. *U.S. Dep. Agric. Agriculture Monograph no.* 16.

SMITH, R. S. & FREE, A. H. (1962). A simple chemical test for the differentiation of Proteus. *Amer. J. med. Tech.* **28**, 24.

SNEATH, P. H. A. (1956). Cultural and biochemical characteristics of the genus *Chromobacterium*. *J. gen. Microbiol.* **15**, 70.

SNEATH, P. H. A. (1957*a*). Some thoughts on bacterial classification. *J. gen. Microbiol.* **17**, 184.

SNEATH, P. H. A. (1957*b*). The application of computers to taxonomy. *J. gen. Microbiol.* **17**, 201.

SNEATH, P. H. A. (1960). A study of the bacterial genus *Chromobacterium*. *Iowa St. J. Sci.* **34**, 243.

SNEATH, P. H. A. & COWAN, S. T. (1958). An electro-taxonomic survey of bacteria. *J. gen. Microbiol.* **19**, 551.

SNEATH, P. H. A., WHELAN, J. P. F., SINGH, R. B. & EDWARDS, D. (1953). Fatal infection by *Chromobacterium violaceum*. *Lancet*, ii, 276.

SNYDER, M. L. (1954). Paper discs containing entire culture medium for the differentiation of bacteria. *J. Path. Bact.* **67**, 217.

SNYDER, T. L., PENFIELD, R. A., ENGLEY, F. B. JR. & CREASY, J. C. (1946). Cultivation of *Bacterium tularense* in peptone media. *Proc. Soc. exp. Biol., N.Y.* **63**, 26.

SOLTYS, M. A. (1948). Anthrax in a laboratory worker, with observations on the possible source of infection. *J. Path. Bact.* **60**, 253.

SPICER, C. C. (1956). A quick method of identifying Salmonella H antigens. *J. clin. Path.* **9**, 378.

SPRAY, R. S. & JOHNSON, E. J. (1946). The preparation of Loeffler's serum and similar coagulable mediums. *J. Bact.* **52**, 141.

STABLEFORTH, A. W. & JONES, L. M. (1963). Report of the Subcommittee on taxonomy of the genus *Brucella*. *Int. Bull. bact. Nom. Tax.* **13**, 145.

STEEL, K. J. (1958). A note on the assay of some sulphydryl compounds. *J. Pharm. Pharmacol.* **10**, 574.

STEEL, K. J. (1961). The oxidase reaction as a taxonomic tool. *J. gen. Microbiol.* **25**, 297.

STEEL, K. J. (1962*a*). The practice of bacterial identification. *Symp. Soc. gen. Microbiol.* **12**, 405.

STEEL, K. J. (1962*b*). The oxidase activity of staphylococci. *J. appl. Bact.* **25**, 445.

STEEL, K. J. & COWAN, S. T. (1964). Le rattachement de *Bacterium anitratum*, *Moraxella lwoffi*, *Bacillus mallei* et *Haemophilus parapertussis* au genre *Acinetobacter* Brisou et Prévot. *Ann. Inst. Pasteur* **106**, 479.

STEEL, K. J. & FISHER, P. J. (1961). A fallacy of the nitrate reduction test. *Mon. Bull. Minist. Hlth Lab. Serv.* **20**, 63.

STEEL, K. J. & MIDGLEY, J. (1962). Decarboxylase and other reactions of some Gram-negative rods. *J. gen. Microbiol.* **29**, 171.

STEWART, D. J. (1961). A micro-method for performing the phenylalanine test on cultures from multi-carbohydrate media. *Nature, Lond.* **191**, 521.

STOKES, E. J. (1960). *Clinical Bacteriology*. ed. 2. London: Edward Arnold.

STUART, C. A., FORMAL, S. & McGANN, V. (1949). Further studies on B5W, an anaerogenic group in the Enterobacteriaceae. *J. infect. Dis.* **84**, 235.

STUART, C. A., VAN STRATUM, E. & RUSTIGIAN, R. (1945). Further studies on urease production by Proteus and related organisms. *J. Bact.* **49**, 437.

STUART, C. A., WHEELER, K. M. & McGANN, V. (1946). Further studies on one anaerogenic paracolon organism, type 29911. *J. Bact.* **52**, 431.

STUART, R. D. (1959). Transport medium for specimens in public health bacteriology. *Publ. Hlth Rep., Wash.* **74**, 431.

SULKIN, S. E. & WILLETT, J. C. (1940). A triple sugar-ferrous sulfate medium for use in identification of enteric organisms. *J. Lab. clin. Med.* **25**, 649.

SUNDMAN, V., BJÖRKSTEN, K. AF & GYLLENBERG, H. G. (1959). Morphology of the bifid bacteria (organisms previously incorrectly designated *Lactobacillus bifidus*) and some related genera. *J. gen. Microbiol.* **21**, 371.

SWAN, A. (1954). The use of a bile-aesculin medium and of Maxted's technique of Lancefield grouping in the identification of enterococci (group D streptococci). *J. clin. Path.* **7**, 160.

SYMPOSIUM (1962). Society for Applied Bacteriology Symposium on Staphylococci and Micrococci. *J. appl. Bact.* **25**, 309.

SZTURM-RUBINSTEN, S. (1963). Les biotypes de *Shigella sonnei*. *Ann. Inst. Pasteur* **104**, 423.

SZTURM-RUBINSTEN, S. & PIÉCHAUD, D. (1962). Sur l'utilisation du lactose par les germes du groupe *Alkalescens-Dispar*. *Ann. Inst. Pasteur* **103**, 935.

SZTURM-RUBINSTEN, S. & PIÉCHAUD, D. (1963). Observations sur la recherche de la β-galactosidase dans le genre *Shigella*. *Ann. Inst. Pasteur* **104**, 284.

TAYLOR, A. W. (1950). Observations on the isolation of *Mycobacterium johnei* in primary culture. *J. Path. Bact.* **62**, 647.

TAYLOR, C. B. (1945–6). The effect of temperature of incubation on the results of tests for differentiating species of coliform bacteria. *J. Hyg., Camb.* **44**, 109.

TAYLOR, C. B. (1951). The soft-rot bacteria of the coli-aerogenes group. *Proc. Soc. appl. Bact.* **14**, 95.

TAYLOR, C. E. D., LEA, D. J., HEIMER, G. V. & TOMLINSON, A. J. H. (1964). A comparison of a fluorescent antibody technique with a cultural method in the detection of infections with *Shigella sonnei*. *J. clin. Path.* **17**, 225.

TAYLOR, J. (1961). Host specificity and enteropathogenicity of *Escherichia coli*. *J. appl. Bact.* **24**, 316.

THIRST, M. L. (1957a). Hippurate hydrolysis in Klebsiella-Cloaca classification. *J. gen. Microbiol.* **17**, 390.

THIRST, M. L. (1957b). Gelatin liquefaction: a microtest. *J. gen. Microbiol.* **17**, 396.

THJÖTTA, TH. & BÖE, J. (1938). *Neisseria hemolysans*. A hemolytic species of *Neisseria* Trevisan. *Acta path. microbiol. scand.* Suppl. 37, 527.

THOMAS, C. G. A. & HARE, R. (1954). The classification of anaerobic cocci and their isolation in normal human beings and pathological processes. *J. clin. Path.* **7**, 300.

THOMAS, M. (1963). A blue peroxide slide catalase test. *Mon. Bull. Minist. Hlth Lab. Serv.* **22**, 124.

THOMPSON, R. E. M. & KNUDSEN, A. (1958). A reliable fermentation medium for *Neisseria gonorrhoeae*: a comparative study. *J. Path. Bact.* **76**, 501.

THORNLEY, M. J. (1960). The differentiation of *Pseudomonas* from other Gram-negative bacteria on the basis of arginine metabolism. *J. appl. Bact.* **23**, 37.

TITTSLER, R. P. (1938). The fermentation of acetyl-methyl-carbinol by the Escherichia-Aerobacter group and its significance in the Voges-Proskauer reaction. *J. Bact.* **35**, 157.

TITTSLER, R. P. & SANDHOLZER, L. A. (1936). The use of semi-solid agar for the detection of bacterial motility. *J. Bact.* **31**, 575.

TODD, E. W. & HEWITT, L. F. (1932). A new culture medium for the production of antigenic streptococcal haemolysin. *J. Path. Bact.* **35**, 973.

Topley and Wilson's Principles of Bacteriology and Immunity. (1964). ed. 5. Edited by Wilson, G. S. & Miles, A. A. London: Edward Arnold.

TRABULSI, L. R. & EDWARDS, P. R. (1962). The differentiation of *Salmonella pullorum* and *Salmonella gallinarum* by biochemical methods. *Cornell Vet.* **52**, 563.

TRÖGER, R. (1963). Eine Vereinfachung der Kapillar-Methode zur Ermittlung der Gasbildung bei Mikroorganismen. *Zbl. Bakt., II Abt.* **116**, 644.

TULLOCH, W. J. (1939). Observations concerning bacillary food infection in Dundee during the period 1923–38. *J. Hyg., Camb.* **39**, 324.

TURNER, G. C. (1961). Cultivation of *Bordetella pertussis* on agar media. *J. Path. Bact.* **81**, 15.

ULRICH, J. A. (1944). New indicators to replace litmus in milk. *Science* **99**, 352.

VALLÉE, A., THIBAULT, P. & SECOND, L. (1963). Contribution a l'étude d'*A. lignieresii* et d'*A. equuli*. *Ann. Inst. Pasteur* **104**, 108.

VARNEY, P. L. (1961). A new closure for bacteriologic culture tubes. *Amer. J. clin. Path.* **35**, 475.

VAUGHN, R. H., OSBORNE, J. T., WEDDING, G. T., TABACHNICK, J., BEISEL, C. G. & BRAXTON, T. (1950). The utilization of citrate by *Escherichia coli*. *J. Bact.* **60**, 119.

VENDRELY, R. (1958). La notion d'espèce bactérienne à la lumière des découvertes récentes. La notion d'espèce a travers quelques données biochimiques récentes et le cycle L. *Ann. Inst. Pasteur* **94**, 142.

VÉRON, M., THIBAULT, P. & SECOND, L. (1959). *Neisseria mucosa* (*Diplococcus mucosus* Lingelsheim). I. Description bactériologique et étude du pouvoir pathogène. *Ann. Inst. Pasteur* **97**, 497.

VÖRÖS, S., ANGYAL, T., NÉMETH, V. & KONTROHR, T. (1961). The occurrence and significance of phosphatase in enteric bacteria. *Acta microbiol. Acad. Sci. hung.* **8**, 405.

WAHBA, A. H. & TAKLA, V. (1962). A new chemical flocculation test for cholera vibrio identification. *Bull. World Hlth. Org.* **26**, 306.

WEINBERG, M. & SÉGUIN, P. (1915). Flore microbienne de la gangrène gazeuse. *C.R. Soc. Biol., Paris* **78**, 686.

WETMORE, P. & GOCHENOUR, W. S. JR. (1956). Comparative studies of the genus *Malleomyces* and selected *Pseudomonas* species. I. Morphological and cultural characteristics. *J. Bact.* **72**, 79.

WHITE, M. L. & PICKETT, M. J. (1953). A rapid phosphatase test for *Micrococcus pyogenes* var. *aureus* for detection of potentially pathogenic strains. *Amer. J. clin. Path.* **23**, 1181.

WHITE, T. G. & SHUMAN, R. D. (1961). Fermentation reactions of *Erysipelothrix rhusiopathiae*. *J. Bact.* **82**, 595.

WILKINSON, A. E. (1962). Notes on the bacteriological diagnosis of gonorrhoea. *Brit. J. vener. Dis.* **38**, 145.

WILLIAMS, O. B. & CAMPBELL, L. L. JR. (1951). The detection of heterofermentation by lactic acid bacteria. *Food Tech.* **5**, 306.

WILLIAMS, O. B. & MORROW, M. B. (1928). The bacterial destruction of acetyl-methyl-carbinol. *J. Bact.* **16**, 43.

WILLIAMS, R. E. O. (1956). *Streptococcus salivarius* (vel *hominis*) and its relation to Lancefield's group K. *J. Path. Bact.* **72**, 15.

WILLIAMS, R. E. O. (1958). Laboratory diagnosis of streptococcal infections. *Bull. World Hlth Org.* **19**, 153.

WILLIAMS, R. E. O. & HARPER, G. J. (1946). Determination of coagulase and alpha-haemolysin production by staphylococci. *Brit. J. exp. Path.* **27**, 72.

WILLIAMS, R. E. O. & HIRCH, A. (1950). The detection of streptococci in air. *J. Hyg., Camb.* **48**, 504.

WILLIAMS, R. E. O., HIRCH, A. & COWAN, S. T. (1953). *Aerococcus*, a new bacterial genus. *J. gen. Microbiol.* **8**, 475.

WILLIAMS, R. E. O. & RIPPON, J. E. (1952). Bacteriophage typing of *Staphylococcus aureus*. *J. Hyg., Camb.* **50**, 320.

WILLIS, A. T. (1960a). *Anaerobic bacteriology in clinical medicine.* London: Butterworth & Co.

WILLIS, A. T. (1960b). The lipolytic activity of some clostridia. *J. Path. Bact.* **80**, 379.

WILLIS, A. T. & GOWLAND, G. (1962). Some observations on the mechanism of the Nagler reaction. *J. Path. Bact.* **83**, 219.

WILSON, G. S. & ATKINSON, J. D. (1945). Typing of staphylococci by the bacteriophage method. *Lancet*, i, 647.

WILSON, G. S. & SMITH, M. M. (1928). Observations on the Gram-negative cocci of the naso-pharynx, with a description of *Neisseria pharyngis*. *J. Path. Bact.* **31**, 597.

WILSON, W. J. (1934). A blood agar tellurite arsenite selective medium for *B. diphtheriae*. *J. Path. Bact.* **38**, 114.

WOOD, M. (1959). The clotting of rabbit plasma by group D streptococci. *J. gen. Microbiol.* **21**, 385.

WRIGHT, H. D. (1933). The importance of adequate reduction of peptone in the preparation of media for the pneumococcus and other organisms. *J. Path. Bact.* **37**, 257.

WRIGHT, H. D. (1934a). A substance in cotton-wool inhibitory to the growth of the pneumococcus. *J. Path. Bact.* **38**, 499.

WRIGHT, H. D. (1934b). The preparation of nutrient agar with special reference to pneumococci, streptococci and other Gram-positive organisms. *J. Path. Bact.* **39**, 359.

ZINNEMANN, K. (1960). *Haemophilus influenzae* and its pathogenicity. *Ergebn. Mikrobiol.* **33**, 307.

ZINNEMAN, K. & TURNER, G. C. (1962). Taxonomy of *Haemophilus vaginalis*. *Nature, Lond.* **195**, 203.

ZINNEMANN, K. & TURNER, G. C. (1963). The taxonomic position of '*Haemophilus vaginalis*' [*Corynebacterium vaginale*]. *J. Path. Bact.* **85**, 213.

ZOBELL, C. E. (1932). Factors influencing the reduction of nitrates and nitrites by bacteria in semisolid media. *J. Bact.* **24**, 273.

ZOBELL, C. E. & FELTHAM, C. B. (1934). A comparison of lead, bismuth, and iron as detectors of hydrogen sulphide produced by bacteria. *J. Bact.* **28**, 169.

INDEX

abbreviations used, x
aberrant forms, 9
acetoin, 32. *See also* V–P test
acetone-iodine decolorizer, 137
acetylmethlycarbinol, 32, 167. *See also* V–P test
Achromobacter, 4, 61. *See also Acinetobacter*
acid ferric chloride, 146
acid mercuric chloride, 146
acid-alcohol decolorizer, 137
acid-fast bacteria, 51, 52, 59, 60
acid-fast stain, 142
acid-fastness, 20, 21, 52
Acinetobacter, 3, 4, 61, 76, 89, 90, 91
   A. anitratus, 4, 22, 61, 77, 81
   A. lwoffii, 4, 22, 81, 87
   A. mallei, 4, 81
   A. parapertussis, 4, 81
acne, 84
Actinobacillus, 3, 62, 76
   A. actinomycetemcomitans, 85, 86
   A. equuli, 62, 79, 80
   A. lignieresii, 62, 79, 80
   A. mallei. See Acinetobacter mallei
Actinomyces, 3, 45, 55, 91
   A. bovis, 45, 57
   A. israelii, 14, 45, 57, 85
   A. naeslundii, 45, 57
   A. suis, 45
A–D group, 62, 67, 73, 79
Adansonian concept, 2, 17
addresses,
   ATCC, 175
   media makers, commercial, 97
   NCTC, 175
Aerobacter, 6, 68. *See also Enterobacter* and *Klebsiella*
Aerococcus, 3, 44, 45, 55
   A. viridans, 22, 44, 53, 56
Aeromonas, 3, 62, 63, 76
   A. formicans, 63, 80

A. hydrophila, 63
A. liquefaciens, 63, 80
A. salmonicida, 63, 80
A. shigelloides, 63, 80
aesculin, hydrolysis, 24, 151
   media, 112
agar, 10, 98, 128
   concentration, 8, 10, 98
air, ability to grow in, 24
Albert's stain, 137, 144
Alcaligenes, 3, 4, 63, 76, 90
   A. bronchiseptica, 4, 17, 64, 81
   A. faecalis, 17, 64, 72, 81
American Type Culture Collection address, 175
ammoniacal silver nitrate solution, 138
ammonium oxalate-crystal violet stain, 138
ammonium-salt, sugar media, 109
   as nitrogen source, 45
amylase in serum, 12, 133
anaerobes, motility of, 22, 48
anaerobic, facultatively, meaning of term, x
Andrade's indicator, 23, 93, 108
anonymous acid-fast bacilli, 51, 52, 60
antibiotic sensitivity, 19
aqueous solutions for staining, 138
arginine, hydrolysis, 26, 72, 114, 115, 152, 154
   media, 112
Arizona group. *See Salmonella arizonae*
asbestos pad filters, 16, 95
ascitic fluid, 12
asporogenous state, 21, 43
autoclaving, 15
   'momentary autoclaving', 15
   pressure-temperature relations, 15

B 5 W biotype, 61
Bacillus, 3, 21, 31, 32, 45, 46, 55, 64, 84, 87
   asporogenous strains, 21, 43
   morphological groups, 46
   B. alcalofaciens, 71